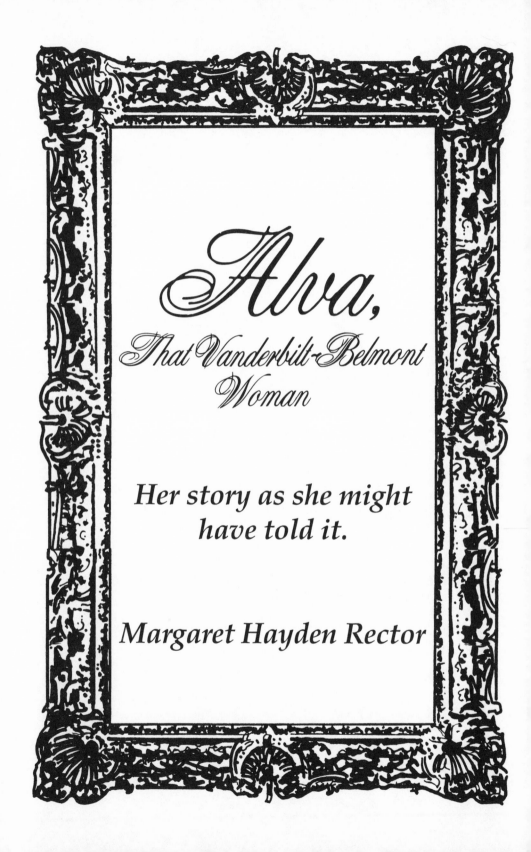

Alva,
That Vanderbilt-Belmont Woman

Her story as she might have told it.

Margaret Hayden Rector

Alva,
That Vanderbilt-Belmont
Woman

Alva,
That Vanderbilt-Belmont Woman

Margaret Hayden Rector

ISBN: 0-934881-13-8

Library of Congress Number: 91-73210

Second Edition: November, 1992
Third Printing, January, 1995
Fourth Printing, June, 1997
Fifth Printing, June, 1999
Sixth Printing, January, 2001
Seventh Printing, July, 2002

Cover Design by Charles J. Cronin

Front cover photo from the collection of
The Preservation Society of Newport (R.I.) County

Back cover photo by Greenberg and McConnville, Los Angeles

Printed in the United States of America

The Dutch Island Press
A division of Clarkson/Maine

Dedication

To my magnificent husband, Dr. Robert W. Rector, for ten solid years of support on this book, and fifty-two years of unquestioning back-up on all my other literary efforts.

Acknowledgments

TO:

Professor Peter Geidel. For eight valuable years of gracious exchanging of books, documents, articles, photographs, and contacts; in preparation for his doing his own book on Alva Vanderbilt Belmont (hereafter referred to as A.V.B.) as his PhD thesis at Columbia University in History. And to his extended family for their many courtesies.

Dr. Robert W. Rector, my husband. For fifty-two years of financial support and back-up on all my literary efforts. And for his success at the task of obtaining permission for the illustrations in this book.

My Family: Cleone and Fred, Robin and Edwin, Bruce and Paula; and our three grandsons, Ethan, Blake and Clark. For believing I could do this book; for supporting me through the difficult days and providing diversion during the pleasant ones.

Peter Crolius. For recognizing there was a need for this book and being willing to take on the complications of doing a first biography. And to the long efforts of his staff and crew.

Anne Toll. As Director of the Newport Public Library, for her insistence that I do this book. For her statement, "I constantly get requests for a biography on Alva Vanderbilt Belmont." And to her staff for their gracious and professional assistance.

Dr. Ray Scungio. For his valuable referrals, as a former professor at both Yale and Brown Universities, and as an assistant in the Newport Public Library. And for his gifts of fine architectural books out of his own library.

Bertha Klausner, my New York literary agent. For her efforts in placing this book and for her belief in its being material for a television series on the life of A.V.B.

The Tinney Family. As owners and managers of Belcourt Castle: Mrs. Harold Tinney, Mr. and Mrs. Donald Tinney, and their staff. For their continued efforts on my behalf in sharing photographs, newspaper columns, articles, and information on the early days of Belcourt and Mr. and Mrs. (A.V.B.) Oliver Hazard Perry Belmont. For their generous luncheons dinners, and teas granted me, my family, and friends on our frequent visits.

Countess Anthony Szapary. For being the faithful "watcher" over Vanderbilt family history and graciously correcting all discrepancies.

Consuelo (Mimi) Russell, the great-great-granddaughter of A.V.B. For lively interviews, the loan of family material, and carrying on the Vanderbilt talents.

The Duke of Marlborough. As the eleventh Duke, for his multiple letters exchanged, for his gracious arrangement for my husband and me to have a day at Blenheim Palace, and for his steady encouragement on this book concerning his grandmother and his great-grandmother A.V.B.

Consuelo Heddens. For early information on her Vanderbilt family and her personal memories of Beaulieu.

Shirley C. Burden. For a memorable interview, the gift of his books, and his professional contributions to his Vanderbilt family.

Allen Churchill. For his great good humor, his gift of books and exclusive information, and his "But, my dear, I've done it all" attitude toward what he considered the great finale of death.

Cleveland Amory. For striking the table, when I told him about this book, and exclaiming, "It's about time somebody did a biography on her!"

Louis Auchincloss. For his information and contacts, and for his correcting my dates, spelling, and pronunciation.

Katharine Hepburn. For her kind verification of her mother's attendance at The Conference for Great Women, July 8 – 9, 1914, at Marble House and its Chinese Teahouse, Newport, R.I.

J. Watson Webb, Jr. For the gracious opportunity to view family memorabilia and to enjoy the house and garden of this most charming of the Vanderbilt gentlemen.

David Black. For telephone conversations, identification of photos, and — as the biographer for August Belmont — setting an example for the rest of us to live up to. Plus checking on my entire manuscript.

Monique M. Panaggio (Mrs. Leonard J. Panaggio). As the editor of Newport Gazette and Public Relations Director for The Preservation Society of Newport County, for her great assistance with documents and photographs from their collection.

Paul F. Miller. As a Curator for The Preservation Society of Newport County, for his research efforts and corrections on my Vanderbilt Chronology.

Elliott Caldwell. Formerly with The Preservation Society of Newport County, for making arrangements for the use of the excellent portrait of A.V.B. on the cover of this book.

Bertram Lippincott III, C.G. As Librarian of The Newport Historical Society, for his research efforts and Chronology corrections. And to M. Joan Youngken, Collections Manager, for assistance with photographs.

Walter Hoving. For kindly directing me around The Newport Historical Society's archives.

Judy Hilliard. For interest and encouragement from The Redwood Library, Newport, R.I.

The Providence, R.I. Public Library. For photocopies of little known suffrage material.

Benjamin Reed. For giving me the information to obtain access to the personal 1914 Conference scrapbook of A.V.B.

The Island Cemetery staff, Newport, R.I. For their kind cooperation and research in locating particular graves.

Gloria Lane. As founder and president of The Women's International Center, San Diego, Calif., for her constant belief in this book as "an important contribution to The Women's Movement". And for her gracious video of me, talking at length about A.V.B., as filmed expertly by Kenneth Rooney.

Anne and Robert DeStefano. As directors of the very successful CMAC in East Greenwich, R.I., for their constant assistance with contacts. And for the gracious concern and attention from their greater family.

Mary and Barnaby Conrad. As Directors of the Santa Barbara writer's Conference, for their offered courses in which I developed this book.

Faculty Wives Writer's Workshop of UCLA. For their 18-year belief in me and valuable suggestions on each chapter of this book.

Surfwriters. As a Palos Verdes, Calif. writer's organization, for their workshops and backing since 1958.

UCLA Research Library staff and Friends of the Library. For their collections, single sources, and professional courtesies.

Los Angeles County Library staff, West Los Angeles, Calif. For their cooperative reference desk in tracking down rare sources.

Santa Monica Public Library staff, Santa Monica, Calif. For their Xeroxes of old newspaper photos of The Vanderbilt Cup Races.

National Woman's Party Headquarters staff, Washington, D.C. For the interest of Belmont House in my work on the life of A.V.B., and for their stressing the need for it.

Feminists: Betty Friedan, Eleanor Smeal, Molly Yard, Peg Yorkin, and Toni Carabillo. For always showing real interest when I talked to them about this book and agreeing there was a need for it.

System One staff, West Los Angeles, Calif. For the great skill of their photography studio and color lab in processing photos, slides, and rare prints for use in this book and in my three lectures: The Vanderbilts in the Gilded Age. A.V.B., the Financier and Manager of the American Woman's Suffrage Movement. The Vanderbilt Cup Races, the Establishing of the American Automobile Through Racing.

Needham Bookfinders. For their considerate handling of all my requests for books long out of print.

Harbour Jewelers, East Greenwich, R.I. For the professional skill of Kenneth and Elaine Roberts in framing Vanderbilt cameo portraits from their extensive Victorian collection.

Mrs. Persifor Fraser. For lively phone conversations from Florida and Rhode Island regarding her friendship with the William Kissam Vanderbilt family.

Cdr. John C. Mathews III. For reading and advising me on the entire log of the world cruise of the second yacht Alva. And for the gifts from him and his wife Corinne of magnificent gowns, coats, hats, and accessories to make my fine lecture wardrobe possible.

Col. John M. Burnside. For loaning me his automotive library so that I might have slides made from the illustrations.

Matthew R. Leizer. For his architectural knowledge and for his obtaining information on A.V.B. at the A.I.A. headquarters in Washington, D.C.

Helen Sullivan Vogel. For her generous loan of books regarding the Gilded Age from her own library. And for her actress-acquisition of facts.

Amanda and John Stork. For their invaluable interest in this book and for the gift of multiple articles on the Vanderbilts and the Belmonts.

Sue Alexopoulos. For bringing to my attention articles on Marble House and on her hometown of Newport, R.I.

Judith, Henriette and Pedro Miller. For their unflagging support of my literary efforts and for their gifts of valuable research materials.

Pamela Lloyd. For 33 years of both belief in and assistance with my literary career. And for her constant charm, her wonderful sense of fun, and for a devotion on which I could really depend.

Joy Gardner. For watching for articles for me in publications which I might overlook.

Leila Fligelman. For her firsthand information on the Vanderbilt family and for her eyes-open coverage of social customs during the last fifty years.

Robert and June Broughton. For our many illuminating conversations on The Gilded Age and for our memorable group-trip to Newport, R.I.

Robert and Barbara Grabowski. For contacts and professional information regarding the jewelry crafted during The Gilded Age.

Curt and Helen Wagner. For articles on the Gilded Age mansions and for their knowledge of interiors as concurrence on my research.

Lucretia and Carl Cole. For their sophistication and enlightenment on the contributions made by the responsible people of wealth during the Nineteenth and Twentieth Centuries.

Earl R. Schutzius and Victoria L. Woody. For their gifts of valuable architectural periodicals and for their enduring interest in this book and in my physical welfare.

Diane Gertzman. For taking all my dictated chapters off the tape and then doing the typed drafts with professional patience.

Rosamond Hendel, artist daughter Paula Tonkonogy and grandson Gary Tonkonogy. For their dependable hospitality and love granted me during my stay at Bella Vista, Newport, R.I. And for the subsequent trips made there by me and my husband when we found them to be great source material in learning about Newport in former days.

Prof. Herbert Kinsolving. For his personal family information on the wedding of Consuelo and the Duke, and on its subsequent annulment.

Saucy Sylvia Stoun. For the many evenings of pleasure given me and my family by her singalong performances at The Auld Mug in the Newport Islander Doubletree Hotel (formerly The Sheraton) on Goat Island. Hearing "Sauce" after a busy day of study and research always made the writing of this book "worth it all".

Les Carpenter. Also for many hours of listening pleasure during those "dig it out" days. For his skill at doing unusual arrangements and playing them on the grand piano for the fortunate customers of Canfield's Restaurant (a former haunt of Reginald Vanderbilt), Newport, R.I. And for his taped compositions and lyrics, which I could listen to in California, played and sung by him describing the charms of Newport.

Nonie Watanabe. For the lettering on the Coats of Arms. For the layout on the Genealogy. And for her charm and talent in fulfilling all short-notice requests.

Robin Rector Krupp. For her artistic skills, design-research, advice, and patience on all phases of this book.

Dr. Edwin C. Krupp. For his advice on publication problems, on the cover design, and on the editing of this book.

Contents

Foreword

Because this book is subtitled "Her Story as She Might Have Told It", you as the reader will ask, "How much of this is true?"

The answer is: I tried to work in every truth I could find into the text.

Every date, every person, every place. The assumptions which remain are the result of ten years of detective search in going to the sources of information on her life and digging out the most probable account I could determine.

I emphasize sources because hackneyed, false, and plain unfounded stories about Alva Vanderbilt Belmont have been told for over one hundred years.

I am tired of these stories.

I want this remarkable woman to finally tell her own story. And this is what I've tried to let her do.

Marlborough

Erskine

Smith

Vanderbilt

Belmont

Forbes

Stirling

Alva,

That Vanderbilt - Belmont Woman

1

I T IS THE SUMMER OF 1932 — ON A LOVELY DAY — in the garden of my home outside Paris, near Fontainebleau.

I sit here in my donkey-cart, about ready to take a jaunty spin around this garden. I am seventy-nine and have had a stroke recently, but I can drive the donkey by myself.

We drive our usual route through the garden paths of my Renaissance stone château. And my thoughts always seem to take the same form. Remembering.

Recently I have had an overwhelming desire to dictate a set of memoirs. I've decided it should be done in episodes, and each episode should begin with a background and proceed to a spoken exchange — a sort of scene.

Besides dictating to a secretary or a machine, I have had to ask myself, to whom do I wish to "speak"? To an imaginary listener? Or, when all this gets down on paper or even published, perhaps to many listeners or readers?

But those listeners or readers will say, "She's almost eighty, and she's had a stroke recently. Will she remember any episode clearly and in detail?"

Of course. There's nothing wrong with my memory. Never has been. It is one of the most dependable things about me. I have always lived with my two eyes and my two ears open. In fact, my memory of significant experiences that occurred seventy-five to fifty to twenty-five years ago is far sharper than what occurred of importance the day before yesterday.

So let me begin with the account of the first big hurdle and public challenge I faced after my marriage to W. K. Vanderbilt. But I want to tell this in the literary style of its time. Certainly not in the chatty jargon of 1932! As a matter of fact, I want to do this all the way through from about 1878 to the present, even to the jargon of 1933, if time and God permit.

I wish to tell this only in the milieu and rapport in which it occurred.

Now, I feel this is enough of these guidelines. My donkey, besides knowing he is very important, is getting impatient. I imported him, complete with harness, all the way from Sicily. This dear creature had to be that special, he is pulling Queen Victoria's bath chair. The chair had been made for that royal lady by a famous French carriage builder. The Queen approved but used it only on her visits to Cimiez.

Years later I saw it in an antiques shop, was captivated by its beautiful lines, and bought it. When the day came that I found I could no longer walk, this bath chair became my traveling throne. Though converted, it now looks very intentional, and my donkey has never once questioned it!

So, when I tell you this first episode, seated in my donkey-cart, I am going to give it a literal running start by using my new dictaphone. My son-in-law, Jacques Balsan, rigged up the whole thing for me by first hooking the microphone (looks more, to me, like an outdated horn for the hard-of-hearing) inside the hood of the bath chair. Then he installed the cylinder and battery mechanism under my feet — those feet are both motionless, I can't kick anything over. And tonight I will have my secretary take my words off the cylinder.

When my man-nurse and my gardener lift me into the cart, they put the reins in my still-good hand. All I have to do is give these reins a couple of snaps, and we're off. But, I figure, in order to finish these memoirs, if that good hand also becomes useless — I can always employ my mouth to give the donkey the traditional "glick glick" sounds to start, and I can yell "Whoa!" when it's time to stop.

In any case, right now my "donk" is more than impatient. So here we go. Snap snap!

I knew that I had to do it. I, Alva Erskine Smith Vanderbilt. Born January 17, 1853.

True, I was not a Vanderbilt. I was only a woman who had married one, but I had to get that family recognized.

Even as late as 1878, it was more clear to me every day that none of the Vanderbilts was being recognized by New York Society. Not my husband, William Kissam Vanderbilt. Not his brother, Cornelius Vanderbilt, nor any of his other brothers. Not his marvelous father, William H. Vanderbilt. And not his grandfather, the great Commodore Vanderbilt.

They simply were not being accepted. Especially by the Academy of Music at 14th Street and Irving Place. That Academy did not want *any* of the Vanderbilts as members. The heaviest voice in this decision was that of August Belmont. Heavy indeed, and why? He was the banker who was known as the American Rothschild.

Furthermore, August Belmont's wife, Caroline, shared his opinion. I had heard that this lady was greatly admired for the balls which she gave after the opera performances at the Academy. Not only that, they said Caroline was such a good social manager, she could actually attend the opera *before* the ball.

I was in awe of efficient women, mainly because I intended to be one!

But I was not wrong about the August Belmonts. They considered the Vanderbilts not only as being new in town, but worse than that, newly rich.

I was determined someday to get even with the Academy and with the Belmonts.

I fully realized the Vanderbilts were not the only newly rich family in New York. And I was aware the Belmonts were only one of the Gotham families which ruled society — that I must also face the Schuyler, Van Rensselaer, Jay, Rhinelander, and Astor families.

Especially *The* Mrs. Astor. She ruled everything, even Mr. and Mrs. Belmont.

But I would have to deal with *The* Mrs. Astor later. Right now my defiance should be limited to The Academy.

Why did the Belmonts and these other Gotham families deny the Vanderbilts an opportunity to buy a box? To enjoy the opera? To be accepted?

It was said, "Because the heads of these new wealthy families are uncouth and without background!".

In the case of the Vanderbilts, I knew they were referring to the old Commodore. Yes, I had grown to know my husband's grandfather. And it was true he spit on the floor and pinched the servant-maids. He was never asked to the home of one of the Gotham families more than once! But he was a clever and hard-working man who had established both a shipping and a railroad empire. One of the original and genuine wheeler-dealers.

I liked the name even though my father was from the South and called them Damn Yankees. But wheeler-dealers were the men who got the industrial wheels of America running, and then made deals to *keep* those wheels going.

They soon became manipulators of money. But that was the reason I couldn't understand why August Belmont was so opposed to wheeler-dealers becoming accepted members of society. Wasn't *he* a manipulator of money? And as a banker! What would he have done without them?

I resented this American Rothschild. But little did Mr. and Mrs. August Belmont know that someday I would indeed have a chance to even the score. How? In a personal way — by falling deeply in love with Oliver, their most handsome, fascinating, and flamboyant son. And marrying him!

I, too, would become a Mrs. Belmont. In fact, before a century of New York opera was finished, there would be *three* Mrs. Belmonts connected with it. And I would definitely be one.[1]

But not until twenty years had passed — those twenty years I was married to William Kissam Vanderbilt. Our wedding took place April 20, 1875, when I was twenty-two, at New York's Calvary Episcopal Church at Fourth Avenue and 21st Street. To the non-Gotham families, it was considered an important social event. The church was so jammed, inside and outside, that it took four policemen to get me through the vestibule door. And not just because I was wearing a lace-flounced wedding gown!

Thereafter, cards of admission were issued for all society weddings. W. K. Vanderbilt and I had started something. We would soon be known for that; this was only the beginning of our many subsequent "firsts".

Why did I marry William? Because I loved him, and I wanted him to be the father of any children I might have. But there was another reason. Ah, yes. My sense of responsibility.

After the death of my mother, I felt responsible for the future of my three sisters. Someone had to be. My father was slowly losing his money. The absence of my mother left all of us without a daily counselor. She was the source of our personal strength. In my own case, she had been the *one* controlling and governing influence in my life. I had been a rebellious child.

My father's failure was caused by the upset of old New York business standards. He always had felt no man was worthy to deal with who could not show credentials of integrity throughout his entire business career. But fierce competition was changing all this. To my father, the new transactions seemed underhanded. He could *not* become a wheeler-dealer.

At first, my father didn't disclose his financial state. Then one day he announced, "We must move to a simpler house and learn to retrench."

We did. When that did not keep the wolf from the door, he would joke, "Pretty soon we shall have to keep a boarding house."

It was this practical sense of mine that made me realize none of us four girls was trained to do anything useful. Until this reeducation could be achieved, something had to be done.

On a visit to another newly rich New York family, the Oelrichs, I met the handsome William Kissam Vanderbilt. It was actually Lady Mandeville who introduced us. We fell in love. Very quickly, fortunately. And we planned to marry, soon.

This was the first peace of mind my father had. He took comfort in it to the day of his death. That day was, unhappily, only two weeks after the wedding.

The great W. H. Vanderbilt, my new father-in-law, became aware of my loss. At that time, he was possessor of the largest fortune in the United States. Fortune or no fortune, this dear gentleman said he would like to become "my substitute father".

What could I say? Of course I said, "Yes." I believed him. But I was determined, very determined, to earn the honor!

This was one more reason I now felt it was my job to get the

Vanderbilts recognized. And it was the specific reason I had been building up to a conversation with my husband. For almost a year, I had laid the groundwork, and now I was feeling it was time to make "the presentation". Eventually, of course, I would have to talk to the *father*, but today I could start with the *son*!

The year was 1880. My husband and I were in the living room of our first New York home, a modest one. We had finished our dinner, and I had enticed him into having coffee there.

In this room we had only one antique, a Louis XIV chair. With a table and lamp beside it. When I really wanted something from my husband, I would stand beside this chair and ask for it. I knew the globe of that lamp was open at the top and would illuminate the feature my husband loved best, my softly piled auburn hair. This hair of mine also had a maddening aura of curls escaping at my neck. It was a spot he loved to kiss.

At this important moment, I walked over to my chair and this lamp. I stood there. My husband — always called Willie K. by me, his family and friends — moved over and leaned his regal but casual body against the opposite side of that chair. He began watching me. I think he suspected.

But I began. "Willie K., I have been thinking. There has got to be a second Academy of Music. There is no chance of anyone's buying a box in this present one. They have to wait until the entire family of some member dies off!"

"Yes, Alva dear, I realize this present Academy is plugged with 'Gotham greats'." He liked the phrase.

"They won't even *consider* a second opera house. I feel their refusal is just one more example of their stupid Knicker—" I hesitated.

"— bocracy?" He liked this one too.

"Yes. And I'm sick to death of it!"

Willie K. was gazing at my hair very intently. He always swore it modulated into a true red when I became defiant. "Not just in New York, Alva. Didn't you always say this was true of your father and mother in Mobile?".

"Yes, *the* successful Murray Forbes Smith — and in the export trade, at that. Furthermore, we were related to the DeShas — everybody knew my mother was the daughter of this Kentucky general!"

"But that didn't get either your mother or your father accepted into Alabama society. So you know how *my* grandmother and

8

grandfather felt when they built their mansion at 10 Washington Place. Right in the middle of those Gotham bluebloods!"

I mimicked what the bluebloods said. "So Commodore Vanderbilt and his Sophia Johnson think they are going to achieve acceptance because of money. They should go back to Staten Island, where they came from!"

Willie K. now had his eyes on my second prominent feature, my pugged nose. He further claimed, that as I became more determined, it became more tilted.

Knowing he was right about both my hair and my nose, I decided to reveal the first step of my activities. "That Knickerbocracy crowd will never give a cent toward building a new opera house."

"I presume you are speaking of Royal Phelps, John Bigelow, and Alexander Hamilton?" He waited for my nod. "Very well. Then why not also name families? The Brevoorts, the De Rhams, the Varicks, the Lorillards, the Hones, the Beekmans, the Kanes —

"— the Rhinelanders, and the Astors? Yes. Not a penny!" I was pleased he was just as aware of those families as I was.

He laughed. Then he gave my neck a long, moist kiss. I was delighted, but I also knew he was trying to cool it off. "Soooooooo my Alva wants to build a new opera house. But she has no money to do it." He nudged me. "I have a feeling that won't stop her."

"No. I will try other sources."

"And if you do, what do you intend to call this edifice?"

"The Metropolitan Opera House!"

He thought the name over, then finally nodded. But he asked, "And the location?"

"At Broadway and 39th Street."

"The Academy of Music is on 14th Street. Broadway and 39th is clear uptown!"

"New York City is moving north. Let the Metropolitan Opera House move with it!"

"But, Alva, you know as well as I do that August Belmont is trying to *stop* this."

"By offering to put in twenty-six more boxes at the Academy? Nonsense. What good will just twenty-six boxes do?"

"But it is at least an offer!"

"And from a banker! You're right. I should curtsy. But the offer will be turned down."

"He will be furious."

"But he will be wiser, dear. Wiser."

Cecile, our French maid, came in carrying the tray of after-dinner coffee I had requested.

Indicating a low table in front of my antique chair, I pulled another chair alongside. "Cecile, would you put it here, please? And you may dismiss the other servants for the night."

"Very good, Mrs. Vanderbilt." She was proud of her English. Placing the tray on the table, Cecile walked to the door. "I will turn down your beds. Then may I, too, go to my room, madam?"

"Yes, Cecile. Look in on the children first." I was proud of my French. "Bien. Vous pouvez vous retirer."

As she departed, Cecile smiled and bowed to each of us. "Thank you, Mrs. Vanderbilt. Mr. Vanderbilt."

I was pleased. Most maids would only have said "ma'am and sir". But I wanted all our staff — small though it was — to know us as people.

My husband had given me credit for not only choosing efficient servants, but pleasant ones. "And, furthermore, you know how to keep them," he would say. "You treat them well."

But right now he was watching me pour his coffee. "Alva, listen to me. In this day, my own father, with all his railroad fortune, can't find acceptance."

"I know. Those families I approached won't even admit William H. Vanderbilt has one of the finest art collections in America!"

"And they *still* won't invite him, nor my mother, to their homes."

I knew exactly how much sugar and how little cream he wanted. I handed him his correct coffee, poured mine, and we sat down.

"Willie K. You wait — these twin mansions your father is building — that will turn the trick!"

"Just because they are on Fifth Avenue?" He stirred his coffee with even strokes. "I doubt it. Those families will still call us Robber Barons."

"Barefoot Millionaires," I echoed. "The Suddenly Rich. And Malefactors of Great Wealth."

"And Bouncers." His spoon clicked the saucer as he placed it beside the cup. "Because we bounce back after social rebuffs."

"My dear, that is exactly what I have decided to do, approach the Bouncers. Darius Ogden Mills. Jay Gould. And Collis P. Huntington."

He had to swallow his first sip of coffee in a gulp. "Huntington? He's a railroad rival!"

"I don't care."

"What are you going to do to make these gentlemen give you money?"

"Promise them something, in return, Willie K."

"What?"

"A box."

"Ahah! It will have to be at the ends of the rows — so they can lean back and sleep through the opera safely!"

"No! They will have boxes in the middle, where they can be seen. In their tailcoats, with the usual starched shirts and diamond studs." I posed on my chair to illustrate. "And where their wives can be seen in their Paris gowns, with the diamond necklaces, brooches, and tiaras …. A box where, not only the audience on the orchestra floor, but the people in the balconies above will notice!"

"And stare, up and down, at the ladies' diamond stomachers?"

"That too."

"Then these boxes will have to protrude, actually stick out."

"Exactly. Tiers of them, curving along. That is what I will tell the architect to create."

"Alva Vanderbilt! You already have an architect?"

I knew, now, I must both promote and defend myself. Putting my coffee aside, I arose and walked to a particular chest across the room. "No. But I have a set of rough sketches. I take them with me. And show them." I opened a drawer and pulled them out.

"Show them?"

I brought the sketches to the table and unrolled them.

Quickly setting his coffee aside, Willie K. joined me. He stared down at each one. "Who did these?"

I raised my head until the light from the top of the lamp properly warmed my cheeks. "I did."

"Alva! You are quite a sketch-artist …. More than that, Mrs. William K. Vanderbilt is a real draftsman!" He carefully rolled up the sketches and returned them to me. "But so far, your showing these has done no good."

"Of course not. Those families already *have* boxes." I moved closer. "As I said, I will approach the millionaires who can't get them."

He took me in his arms. "My dear, you are a Robber Baron yourself — using this Southern voice, that hair, these eyes, and the peach color of your cheeks."

"Apricot," I corrected, but it was too late. He had observed all my ruses. And identified every one! I then had to use the only defense left to me. "But don't tell the barons I'm twenty-seven. And the mother of a two-year-old son and a three-year-old daughter."

"Why not? It is arguing every day with little Willie and with Consuelo which has made you strong!" He laughed with the direct heartiness he always had when we talked of our children. But he next asked the question I knew he would. "Alva. What happens if building the Metropolitan Opera House does *not* get all the Vanderbilts into society?"

"Then I will try something else."

"I know you will. Besides being a Robber Baron, you are also a very pretty Barefoot Millionaire."

Delighted, I moved to where I could both tap him on the head with sketches and kiss him on the lips with intent. "With tiers of boxes to sell, my dearest."

"How many?"

"About seventy-three. Rows — in a giant curve."

"Will you approach each one of the Vanderbilt families and promise them a box — to show off all their diamonds?"

"Absolutely. And I intend to start with your father."

"My father?"

"I may find him very willing."

"I hope so. And what will Alva Vanderbilt call these boxes?"

"Well how about — about —"

"Yes, yes — what name?"

"How about The Diamond Circle."

"Fine. But coming from an equestrian Family, I think the name will more likely end up The Diamond Horseshoe."

"Because of its shape?"

"Exactly."

"Very well. Circle. Then Horseshoe."

"Whatever, my darling."

2

I T TOOK MY DONKEY AND ME SEVERAL TRIPS around the garden to tell that episode, and my secretary several "trips around the cylinder" to take it off.

And it took me a few more to edit it and make it flow. But I find I like recording a conversation. It "brings it alive", and more than that, it brings it back.

Naturally, now I want to tell you about my first session with the architect, Richard Morris Hunt, concerning our proposed house at 660 Fifth Avenue. Richard always said I worked "shoulder to shoulder" with him, pouring over the plans for this. And I did.

That's why I think — if Richard were alive and my houseguest now — he would be very amused (but not amazed) at a "remodeling project" I am starting today.

I am remodeling a river.

This river runs by my château, but it is the wrong size for it. The river should be twice as large. So, this morning, I will be watching the arrival of an army of workmen I've hired to make it larger.

If he were here, Richard and I would choose the best second story window to overlook the whole project. And we would laugh and poke each other as we recalled special project after special alteration after special quirk we performed on all the houses we created together.

This widening of a river would be only one!

I will get my donkey started and tell this next episode. But, instead of being upstairs, I will be peeking through the trees, shrubs, and hedges to see how everything is coming along. And wishing Richard were here.

My wise Willie K. was right when he asked, "What happens if building the Metropolitan Opera House does not get all the Vanderbilts into society?"

I had replied, "Then I will try something else."

But, really, I knew I dared not wait to see if it got them in or not. I *had* to try, in the meantime, something else.

So, very soon, there were two of my projects under construction: The Metropolitan Opera House; and a new house for the W. K. Vanderbilts, on the northwest corner of 52nd Street and Fifth Avenue.

The first had as its architect Josiah Cleveland Cady. And it was slated to open in October of 1883, with a production of Gounod's "Faust". I had been successful with my planned approach.

But it took a conflagration to get me my Diamond Horseshoe. Not until 1892 was it put into the Metropolitan restoration plans, *after* a fire had gutted the interior.

The second project had as its architect Richard Morris Hunt. This great man had first been approached by us in early 1878, to design a country house for our family at Oakdale, Long Island.

He did so — a big, rambling, stick-style house. It was to be completed two years later. We and the children were to spend so many happy hours there that we called it Idlehour.

I was the one who first found this remarkable Richard Morris Hunt. I had heard of his atelier in the Studio Building he had created in Greenwich Village.

Willie K. and I had gone there together for the design sessions for our Long Island house. But for the second series of sessions with Mr. Hunt for our Fifth Avenue house, my husband did not accompany me, even though the year was still 1878.

Mindful that I was doing it alone, Willie K. was even more

insistent in asking, "Alva, where are you going to get the money for *this* building?"

He was right. I knew I had to have a benefactor. And I knew exactly the person I would ask. But it had to be kept a secret. Right up to the last second of revelation. A true surprise.

So I replied, "I am not going to ask *anybody* for the money, until I have the plans in my hand, the best plans Richard Morris Hunt and I can draw up."

"Very well, my darling. I have time on my side. But I will at least pay for the plans!"

That was enough for me. And I wrote Mr. Hunt a note that I was coming. Alone. That was a rather remarkable thing for a wife to do at that time. I shall never forget the day.

Dressed in my best fall velvets, I called for our carriage. As its beautiful horses trotted toward Greenwich Village, I sat there in the cab and could hardly wait to be back in Mr. Hunt's Studio Building. It seemed to me that here creativity was swirling about. He had designed a painting center for artists — such as Winslow Homer, John La Farge, Frederic Church, and William Merritt Chase. A four-story building with a central gallery, roofed over by a high skylight. This gallery was surrounded by twenty-five studios, twelve of which had adjoining sleeping rooms. What more could they ask? I knew I wouldn't see those artists that day, but it was wonderful even to be in the same building!

This being thrilled by the creativity of men went back a long way with me. As a child I was a tomboy — I could be found either out riding horses or playing explorer with the boys in my neighborhood. Even the one creative streak I had was usually associated with males: I could be found in my father's library — lying on the floor, surrounded with books I had pulled off his shelves. All sizes, shapes, and kinds. Not to be read. Oh no, not me. All through my life, I always preferred to observe rather than to read. I liked books — but to build houses! I leaned them against each other, creating entrances, parlors with nice windows, second floor bedrooms, and steep roofs with chimneys. I was very careful about the placement of each. I wanted to create the grandest house I could.

And for my entire life I did exactly that. Some people said, "She is only happy when she has one leg knee-deep in mortar!"

But this particular day took place when I was twenty-five, two years earlier than my conversation with my husband about the Metropolitan Opera. Even my horse and driver seemed to be pleased to again approach 15 West 10th Street. This was a building! It had excellent placement of windows, nice masonry detail, and even wrought iron accents. For a structure that had been completed in 1858, it obviously had tenants who thought enough of it to maintain it well. Even twenty years later, I could still see its original grandeur.[2]

As I descended from the carriage, I walked across the small wrought iron bridge and through the tall, double front doors. I was grateful for the wide entrance — my hat was a very large sailor, with swirls of peacock feathers across the brim. On the wall directory, again I found the name Richard Morris Hunt. I was impressed that it was still listed as though he were any other occupant. I happily and humbly approached his door.

My knock was answered by one of the apprentice architects. I nodded and then stood for a moment, again feasting my eyes on all the books, prints, plaster casts, and photographs of classic European buildings. He had told me these were the things he brought back from Ecole des Beaux-arts when he finished his training and returned to America.

But for an architect who had been back since 1855, I was once more puzzled by the small number of drafting tables and personnel in the room. No more than eight. On my first visit, I had expected fifty. But even on today's visit, I expected the number eight to be increased to at least twelve.

And why not? Look at all the work this great man had done. I felt like saying, "Forget all those photographs on your wall of classic European buildings. Why don't you have some photos of your New York Tribune Building? The Marquand Chapel at Princeton University. Your charming summer 'cottages' in Newport, Rhode Island? Or something practical, if you prefer, your Presbyterian Hospital here in town? Or your great Lenox Library?"

Didn't he realize the initials R. M. H. on a building *stood* for something? Then why not have a big, showy office to say all this?

What I had to "get through my head" was that Hunt was trained in the atelier of Hector Martin Lefuel, who, besides being a teacher, was one of the designers and builders of the Louvre. These French ateliers were small. Hunt was doing the same thing Lefuel did — teach as he worked. The four, and sometimes five, apprentices were draftsmen, learning as *they* worked alongside Hunt, designing his homes and buildings. Over the years, each one of them would become famous in his own right. One of them was William R. Ware, the great professor of architecture, first at the Massachusetts Institute of Technology and then at Columbia University.

While great architectural firms, such as McKim, Mead and White, employed about eighty draftsmen in their offices, Mr. Hunt never did. He always *preferred* to remain small.

While comprehending all this, I saw the great designer himself come into the room, still the erect and handsomely bearded gentleman.

"Mrs. Vanderbilt. How stunning you look, and how good of you to make an appointment. Many people just walk in."

"That's because they are not sure they really want to build a house, Mr. Hunt. But I am!"

"Even when the first one is not yet completed?"

"That one will be completed, you say, in 1880. I would like this new one to be completed by the end of 1882."

"Are you planning to give a party the *next night*?"

"No, but very soon after. And a very large party!"

He laughed but took note, then he introduced me to his new men. I can't remember now if one of them was Frank Furness, Charles D. Gambrill, George B. Post, or Ware himself. But all of those men came out of that room.

"Every time I look around these walls, Mr. Hunt, I feel as if I am back in France."

"How fortunate we were both educated there. We understand each other."

"You compliment me. Remember, sir, you had the formal Ecole education, but I simply opened my eyes and looked around."

"It can amount to the same thing."

"It almost did. That is why I am here. I want you to build me a French château."

"Ah. Indeed?"

"Yes. But to protect my husband from heart failure, I had to *start* with a Long Island country house."

"A wise and splendid approach, Mrs. Vanderbilt!"

This time, the whole room broke into laughter, and I was invited to sit down. "Would you care for some tea?"

"Yes, thank you." I pointed around the room. "These living quarters I hear about should be put to use."

"Oh, but we have no kitchens. Only a gas burner for the tea-kettle."

"Never mind. I am quite aware that next year you are going to build what they are already calling New York's first apartment building."

"The Stuyvesant?"

"Yes, Mr. Hunt. There will be kitchens enough in that structure!" I laid my purse aside, and he helped me remove my coat. Then I sat down. "A cup of tea will be fine. And some of your cookies, of course. I will need the strength." He nodded, grinned, and reached for a nearby jar. The cookies again appeared to be homemade. Still by his wife, Catherine, no doubt.

One of the apprentices, while he was putting on the kettle, observed, "Mrs. Vanderbilt, may I say how impressed we are with the acreage you and your husband have chosen in Oakdale. I have seen the site — all those tall trees and that river running by!"

"And don't forget the train stops in Oakdale. That will be a help, too."

"My dear madam, I would think the train would stop for the Vanderbilts anywhere!"

Once again, everyone in the whole room loved the irony. I admired my architect for his informality and camaraderie with his men.

Then Mr. Hunt motioned. "A French château, you say? Shall we begin sketching?" He invited me to come over and stand by his side.

"But you won't have to worry about sketching the trees or a river on these. Just draw them the French way — the building and no more."

"You are forever French, madame. All my American clients require me to draw sidewalks, people, bicycles, carriages and horses passing by. Some of them even want the sun and clouds!"

"Just a *house*, Mr. Hunt. A very elegant, Gothic, Renaissance combination, but with all the romance of a château"

"Ah yes. With a surrounding pillared fence? An elegant entrance —"

"— on Fifth Avenue, with tall light stands."

"And recessed balconies above." He was quickly sketching in every item ….

"Three will be fine, sir. Accented by a round tourelle for each."

"Very good. And some dormer windows?"

"With beautifully carved, elaborate jambs and hood-molds."

"What about at least one oriel window Mrs. Vanderbilt?"

"Of course. Now let's talk about the roof line. I'd like it steeply hipped and of blue slate. Never mind the blue right now."

"How about some copper cresting and finials?"

"With high chimney stacks, massive and richly carved." Richard Morris Hunt could certainly have sketched all these requests and suggestions in cartoon style. But no — the lines, details, and even the shading were serious. The house was taking shape before me. I was enthralled.

"And bay windows, Mr. Hunt? We must have them along 52nd street, to pick up and retain all sun angles."

"You are quite right, Mrs. Vanderbilt." He glanced around. "As you can see, all of my men are astonished at your knowledge of architecture." Then he drew in the windows.

I nodded my approval and turned to the men. "You see, I have a responsibility to spend Vanderbilt money for something that is beautiful and something which will last."

Mr. Hunt checked the expressions he saw around him, then broke into a broad grin. "My dear lady, as you are witnessing, every one of my men would *welcome* the opportunity of having just such a responsibility!"

I joined the amused murmurs, literally at my own expense, and finished my tea. "Gentlemen. I think it is time for me to go. And — if you will all just look the other way — I will now put some of your delicious cookies into my purse."

Mr. Hunt was quick with a smile. "Can't I wrap those for you?"

"No. Thank you. But next time I will have enough common sense to bring a pocketbook!"

"And speaking of pocketbooks, Mrs. Vanderbilt."

"You are wondering if my husband has the money to pay for all this? No. Not after paying for the lot on which to build this dream of mine. But he *has* promised to pay for the plans."

"Very good. And we will work very hard, and confer with you often. But we *do* like to see our buildings actually take shape."

"Mr. Hunt. When I am armed with those plans, I intend to find the money — all of it. I, too, am opposed to castles in the air. I would rather have a mansion on the ground!"

He laughed, "A château, Mrs. Vanderbilt, with Renaissance Gothic overtones."

I was laughing, too. "Yes. But complete overtones of financing, as well …. I shall have to go about looking for a mythical benefactor, won't I, Mr. Hunt?"

"If by mythical, you mean a fairy godmother, I suppose so."

"Godmother? My dear man, why the traditional female?"

"Why not?"

"Wouldn't it be just as wise to look around for a male?"

"Perhaps."

"Then that is what I shall do. I shall search for and approach a fairy *godfather* ...."

3

I 'VE TAKEN A WEEK OFF FROM DICTATING TO supervise the widening of that river. It went very well. Even the workmen agreed that it looked better.

These workmen are from our nearby village. They refer to me as "that woman who has American ideas but speaks French like a native".

So be it. They also know my money is good and they get paid promptly.

Yesterday, as I stopped my donkey near the river, and we parted the bushes and looked through for the last time, I felt he also approved. Today he even seems to have matured. Perhaps it's because he knows I have an important episode to dictate, and it might take several days!

I'm referring, of course, to the house at 660 Fifth Avenue.

During the period of construction from 1881 to 1883, if you were standing on the steps of St. Patrick's Cathedral, you would have seen our house going up, diagonally across the street, to the right, and on the corner.

Vanderbilt money was finally going to be used to promote Vanderbilts effectively.

When I talk about this, I find I again enjoy dictating "in period". It brings back not only the things our family said, but also the formal way in which they said them.

And the time we all willingly took to say them. Conversation was a technique. There were no radios, and the telephone had not become an instrument for social visit. Head-to-head and eye-to-eye verbal exchange was it. And only it.

It's true I had a male in mind to pay for our new house. But this godfather was still to be a surprise.

I was consumed with my head-on concern to get the Vanderbilt family recognized.

Even late in the year 1879, my mother-in-law and father-in- law were not receiving invitations to the top New York social events. Not as long as Mrs. Astor had control. I was determined to meet that woman, somehow, someday, and have a talk with her. Of significance.

In the meantime the W. H. Vanderbilts and my husband and I had come to the same conclusion. What we *both* needed was a new house. In their case, for their very fine European art collection. In our case, for entertaining. I, again, intended to give that all-important first party.

But Willie K.'s parents decided one new house was not enough — they would build two. These were the houses always referred to, later, as the W. H. Vanderbilt twin mansions. The second house was for their two married daughters, Mrs. Elliott F. Shepard and Mrs. William D. Sloane — Margaret and Emily. And their husbands, of course!

On subsequent visits, I told Richard Morris Hunt about these two prospective houses. One day he finally said, "Ah yes, Mrs. Vanderbilt, I think you are happy they have chosen another architect — not me."

"Absolutely," I replied. "Since I have chosen you, there will be no comparison."

"Comparison?"

"Yes. We all have agreed to bring our separate plans, when we are finished, to the home of my mother-in-law and father-in-law on a particular evening."

"How I would love to be there, my dear! But only as a mouse in the corner."

"Mouse? Certainly not. I will report every word to you, Mr. Hunt. Trust me — a real report!"

Finally the evening was agreed upon. By 1880 almost two years of planning and working with this marvelous architect were paying dividends greater than any Vanderbilt railroad stock. If Mr. Hunt and I had been having an affair, the result would not have been more dominant in my mind. Together we felt we had created a masterpiece!

All those years of planning and drawing he had done at the Ecole, in the competitive concours, had paid off — those times when he had to design a bridge, or a bank, or a bandstand in twenty-four hours. Followed in New York City by twenty-three years of designing town houses, public buildings, and pedestals for the most famous of statues. Plus doing country homes both on Long Island and in Newport.

How could I lose on my prospects for a financier? I realized the house Mr. Hunt and I had designed would cost about three million dollars, but I felt that was a good round sum for any prospective godfather!

I was also aware, very aware, that W. H. Vanderbilt had set aside three million for the construction of his *two* mansions together. What would he and his wife, Maria, think about that sum for their son, William K.'s, construction of *one* mansion?

My W. K. — I called him by his initials sometimes — was worried about this. "Alva dear, I will join you on the evening of this 'presentation', but what happens if my father and mother think we are imprudent, unwise, and possibly crazy?"

"We go right ahead."

"Impossible!"

"Then let him throw you out of the business for being insane. You can tell him you will get an executive post with his greatest railroad rival, Mr. Collis P. Huntington. Or Mr. E. H. Harriman!"

"Alva!"

So, when that decisive evening came, Willie K. and I approached his parents' house at 450 Fifth Avenue without speaking. The plans were tightly rolled up in my hand. I intended to be the last one to make a presentation. For a reason.

But W. K. took my arm and made me stand still for a moment. "Alva, do you realize my father and mother have given up on this quest for social prestige? They are building one house for themselves, and the second for Margaret and Elliott and Emily and William — to live in, Alva, to live in—that is all!"

"Nonsense. Your father expects to spend one third on the furnishings alone. Including a gallery for his paintings. And he has chosen Herter Brothers for the job!"

"But one thing is clear, Alva, you are building our house for the social advancement of the Vanderbilts!"

"*Somebody* has to be honest."

"But why — why do you so desperately want all of us to be accepted?"

"Because I don't want Mrs. Astor to run my life. I am as good as she is! But if you want a formal reason, I can give you that too. The 1880s will be one of the great cultural periods of this country. We will have more opportunity to use our money than ever before, or again"

"So, if the Vanderbilts don't make it in the next ten years, they never again will have such a chance?"

"No. Never. But what we *do* with our money will be the answer. That is why you and I intend to build the most beautiful house on Fifth Avenue!"

"But you still haven't told me why."

I looked at him. I couldn't believe my ears. Had he not understood what I just said? All right — I would give him some flippant reasons — perhaps he would understand *those*. "Because I was born to be rich. I intend to stay that way. And I am demented and determined enough to make the best use of money that I can!"

"Good lord, you make it sound like a crass responsibility."

"It is. And if you don't want to shoulder it, I will!"

"But, Alva, you're not even a Vanderbilt!"

"Willie K., so far, it is the women who have *married* into this family who have made the difference!"

And with this statement, I marched up the steps and rang the bell. Whang whang!

Their butler let us in. My husband was surprised at how well the butler knew me. It was true — I visited my father-and- mother-in-law as often as I wanted to. Sometimes I brought one of the children and sometimes brought both. But my in-laws always gave me time, advice, and love. I had continued to be lonely for my own mother and father, so I was warmly grateful for this.

As we left our wraps with the maid, W. K. and I moved on into the living room hand in hand. No matter what our differences had been outside, we knew that, inside, we were presenting our life, together.

The W. H. Vanderbilts were grateful for our having had two children. Cornelius and Alice had tragically lost little Alice, but subsequently had had William II, Cornelius III, and Gertrude. It was time for the W. K. Vanderbilts to get into the grandchildren picture. We had done so, and this fact was duly noted.

So our intention to build a new house could be predicated on the fact that we needed more room. However, I wondered if that thought would go out the window when the senior Vanderbilts saw the *size* of the house we were presenting. I would have to take my chances, but I was sure that my sisters-in-law and brothers-in-law, not the parents, would blame *me* for it — never Willie K. So I extended a very warm hand toward Maria and W. H. Vanderbilt.

Maria responded, "Alva, darling. Willie K., my dear. Come in, come in."

W. H. followed with, "This is going to be an important evening, isn't it? But never mind that. Tell me, how are Consuelo and little Willie?"

"Fine, thank you." I was both amused and beaming at the same time. "We read some stories to them before we left. Now Cecile is tucking them in."

We moved on into their comfortable living room, where there was a fire burning. Soon there was a buzz of conversation. After-dinner coffee and cake was provided for everyone. Margaret's husband, Colonel Elliott Shepard, and Emily's husband, William Sloane, gravitated toward Willie K. and W. H. The four men formed a talking circle, grateful for the protection of each other. They proceeded to eat. While I observed this, I wondered if this was to be a presentation of plans — three sets — by the *women* of the family?

After we finished all our chatting and eating, W. H. called us all together. He stood in front of a table, cleared his throat, and began to unroll his plans, announcing that his artistic adviser would continue to be Samuel P. Avery. His builder would be J. D. Snook. And his decorator, of course, the renowned firm of Herter.

Little did he know that I, too, intended to engage these Herter Brothers to do *our* house. But I was determined the Herters were not going to send me cables from Europe about what they were buying. "Do you approve, Mrs. Vanderbilt?" I was going to be over there, myself, helping select the very important interior of my house.

W. H. sat down and laid the plans of the twin mansions side by side. I could see some contrast in floor plan, and the second house was in many ways divided in half for the two couples. But the rooms on the ground floor were to be used in common by them. Not so with ground floor of Maria and William — it was all for them. So we began concentrating on this first house and only referring now and then to the second.

I was right. A woman led off the presentation by pointing to the plan's main floor. Maria said, "You see this, my dears? Everyone seems to feel it is very important for William and me to have a great entrance hall, so that we may properly receive our guests at balls and formal receptions."

W. H. nodded solemnly. He was quick to point, then ask, "But, Maria, what's this anteroom for?"

"That is where our guests will play cards after dinner."

Margaret cut in, "Since this is the ballroom over here —between dances, won't the guests need a place to gather? Yes. Father, it will have a second use!"

"Playing cards is good enough for me." W. H. put his finger squarely on the plans in another area. "If we have a ballroom, why do we need a music room?"

Emily explained, "For musicales, father. We can have the finest violinists, pianists, and harpists."

"Eh? I like people who can *sing*. Emily, are you going to have a music room in the other house?"

"Of course. Right here."

"But we are going to have a large passageway between the two houses. So *you* have the fiddlers, the piano players, and the harp pluckers in your house. I will have only vocalists in mine!"

"Ours," corrected Maria, then diverted by pointing to the large floor plan for his gallery. "William, Mr. Avery has made room for *all* your paintings. The entire back of the house. Complete with skylights."

"I told him to. There is a million and a half invested in those pictures alone!" As he leaned over, he nudged her. His index finger tapped the middle of that room. "But I suppose, Maria, you will request this location for your huge Christmas tree you insist on decorating every year?"

"What better spot? The whole family can gather around it."

Emily chided, "And, father, you can invite your favorite opera tenor to lead us in singing carols!"

W. H. laughed. He was always pleased when his children bested him in an argument. After all, that was the way he had finally been accepted by his own father, the old Commodore himself. After receiving years of insults from him, William was persuaded by his new bride, Maria, that this shipping king and ex-vegetable peddler would never respect his own son until he was bested in a business deal. William agreed and proceeded to get the better of him in a transaction about something his father knew well—fertilizer. After that, the Commodore changed his tune and took William into his maritime empire.

It was this W. H. Vanderbilt laugh I was depending on to save me after I had presented our own plans. He might approve, but he would inevitably ask the question. *The* question. In any case, I would have to wait.

Maria again diverted by noting, "William dear, you haven't said anything about the small salon."

He again tapped the plans. "It's just off the music room, isn't it? So that must be where my tenors — and sopranos — are expected to warm up."

Margaret corrected this time. "No. This is where the most important guests are to be entertained during a ball."

"Why aren't they out on the dance floor?"

"This room is for the ones who don't dance."

"Oh? Then I think we should provide them with a lot of dull card games — and maybe they will forget their importance and go dance."

Everyone chuckled, in either enjoyment or deference. After all, this was an important evening to seek approval. By everyone.

Next Emily asked, "What happens if you and mother are having your own ball? Does that mean the four of us have to give a ball too?"

"Yes!" roared W. H. "But you have to pay for your own orchestra!"

W. H. observed my laughing the hardest at this joke. He was pleased. "Alva, dear, when are we going to see *your* plans?"

"Soon." Glancing at Maria, I was very willing to delay. "But I'm sure your wife wants to talk about the dining areas, first."

Maria was pleased. "Yes I do. William, the formal dining room will also have a magnificent marble fireplace."

"What for? Avery tells me this room will seat fifty at one long table. There isn't room!"

"It will also seat one hundred at small tables for supper. So there is room."

"Maria. Fifty is enough. It will take me three months of railroading to pay for the first dinner party!"

Margaret hastily pointed out, "But think of the clients you can entertain!"

W. H. acknowledged the point by winking toward Elliott, William, and my own Willie K. They grinned back, smugly.

Maria was determined to get through the rest of the plans. "But, dear, are you aware of where you eat breakfast?" He shook his head.

Emily's finger was overly helpful in drawing a circle around it. "Right here, father, in the small dining room."

"What? That is where J. D. Snook said he would put a secret door back of one of the panels. To a little elevator. He promised. This elevator will go down to what he called 'a very inconspicuous exit and entrance' onto 51st Street."

Maria was shocked "William! You mean you are not going to leave and enter our house by the front door? Are you aware it will be made of wrought iron and beveled glass?"

"I shall only use that entrance at midnight. Otherwise, people will stare. And point. Plus those reporter fellows. They're always after me."

"And it isn't fair," I defended. "You never made that statement, 'The Public Be Damned'."

"Yes, Alva, I know. I remember that day very well. It had been long and hard. I had finally gone to my sleeping car for a rest."

"That was when that swarm of reporters wanted to come on board your train for an interview?"

"Correct. I sent word I was tired and would receive one representative of them all for a few minutes. But they weren't satisfied. That young man who arrived announced, 'Mr. Vanderbilt, *your* public demands an interview!' I laughed and said, 'Oh, my public be damned.' But the next day he did an article with the headline, 'Vanderbilt says THE PUBLIC BE DAMNED'."

I was incensed enough to stamp my foot. "But people have been repeating that all year! Will they still be saying it in ten years when 1890 rolls around?"

"Probably. And for a hundred years more."

"It isn't even careless reporting. It's dishonest!"

He smiled, then leaned over and kissed my forehead.

Maria took my hand. "Alva dear, thank you for trying to set the record straight." Then she turned to her husband and breathed a very heavy sigh. "Does something like this happen because Mr. W. H. Vanderbilt is always news?"

"Probably so, Maria." He gazed again at the plans. "Look. The exterior of these two houses will be impressive enough, but we haven't even talked about the interiors. You *know* they will be just as grand. These are going to be two, huge, opulent mansions. I will probably *die* in one!"

"And so shall I. And that will again be news — for both of us. But this is not necessary. May I remind you, my dear husband, of what I have said time and time again? This very house you are sitting in at this very moment is good *enough* for me!"

Emily stepped forth. "Mother. Father. Please. We have all made our decision. We must stand by it. There are already 700 workmen being engaged." She began shaking a finger for emphasis. "Sixty of these are sculptors from Italy — imported to carve the cornices, pilasters, columns, entablatures, balusters, arches, and pediments!"

W. H. sawed the air with his own finger. "See what I mean? She sounds like a contractor!"

Margaret moved protectively to his shoulder. "There, there, father. Both of these houses will only be three stories. With flat roofs. We are not building ridiculous towers in the sky." She turned to me for a needed diversion. "Though, perhaps, that is what W. K. and Alva have in mind. Yes?"

It was time for me to step forth. With a reassuring glance toward Willie K., I did. Unrolling our plans, I laid them intentionally on top of their two.

Richard Morris Hunt's ability to draw was my ace card. I played this card at the beginning without waiting.

W. H. and Maria were still seated at the table. The Sloanes and the Shepards were standing behind them. W. K. was beside me.

Everyone on their side of the table gasped.

The exterior of the house not only had all the features Mr. Hunt and I had delightedly called out at the first sketching, it had more. Much more in great balance and beauty. When I first saw this finished drawing, I remarked, "A real Venetian palace, sir, just as the Doges had!"

But to my audience in this living room, I carefully said something quite opposite. "My dear family, let us be honest. We are all building country houses in the city. Your houses and mine should be surrounded by gardens, hedges, and greensward rolling to the forest.

But the cost of lots on Fifth Avenue is already prohibitive. W. K., Richard Morris Hunt, and I feel we should have purchased the whole block. But we could not. So we must all compromise before we have even started."

Willie K., bless him, pointed out, "The best we can do is this beautiful stone railing around our house — on both Fifth Avenue and on 52nd Street. It gives a continuous feeling of unity, don't you think?"

W. H. agreed, but asked, "Is this house a copy?"

My husband turned to me to make the reply. "No," I explained. "It combines, we hope, the most graceful features of both the Chateau de Blois in Touraine and of the Jacques Coeur castle at Bourges."

Emily commented, with the first definite sign of envy, "Reflecting your childhood in France, no doubt?"

"Reflecting the best in European architecture," I qualified. "We have also taken certain features from the château at Chenonceaux and from the one at Azay-le-Rideau."

W. H. and Maria seemed interested, but I knew this architectural derivation would cost me the approval of the Shepards and the Sloanes.

Willie K. quickly added, "Instead of doing a box style, we hope we are creating an irregular line of silhouettes from all these past glories."

For a man who attended precious few designing sessions, I thought my husband was doing very well!

So I went on, undaunted. "Yes. You can see these pinnacles and gables rimming the roof."

W. H tapped the plans, harder than he had his own. "Such a remarkable amount of frieze work. And these medieval spires, here, rather eye-catching. Is that what you intended, Alva?"

"Our intention, in choosing the lines of the exterior, is very frankly to impress, yes sir."

He laughed — the very laugh I wanted.

Maria asked quietly, "And this goes for the interior, too?"

"Yes, ma'am. It is designed as a house in which to entertain."

"Not live?"

"That too. For example, the gymnasium on the third floor, here — designed for our children — will double on the ball nights. Decorated with vines and flowers, it can become a bower for our guests to enjoy a midnight supper."

Emily sucked in a covetous breath. "But a gymnasium?" W. K. outlined this room on the plans, with fatherly pride. "Yes. Large enough for roller skating and bicycle riding."

Margaret's voice became sardonic. "Oh, very good. When the staff at Delmonico's caters for you, the waiters can all do it on bicycles!"

Everyone thought her joke to be a huge one. I thought it to be small avarice. But I waited for her to do the proper amount of basking before I continued. "Speaking of ball nights, let's go back to the first floor plans. Right here, the doors of our Louis XV salon may be opened into the banquet hall — really our two-story dining room — to create a very large dancing area."

Elliott Shepard noted, "With two fireplaces? They look a bit large. And what's this? A stained-glass window?"

W. K. nudged him, "You're right on both counts. Want to know what the window will depict?"

"A bunch of dancing gluttons, no doubt!"

"No. Francis I and Henry VIII, midst their courtiers, meeting on the Field of the Cloth of Gold."

"Dear me. I would have preferred the gluttons .... But what about these windows shown along the *sides* of the hall?"

I tried to identify them for Elliott, but I knew I was already trying to forecast a party atmosphere. "These windows will be designed by Oudinot, and we told him to use very bright colors. These colors, I hope, can be picked up by the glass in the wrought iron chandeliers."

William Sloane pointed a finger of caution. "This balcony — is it for the musicians?" He accepted my nod. "For how many?"

"It can hold twenty."

"Then be careful with all this glass. They'll shatter it with vibrations. Francis I and Henry VIII will find themselves in the middle of the floor doing a polka!"

The uproar of hilarity was once again at the expense of Willie K. and myself. We tried, unsuccessfully, to join in.

Maria was sensitive to this. She decided to immediately restore order. "Alva dear. Tell us about some of the other interiors. We are so anxious to hear about those."

Silence set the stage.

"You are referring to the furnishings?" I received a pleased nod from her. I would now be forced to mention Herter Brothers.

But W. H. cut in. "Furnishings! Alva sounds as if she, herself, will choose every one of them."

I gave him a broad and relieved smile, and waited until he returned it. "You are right, sir. Mr. Hunt and I both intend to go to Europe to choose the furnishings."

"At the same time?"

The two couples snickered.

"No," I grinned at them. "I intend to go to estate sales and bring back whole rooms. While Mr. Hunt will be looking for doorways, wainscoting, flooring, tapestries —"

"— and suits of armor!" Willie K. sang out.

I blew my husband a grateful kiss. "Don't forget I also told him he must find an alabaster bathtub!"

Emily snapped at the drawings with her fingers. "Yes, I have been noticing the design of these second floor bathrooms. Yours is the most elegant. So I assume the alabaster tub is for you?"

"With modern plumbing and solid gold fixtures."

Emily nodded. "Adjoining your boudoir, of course. But this next room looks more like a state bedroom. I assume Willie K. is going to have one, too?"

"On the floor directly above, connected by a circular stairway."

Maria reminded Emily, "Dear, that is the custom. A bedroom for the husband and one for the wife."

"But, look here, that doesn't explain why *his* always seems to be smaller!"

W. H. slapped the table. "Emily. That is because the husband is usually nocturnally residing in the bedroom of his wife!"

He followed with a booming laugh, much to Emily's embarrassment. But Maria gave her a pat, and then cast a cautioning glance at W. H.

His rejoinder to her warning was, "Whether he has to ascend a spiral stairway in the morning or not!"

At this moment, the presentation seemed to belong only to the amused men in the room. The women needed to get it back. Particularly one Alva Smith Vanderbilt. This woman who was not even a Vanderbilt!

Maria very adroitly helped me by rising and directing everyone's gaze toward the plans. "My dear, we have talked about everything but the design of this magnificent main hall. What a useful reception area."

W. K. made his own return to the plans. "Mother, if you're talking about *use*, why not say something about this children's study, here?"

"Yes, my dear William, what a charming idea."

"And let's not overlook the parlor, the library, and especially this billiard room, right here!"

As all three of the covetous men "Ohhhhhhed and Ahhhhhhed", Willie K. puffed out in satisfaction.

Margaret deflected, not to be upstaged. "I must say that is the grandest stairway I have ever seen!"

Emily joined. "And that archway to it, leading off the main hall, it looks like the entrance to an Exposition!"

I was aglow. "You are right. That's what I hope the whole structure will be — such a credit to Richard Morris Hunt that he will be asked to do the central building for the next World's Fair!"[3]

But, right now, I felt the time had come to begin to discreetly roll up our plans.

W. H. himself prevented me. "Just a moment. We've seen it all?" He received a nod from me. Then he leaned back, thumped his stomach, and asked *the* monumental question, "Well, well, then, where do you expect to get the *money* for all this?"

It was not too late. Here was my moment. The secret I had kept. My own surprise.

"From you!" I answered, giving him an affectionate slap on the back.

The others were appalled at my temerity. Even Willie K. It was as though I had slapped the back of The Established Power Himself.

Everyone that is, but W. H. He began murmuring very quietly, then broke into a soft chuckle.

I continued to roll our plans until they were in a tight and safe cylinder. I was thirsting for another cup of coffee, but I felt the tactful thing to do was for Willie K. and myself to just thank them all for their hospitality, their attention, and the opportunity to see their own plans. And leave.

We did.

As we climbed into our waiting carriage, we said nothing. And not a word all the way back to our house.

And nothing but "Goodnight" before retiring. Separately.

After two days of only routine exchanges between us, I could stand the suspense no longer. When my husband returned from the office that night, I asked him a simple, direct question. "Is there any word?" Then I added, "Or was I too overbearing?"

"No, you weren't." He put his arms around me. "Alva dear, that night—I know you must have wondered why I didn't tell you what a magnificent presentation you made. But it was because I didn't know. I really didn't." He leaned his forehead against mine. "But I know *now*... Late this afternoon, father called me into his office after everyone else had gone. Only the two of us were there. He didn't even ask me to sit down. Father simply gazed at me hard and said, 'How much will it cost?'"

"I had to answer. Finally I said, 'More than it should, I'm afraid'."

"He insisted, 'How much?'"

"I told him. 'Three million'."

"And guess what? All he said was, 'Tell Alva she has it .... Start building'."

Willie K. waited for me to explode. I did. I followed it with ascending outbursts.

When I finally stopped to catch my breath, I realized I was hugging Willie K. even harder than he was hugging me.

But when we both stood off and looked at each other, I didn't say "Really?" or "Isn't that grand?!" I said nothing. I couldn't.

My eyes were wet. I simply was glad I had ordered our cook earlier to prepare an especially fine dinner for him. Very glad.

As we moved into the dining room, our arms were again around each other. It was over, but I could hardly wait for tomorrow.

First, to go to the W. H. Vanderbilt's house, before W. H. left for his office, and *thank* him. And thank Maria.

Second, to go down to The Studio Building and see Richard Morris Hunt. To give him a report.

As I had promised, "Trust me — a real report!"

4

T HIS IS NOT THE FIRST TIME I HAVE DICTATED MY
memoirs. Perhaps that is why I have the courage to try again.
But this second time I have decided to do it in a different way.
Years ago I had dictated directly to Sara Bard Field, a fellow
worker in the American Woman's Suffrage Movement.

We had done this dictation in my Chinese Teahouse in Newport, Rhode
Island. This Teahouse is located at the far edge of the broad lawn on the
Atlantic seacoast side of my Marble House. My Chinese creation is
perched on the very edge of the cliff, above Cliff Walk. The lapping of the
waves can be heard far below.

Somehow I felt this location was appropriate to my dictation. I had lived
dangerously many times in my life.

But, at this time, what really was the need for putting my life down on
paper? I had had several requests from members in the Woman's Movement to do so. But more than that, it was wartime. It was 1917, and
everyone was feeling the need to make a record of American life, lest the
Germans in their U-boats come across the Atlantic and destroy it!

So, for much of that summer of 1917, I dictated to Sara, she took it down
in shorthand, and then typed it up at night.

We did it in a series of essays. On my early childhood. On travel. On
marriage. On divorce. And so on.

But this time, in 1932, I want to continue to do it as a panorama.
Chronologically. I feel a life is a life, not a series of subject matters.

Unfortunately, during that war, we were only part way through when
Sara had personal problems, followed later by the tragic accidental death
of her son. Even though this was at the time she was editing the copy, we
stopped the project.

I gave Sara the option of beginning again when she cared to. But her
life had changed. That day never came.

Thus I feel I am wise — if not also free — to start the project again, in a different way. And this time, I hope to finish it.

My donkey hopes so, too. He feels it is all too obvious we should start the rounds, right now, and continue on to this next part of the story.

CONQUEST OF *THE* MRS. ASTOR

And report on the conquest for a godfather I did. Richard Morris Hunt was amused and grateful but wasted no time. This great man went to work.

So did I. Plus hundreds of carpenters and masons —construction workers of all types, including sculptors. Many of them had old-world backgrounds and experience, and all worked to create our new house at 660 Fifth Avenue.

From the time Mr. Hunt and I started sketching in 1878, until the time of completion in 1882, there were four full years of intense planning, checking, adjusting, and a *daily* workload to push through, regardless of obstacles.

As I had stated, Mr. Hunt and I both made trips to Europe to choose the various types of furnishings. It may have sounded like an elegant search, but it was often a case of hard sleuthing and sometimes a wild-goose chase.

I fully realized I could not have done this if there were not servants at home to take care of Consuelo and little Willie. Money was the key to everything. And I fully respected its use.

To build a house in which the William K. Vanderbilts could entertain was fine, but, again, it was to gain the social recognition of *all* Vanderbilts.

To do this, and to celebrate the completion of the house, I felt Willie K. and I must not only give the most interesting but the most lavish costume ball of the decade. Yes, decade. I also wanted New York to remember this party for the rest of this century. And possibly into the next.

But there was still one very large conquest that I had to make. It stood directly in the way of our ever giving this ball. That was the conquest of Mrs. William B. Astor — Caroline Astor — The Mrs. Astor. She had to be present at the ball. Her presence was indispensable.

I knew I must plan my strategy carefully. And secretly. I could not even tell my husband. I believed the element of surprise was, as usual, the key to my success.

So, in sending out the invitations, for Monday evening, March 26, 1883, I subtracted two.

One, the invitation for The Mrs. Astor.

And, two, the invitation for her daughter, Caroline, known as Carrie.

These invitations were already addressed to each. But they were *not* to be sent. Not yet.

So, as the evening for the gala costume ball approached, I awaited the reaction to this subtraction.

The reaction finally came one day at noon, after Willie K. had come home to have lunch with me and the children in our new house. We all had finished eating and putting our napkins back into their individual rings. Consuelo and little Willie then asked to be excused to go upstairs and play in the "indoor playground".

Herter Brothers and I were still receiving shipments of furniture to put in their proper places. Everything was new and exciting, and the two children could not get over the fact that they had their own gymnasium.

"They are very content up there, so let's move into the parlor, dear," I suggested.

"The parlor has become your office, your sitting room, and your command post."

"And my receiving center. So what better place to go and discuss the ball?"

We moved into the room and stood looking over the piles of acceptances on the table. W. K. pointed out, "You realize, Alva, we had no chance of giving this ball until my grandfather died."

"Yes. The Commodore would not have fitted in."

"Furthermore, he had to pass on his money to his son, so that it could be passed on to us, so we could build this house!"

"True. Every time I look at your father, I am grateful. But honestly, my dear, for the last two years, I think he has received a thrill from passing by this house, to see what has been added *today*."

"My father has a great sense of the competitive. And he knows, Alva, that you are competing."

"W. H. Vanderbilt also knows a lot about life. Sometimes I sit at a family dinner party, look across at him, and wonder, 'Did this great financier and railroad magnate once take on an unusual responsibility for his father's so-called welfare? Did W. H. actually have to select healthy and willing backstairs maids for the old Commodore?'"

"So they say. And I'm sure my *grandfather* would have considered them 'necessary to his welfare'."

"On those sedate Sunday afternoons we visited your father and mother, I had to pinch myself, once I believed it to be true."

"Pinching was what the Commodore was supposed to be good at — and doing exactly this to anyone's maid on any visit. I think it was when he missed the girl, that he, reportedly, 'missed the cuspidor and spit on his host's rug'!"

"That's why he was never asked to anyone's home more than once?"

"That's why."

"But — this choosing healthy and willing backstairs maids for his father — how many sons, today, would be willing to do *that*?"

Willie K. roared. Then he nuzzled my ear. "Alva, darling, let us hope that our son, Willie, does not have to do that for *me*."

I joined his laughter but not his humor. As a young wife, I was hoping this day would never come. Probably it would. But this generation was different. The fathers undoubtedly preferred going out to look for their "maids" themselves!

Regardless of founded and unfounded gossip about the old Commodore, his grandson and I were truly grateful for this man's ability to practice sound business methods. For example, when he expanded into the national and international shipping industry, he learned it from the bottom up, so that he knew what he was talking about. But also so that he would not be cheated. He still hated to be bested in any deal.

This was also true of his venturing into the railroad industry. And he didn't even go into that business until he was sixty-six years old. I would say to Willie K., "Two careers, already, in the Vanderbilt family? Shipping and railroads? Amazing."

I was fully aware of what made me discuss this with Willie K. right now. It was because I was, once more, thinking of Mrs. Astor. There was a great similarity between the Vanderbilts and the Astors. The Astors were in the fur-trading business, tracking all the way out to the territory of Oregon. But when they wished to enter New York Society, this was not acceptable. They were thought of as coonscap-wearing frontiersmen. So they went into the real estate business. That was respectable.

In arranging my "trap" for Caroline Astor, I knew I must think about this similarity, and I intended to create an opportunity, soon, to point it out to her.

Willie K. would have thought me much too aggressive. But I had my reason. And it involved his welfare.

All that would be taken care of in due time. I hoped. But right now I had the daily task of quieting my husband's fears about the impending "fancy dress ball" as he called it.

"Alva, anything else new? If not, I must be getting back to the office. We have a two o'clock board meeting."

"Give yourself time to digest your lunch."

"Once again, you planned a delicious one. Even Consuelo and little Willie liked it. Compliment the cook for me."

I prevented him from starting for the door by pointing to the invitations. "We will have to have someone announce each person or couple, as they arrive. Otherwise, we won't know them in costume."

He leveled a William K. Vanderbilt gaze at me. "We won't know them anyway!"

I grinned. "What does it matter? They're curious and inquisitive. They want to see the interior of our new home."

"And you expect all of them to ask us back?"

"My dear, that is the general idea."

"Good lord. We'll be going to dinners every night for the next three years!"

Fortunately Cecile entered at this moment. She went directly to my husband and bowed. "Sir. Mr. Ward McAllister asks to see you and Mrs. Vanderbilt." And she presented the proper plate with the proper card on it.

With a pounding heart, I watched Willie K. read it. This man, Mr. Ward McAllister, had arrived. My plan was actually working.

W. K. exchanged a glance with me, returned the card to the plate, and instructed, "Thank you, Cecile. Show him in." When he made sure she was out of the parlor, he turned and confronted me. "What is Ward McAllister doing here? I thought he was a social secretary for Mrs. William Astor."

I delayed by trying to clarify. "Secretary? He's more than that. Ward McAllister is a social arbiter, a major domo, a planner of her magnificent parties, and even a choreographer for her quadrilles."

"Her quadrilles!" He felt it was time to shake his finger and speak in full tones to me. "Alva. Are you trying to woo him away from

Caroline Webster Schermerhorn Astor?"

I was impressed he knew her entire family background. And that he had guessed …. My attempt at secrecy was again over.

"There isn't a chance, W. K. But we must face her. Fancy dress ball or not, unless *The* Mrs. Astor attends, there will be a very important group of people who will not."

"All the money and all the planning for this party will be lost?"

"Yes!"

He knew I meant it. And he knew I was desperate. So, when Cecile showed Mr. McAllister into our parlor, my dear husband decided that the battle was mine. Of course he could stand on the side and guard me, but the in-fighting was something I had planned. And must see through to the finish.

Ward McAllister was the handsome and professional representative of Caroline Astor that I had expected. He was dressed and groomed impeccably, and apparently determined not to fail his mission. At that moment, when Cecile was leaving the room, carrying his cape, hat, and cane, he was careful to give her a grateful nod. But I knew he was surprised that a butler had not greeted him at the door.

However, I did not intend to explain to Mr. McAllister that this was the day off for our butler, Harwood. One of two days, actually. I believed in the necessity of a five-day week. And I intended to set an example.

I think Mr. McAllister figured this out, because he seemed to be impressed with our informality.

And I was with his. He shook hands. "Mrs. Vanderbilt… Mr. Vanderbilt."

The fact that he addressed me and reached for my hand first meant already that he knew who was making the calls in this shooting gallery. Ahhhhh — a true Southern sportsman. Furthermore, he was inclusively tactful. "I am so pleased that both of you would see me."

Willie K. smiled. "Thank you, but I'm afraid, sir, very soon I must get back to the office."

"Indeed, I understand, Mr. Vanderbilt."

"Office?" I indicated the table. "But, as you can see, Mr. McAllister, *mine* is right here."

"Ah yes, for those grateful replies. Including my own, no doubt."

I knew where he was leading. "We are so pleased you can come."

"With your permission, I am coming in costume as Count de la

Mole, lover of Marguerite de Valois." He gazed around our parlor and through to the salon. "And my colors, I believe, will be just right for this interior of your magnificent new château. My couturier says purple velvet slashed with scarlet silk."

"Tres merveilleux." I side-glanced at Willie K., making sure he did not head for the door too soon. "Mr. Vanderbilt will be attired as the Duc de Guise."

Waiting, W. K. gave a flourish. "In yellow silk tights, yellow-band black trunks, yellow doublet, topped by a black velvet cloak embroidered with yellow gold!"

Mr. McAllister raised sympathetic brows and diverted a smile. "Duc de Guise? Wasn't he murdered in the Chateau de Blois?"

"That's exactly the way I feel every time I have a fitting!"

There was little I could say. Mr. Hunt and I *did* pattern our house, both after the Jacques Coeur castle at Bourges and that very Chateau de Blois. I decided to let the men have their fun. It could soften Mr. McAllister for the blow.

He corroborated, "Mr. Vanderbilt, I can share your feelings. I find my doublet and hose so intricate that I have to climb into them from a stepladder. That is, with the aid of two manservants." He raised an emphasizing finger. "And we are finding the whole process takes one hour!"

W. K. chuckled, "My, my, Mr. McAllister. I hope you will find our ball to be worth all that."

"Everyone says it will be the grandest of the century."

"Century?" I said to myself. Did I hear correctly? Was he even more in agreement with me? "Ah yes. But you, yourself, have arranged some very grand ones for Mrs. Astor." This was the first mention of her name. And he had allowed *me* to bring it up.

"Yes. We keep her ballroom very busy. But she says her next house must have a ballroom which will accommodate at least 400 guests!"

My next shot had more than wig-powder in it. "But never for parties for *more* than 400."

"Indeed not." He made sure my eyes met his. "However. Mrs. Astor and I feel New York society may deserve to be labeled 'The 400', but for more reasons than the capacity of a ballroom!"

"Then, Mr. McAllister, perhaps Mr. Vanderbilt and I can remedy that situation by giving a ball for *1200*."

He gave me an acknowledging bow. I felt it was also to cover a gulp from his throat. Glad to change the subject, he pointed around the parlor and nodded toward adjoining rooms. "And in this French Renaissance Gothic wonder. When we drive by in her carriage, Mrs. Astor always points out such features as your marvelous balconies or your corbelled tourelle."

And I knew exactly what she had to say about them!

But Mr. McAllister was covering nicely. "Then she always asks 'How did Mrs. Vanderbilt *ever* find her architect?'"

Willie K. took over. "In an atelier down in Greenwich Village. Richard Morris Hunt and Mrs. Vanderbilt found that they both had been educated in France."

"So why not celebrate this in the building of a mansion?"

"Exactly. But I must be getting back to the office if we are to pay for the next celebration—this ball!" He extended his hand. "So if you will excuse me, Mr. McAllister."

"Of course. Again, I am very grateful for this visit, Mr. Vanderbilt." He bowed and watched my husband as he was leaving the room.

I was busy giving Willie K. a quietly amused eye. He controlled a smug grin and hurried out.

Mr. McAllister seemed pleased to be alone with me, now. "Mrs. Vanderbilt. This ball is precisely the reason I am here. Mrs. Astor is very concerned about her daughter, Carrie. May I begin by saying you and Mrs. Astor both have very attractive daughters?"

"Oh? Even though Consuelo is only six?"

"And Carrie old enough to make her debut into society."

"A society which Mrs. Astor controls."

"Exactly. But she desires social appearances for Carrie. Just as you —" He hesitated.

"— will desire appearances someday for our Consuelo?"

"Yes." He hastened on. "For months, now, your guests have been hiring famous French couturiers to design their costumes. But, as is the custom, your guests have also been arranging something else."

"Rehearsing entertainments for our ball?"

"Yes."

"Very nice of them."

"In Mrs. Astor's own ballroom, at this very moment, Carrie and a group of her friends are practicing the Star Quadrille."

"In costume?"

"Indeed. The young ladies wear gray tulle and diamonds, while the young gentlemen wear their Louis XV gray satin court dress."

"Charming."

"And Mrs. Astor is, no doubt, watching and thinking the same thing." He came closer but seemed to stall.

I waited. I was not going to help him with the very thing he had come to say.

"But, madam, we find neither Mrs. Astor nor her daughter have received their invitations. The hour is late, as you know. So I am sure it may have been an oversight."

"It was not an oversight, Mr. McAllister. But I *am* sorry. It is certainly too bad Miss Carrie Astor has gone to all that trouble, and the Star Quadrille shall be wasted."

He stared. "Wasted?"

"Yes. My dear, Mr. McAllister, how can I invite her? How can I invite her mother? Neither Miss Astor nor Mrs. Astor have ever called on me!"

His mouth dropped open. It took him several moments to recover.

Finally he leaned over and took my hand. "Mrs. Vanderbilt. I shall *personally* attend to this matter." Kissing my hand, he began backing away. "May I bid you good day."

I rang for Cecile. She came — bless her cognizant heart — carrying his cape, hat, and cane.

He received them with relieved gratitude. Nodding to me, he followed her out.

In a few moments, I heard the front door open, then close.

I stood there, feeling very pleased. Feeling triumphant, I hoped.

The following afternoon, *The* Mrs. Astor was driven up to my door. She did not get out of her carriage. Her footman got out, instead. He knocked on my door. And presented Cecile with New York's most famous calling card.

Cecile presented it to me. It read only "Mrs. Astor"— meaning that there was *no other*.

The footman then got back into the carriage, and they drove off. An actual visit was not necessary.

Within a half hour, I had the two invitations delivered, by our own footman, to "No Other's" door ....

5

I LOVE HOUSES.
In my fortunate 79 years, I have built one on Fifth Avenue and one on Madison Avenue, in New York; one in Newport, Rhode Island; and two on Long Island. And I have remodeled three in France, one in Newport, and one on Long Island.

Not a bad record.

This present château has required the least remodeling. Actually, parts of the grounds and the surroundings continue to bother me more than the house. The sanding on the fore court, for instance, should all be covered with paving stones. But these things can be changed. If I can change a river, apparently I can change anything.

For me, a house has to have more than beauty. It has to have a history. My château does. That's why it appealed to me. Once again in my life, this appeal concerned women and their status.

The great financier and builder, Jacques Coeur, had given this château to his daughter. The gift was a tribute to the female hierarchy, and I wished it to be carried on.

Of the houses I have either built or remodeled, one has even received distinguished formal recognition. Our house at 660 Fifth Avenue.

Right now, I want to tell you about the great party we gave at that house. I know it will take at least a week or two to remember the special guests, costumes, entertainment, food, encounters, têtes-à-têtes, and gossip.

So it probably will require two sections or chapters to tell it all.

I will not interrupt the second section with my introductory comments. You can read straight through. And enjoy it.

I assure you I will enjoy telling it.

PARTY TO THE ACCEPTANCE

This was the night. Monday, March 26, 1883. The gala event 1200 people were, I hoped, waiting to attend.

I hoped they were also eager to break all the pre-Easter fasting and denial. This could be a double celebration.

"But, Alva," my husband warned, "even with all that, they may find it difficult to believe you built this house just for the party!"

"Why not? I have a monumental cause."

W. K. muttered, took my hand, and led me to the spot where we would receive our guests. It was a dais, especially built for the occasion. In our gold and white French salon, of course. Lady Mandeville, our matchmaker, took her place beside us. I would be depending on her heavily to further identify the guests to Willie K. and me, after they had been announced. She could give the first warm greeting. W. K. and I would follow with our own.

Guests began arriving at 10:30, though the opening of the party was scheduled for 11:00.

"They can't wait!" I bubbled.

From the salon, I would not see our entrance, but I could imagine the carriages arriving and guests descending in their various costumes. I knew the onlookers had long since gathered. What a sight it must be. They should be gaping!

Lady Mandeville leaned toward me. "Of course your guests can't wait, dear. Entering under a striped awning? Walking across a carpet of Vanderbilt maroon? My, oh my!"

Willie K. overheard and reminded her, "But they have to pass the bas-relief watchdogs to do it."

"And every reporter in town wishes he were one."

"I'm not so sure the *New York Herald* hasn't transferred the souls of their two best society critics inside each!"

Lady Mandeville and I wanted to laugh — hard, but we couldn't. Each of our costumes was too elaborately restraining.

She was wearing a dress copied from Van Dyck's portrait of Princess de Croy. It was black velvet, with puff sleeves and a stand-up collar of Venetian lace. True to the lady in the painting, her elegant coiffure was crowned by a Van Dyck hat and Venetian plumes.

I was the Alexis Cabanel re-creation of his painting of a Venetian Renaissance countess. My shoulder-strap bodice (the exact reason I couldn't laugh with abandon) was of blue satin, covered with gold embroidery, with flowing sleeves of transparent gold tissue-material. My double-strand pearls looped to my midriff, then rose to a shoulder-strap anchor.

At that moment, I could feel Willie K.'s eyes noting them, then traveling on down to my puffed-at-the-hips brocade skirt. It was a many-colored wonder, outlined with figures of flowers and leaves, all created by iridescent beads. This iridescence was repeated in my light-blue satin train. Embroidered and lined in Roman red, of course! My husband sighed as his eyes followed its draping line all the way to my slippered feet.

There was nothing like this kind of splendor to beguile a man who has been seeing you every day of his married life ....

Now feasted, his eyes slowly returned to my face. And my hair. He was again rewarded. My auburn curls fell across my bare shoulders. As if this weren't enough for him, this same hair was crowned by an upturned Milan bonnet covered with jewels, including a gem-studded miniature peacock!

Were there photographs of all this? Ah yes. Many. Of Willie K. as Duc de Guise, handsome in his discomfort. And of me. He was relieved when the photo sessions were over. But I loved all that flashing of powder. Because it didn't disturb the doves. Doves? Six of them, stuffed — two on the floor, one near the chair, one about to perch on each of my hands and the sixth intending to perch on my bonnet but never getting into the final photograph! All this was the photographer's idea; he was a real stickler for authenticity. If posterity was destined to view the classic photograph of the hostess of this costume ball, then he wished those six doves to be definitely "fluttering about".

The original Alexis Cabanel painting was not available, and I could not receive my guests "surrounded by all this wildlife", so I did the next best thing. I stood in front of my Raymond de Madrazo portrait. The dais had been deliberately placed so I was able to accomplish this. Either, I could do the portrait justice, or it could do me justice — I didn't care. I knew my husband had many fine wines waiting for my guests. If, by the end of the night, they wanted to see me as a double image, that was their pleasure!

Right now we were waiting to receive our guests, waiting because the whole procedure was going according to my orders. In the main hall, the footmen, in powdered wigs and knee breeches, were relieving the gentlemen of their outer coats. And directing the ladies upstairs, up our grand staircase, to the state bedrooms where maids in French peasant dress attended to their needs.

William H. and Maria Vanderbilt had long since arrived and stepped into the salon at that moment to view us three waiting on the dais. They both looked like old and new portraits which did *not* hang on the wall. She was quietly and softly costumed as a lady-in-waiting to Marie Antoinette. But my father-in-law was not in costume — not in the least. He wore his regular, severe black and white evening attire.

My husband gave him a twinkling glance of admiration for not giving the arriving Gotham guests a last chance to ignore him. It was a reversal. He was not in fancy dress — now they would *have* to notice him.

After returning his son's glance, he looked over at me. As if tonight were the night. His daughter-in-law would end forever the characterizing of the Vanderbilt fortune as "vulgar railroad money". And the referring to our new house and their new twin mansions as "nouveaux riches blights on Fifth Avenue."

I realized that these opinions had been voiced at times by Caroline Astor. That was why I was amazed, when Ward McAllister visited us, that he conveyed her compliments about our new house. Perhaps her opinions were changing. I intended to find out. To-night. I had not only my plan to get her aside and talk with her, I even hoped that I could sit down with her at one of my dining tables upstairs, and the two of us could have a late supper — privately. But that part of my hope would be left to chance.

I still did not tell anyone about my plans, not even my beloved friend, Lady Mandeville, still standing beside me. This was the lady after whom we had named our daughter. I was delighted that, before long, my friend would have three names: Her maiden name, Consuelo Yznaga; second, Lady Mandeville; and last, the Duchess of Manchester. Her husband was soon to become the eighth Duke of Manchester. It was she, bless her heart, who said to me, "Alva dear, I will see to it that there will be precious few 'Regrets' back from the 1200 invitations you sent out." And precious few there were. True to her word, she had personally urged many important people to be our guests.

I was quietly convinced that having a title had been the persuading factor. When a Lady Mandeville speaks, you are very liable to listen. I was always impressed. And I wondered if someday, by some wild scheme or fortunate set of circumstances, we could have a title in *our* family. I was not sure how this could be achieved, but I intended to keep my eyes and ears open.

At the moment, I knew I had to stop my speculating. The first couple was coming through the main hall into the parlor and approaching us. I did not recognize the two. But I was happy to see they both glanced up at my portrait — it gave me a little time. However, one of our footmen appeared on cue. The couple handed him their invitation, and he dutifully announced them. I was saved. All three of us extended our hands, in turn, smiled and spoke their names in welcome. They correctly spoke our own, returned our greeting, and moved on into the ballroom.

This process continued, with delightful interruptions by Lady Mandeville when the guests were friends of hers. She included Willie K. and me into the quick small talk, and made us feel, for the first time, a part of the New York social scene.

At Mrs. Astor's, I thought Ward McAllister probably performed this function. But I wasn't sure. We had never been invited to any party at the William Astor home. However, I was proud, throughout all the detailed planning for our own, that I did most of it myself. I did not need a hired social manipulator.

I hoped this would be true for the rest of my life, because I fully intended to set an entertainment level that would keep my rivals huffing and puffing.

The guests were now arriving and approaching our dais in frequent surges. My friend was kept very busy. Willie K. and I shook hands, nodded, smiled, chuckled, laughed, and complimented costumes for a solid hour.

The common knowledge that Mrs. Astor would be attending our ball had made the presence of the more reluctant a reality. Here were names I had never dared hope would enter our front portal. In addition, they had gone to the expense and trouble of wearing a diverse array of elaborate and innovative costumes. How fortunate could I be?

Finally, Caroline Astor herself appeared. It was literally a stunning moment. She was dressed as a lady of the Venetian court, adorned with jewels. The newspapers later said these jewels were a $200,000 sampling from her million-dollar collection. I was grateful for even that one-fifth!

Because our mansion was a château, most of the guests had chosen to wear costumes of the sixteenth-century French, Italian, English, German, Austrian, and even Russian courts. Men were knights, courtiers, princes, hussars, gondoliers, court jesters, or monks with bare feet! Even the Villonesque troubadours were matched by costumed tattered streetgirls. But most of the ladies chose to come as romantic characters, ranging from Joan of Arc to Juliet to Madame Pompadour.

At this point, I reminded Willie K., "The Hobby Horse Quadrille must begin promptly at 11:30." And as we moved into our dining hall, I remarked, "I *told* Richard Morris Hunt this would make a great ballroom."

"Why not — when it's two stories high."

Then we spotted the great man, himself. He was dressed as Cimabue, the painter Dante chose to symbolize "the transience of fame". Ah yes.

I embraced him warmly. "This cape and hood over your head is a great foil. All the better to view the pretty girls, transient or not!"

Laughing, along with R. M. H., Willie K. continued, "But more than that, it exposes the rest of you. And what great legs you have."

Mr. Hunt posed. "It's what tights and hose can do, my good man!" And his great laugh underlined his pose.

When we finally simmered down, Mr. Hunt pointed out the musicians in the balcony. They were tuning up for the Quadrille. "Alva, my dear, when I drew up the plans for this room, I should have sketched in those very men."

"Yes. Marvelous what a hostess — any hostess — can do with violins, violoncellos, and double basses."

"As long as she has those horns, trombones, and kettledrums to go with them."

He was right. The conductor struck up the music.

To my great surprise, it was not the tune for the Hobby Horse Quadrille. For the first time, I turned away from R. M. H. and my husband and looked at the dancers. They were very properly performing the Mother Goose Quadrille.

I excused myself and went to make prompt inquiry. It seemed that the workmen had been preparing costumes for the Hobby

Horse Quadrille for two months and were still not quite ready!

So I immediately made my way over to Mr. Ward McAllister, the creator and choreographer of the Mother Goose Quadrille. He was dressed as he had promised. I addressed him properly. "Count de la Mole, may I compliment you on your gift to our entertainment. We are honored."

"Mrs. Vanderbilt, thank you." He bowed. "Even though it did not ease my difficulties in getting into this costume, it has all been worth it."

Indicating his dancers on the floor, I remarked, "I can see they are showing off Mary, Mary Quite Contrary to lilting advantage."

"Yes, aren't they splendid? And when this is over, I will be able to relax and view your sister's Opera Bouffe."

"Oh, that will be last, Mr. McAllister." My sister had wanted it that way. She had married Fernando Yznaga, brother of my friend, Consuelo, but this Cuban influence would not be felt in this Opera Bouffe. It could be saved for an outdoor, folk-like festivity. The Opera Quadrille would be quite different. So it must be the final entertainment of the evening.

Willie K. appeared, nodded his greeting to Mr. McAllister, and tugged at my arm. "We must excuse ourselves. The Hobby Horse Quadrille is finally ready."

Mr. McAllister was gracious. "Yes, I understand, Mr. Vanderbilt. Mine is fortunately just finishing."

As my husband and I slowly made our way through the spectators to rejoin Richard Morris Hunt, we heard the music work to its finale. After a few moments, the tune I had orginally expected was struck up.

The dancers began. All three of us watched, but it was my Willie K. who was raising his brow. William Kissam Vanderbilt could never be fooled in the horseworld. He knew it all. "Alva, you didn't tell me this would actually be a steeplechase!"

He was lightly referring to the accompanying ladies in their red hunting-coats and white satin skirts, elegantly embroidered. But his real focus was on the frames of the horse-bodies that had been fitted down over the hips of the male dancers. These frames included false legs, hanging from the gentlemen's waists — legs complete in jodhpurs and riding boots. This gave a satirized but amazingly real appearance of a true rider on a horse. The red hunting coat, white satin vest, red cap, and riding crop of each dancer did the rest.

In spite of all their splendor, I leaned toward Willie K. in apprehension, since I was more worried about the men than the women. "Those panels reach all the way to the floor, let alone the tails of the horses. Let's hope the tempo doesn't increase."

But it did. The dance steps of the gentlemen's feet beneath the horse frames grew more intricate. On one of the twists and turns, two of the riders slipped on my highly polished floor and fell.

"Ohhhhhhh!" I was ready to call for a "doctor in the house." But, to my amazement, the two dancers stood up, laughed, straightened their horse-frames, and continued.

With a horse-breeder's glee, my husband pointed to the two, "A *real* steeplechase!"

Mr. Hunt clapped him on the shoulder. "Mr. Vanderbilt, perhaps you could purchase those two and assure my winnings at the track."

W. K. agreed that he would find out who had planned and rehearsed this Quadrille for us, and make inquiry.

Thus our masquerade of fun and gaiety was definitely sparked.

Willie K. was still applauding wildly when he turned and asked, "It's time for the Astor's Star Quadrille?"

"No, the Dresden China Quadrille comes next."

"Whatever is happening, I think you should know I've been told the lighting apparatus that all the young ladies have isn't working."

"Oh dear. Not tonight. Please!"

He tried to comfort me. "Perhaps a little Dresden China thrown at our guests will give them time to repair the apparatus."

I was not diverted nor amused. "Can you help?"

"Harwood is helping."

"But butlers don't know everything."

"Harwood does. *You* trained him."

As I watched the China figures go through the intricacies of their steps, I tried to catch sight of Harwood and the helpless girls. Especially Carrie. Her mother would be overcome. Devastated.

She might even try to quiet the tears of her daughter by leaving! I couldn't bear this. Others might follow. I could accept the other's leaving, but not the departure of *The* Mrs. Astor.

"Alva, what is the matter?"

"Willie K., we *must* have the Star Quadrille .... Where *are* they?"

"In the salon."

It seemed forever before I could applaud the ending and final steps of those China dancers, hand-painted as they were! Then I made my way to our salon. Mrs. Astor was not there. Only the distraught Carrie and the crestfallen other young men and women. Indeed their Star had taken a plunge toward the earth. Was Mrs. Astor not aware?

I tried to comfort Carrie and the others. But Carrie seemed more fearful of what her mother would *think*, than wishing her at her side for consolation.

"Carrie, my dear, I suspect your mother has found a very good vantage point for herself and for Mr. McAllister to view you dancing your Quadrille." I checked. "And that is precisely where she is."

"Then leave her there, Mrs. Vanderbilt. Tell me, will you be substituting something else for our performance?"

"The only thing I can think of — which could informally suffice — is a 'Go-As-You-Please Quadrille'."

"Oh no, Mrs. Vanderbilt. That one is always saved for last!"

"Last? True. But, my dear Carrie, why not have it now? Now. Then your mother can stay exactly where she is and *still* see all of you dance."

As she thought it over, Carrie's unhappy face began changing. "We will, Mrs. Vanderbilt, we will. Every one of us can 'Go-As-You-Please'."

As she asked the other dancers, each one nodded. I was relieved they were doing a complete turnaround of attitude as deftly as they intended to do it on the dance floor.

Carrie hugged me. I was very amazed but cooperative enough to make her feel completely natural about doing it. Then I was off to tell the orchestra leader to start the music for the substitute quadrille.

As they moved into the tune, it was a signal for all guests who cared to, to begin innovating. And that they did, with enthusiasm. Carrie and her group had already formed the swirling center of the floor.

Suddenly, I saw Alice Vanderbilt motioning to more guests to join the Quadrille. Even her husband, Cornelius. I would like to have believed she was doing it to help me. But I doubted that. Alice probably had *not* gone through all the pangs of getting the two of them into costume, plus their children, without wanting a just reward. After all, she was dressed as Miss Electric Light, with a torch in her hand. Alice also had been a well-known Sunday school teacher. Did she also want to be evident to the multitude?

And I had no doubt that when the New York newspapers came out tomorrow, there would be long eye-witness accounts of our party. Column after column. And several of those society writers would say, "Mrs. Cornelius Vanderbilt was very lively on the dance floor as she sparked the 'Go-As-You-Please Quadrille'." But I would know the difference. So would Carrie and Mrs. Astor. And that was enough.

I decided now to wait a few moments until Mrs. Astor could see that they were all completely happy with what they were doing. After being sure, I made my way to the lady of distinction.

"Mrs. Astor. Mr. McAllister. As you can see, there is a change in the program. Your Star Quadrille, so carefully rehearsed and costumed, cannot take place. It seems the lighting apparatus will not work."

She poked a gloved finger into his side. "See, Ward, I told you that gadget fellow didn't know what he was about. And he insisted that I pay him immediately!"

"Mrs. Astor, he will simply have to give back the money."

"What? He probably has already left town." Then she turned as if there had been no interruption. And took my hand. "Mrs. Vanderbilt, how kind of you to explain. Is my Carrie terribly upset?"

"No, no, Mrs. Astor. She is the charming center of it all!"

"So I see. But I thought perhaps all this twirling was simply a warm-up."

"No. No indeed. They are getting very lively out there, but the Opera Bouffe Quadrille will come next, on schedule."

"That should calm them down."

"But it will be our finale."

"And your sister, I hear, will be directing this one." She eyed me. "Will it be a Cuban opera?"

"No, only traditional. But I have been thinking of having an evening of Cuban dances — with a real Cuban band, along with their interesting food — sometime soon."

"Here in this house?"

"Yes."

"I'll come."

I could see that she once again expected an invitation to be automatic. So I simply smiled and said, "Mrs. Astor, the Star Quadrille brought us together. So why should the Cuban dances keep us apart?"

She and Ward McAllister thought it was an acceptable rejoinder and nodded their approval.

My moment had come.

Then he added, "Just tell the Cuban dancers to avoid all lighting apparatus!" As he laughed, he gave me an enigmatic wink.

We three again turned to watch the "Go-As-You-Pleasers". Carrie Astor apparently had been glancing at her mother, whenever she could, to see if she was angry with the substitution. But she could plainly see that Mrs. Astor was beaming. Carrie seemed relieved, turned to tell the others, then caught my eye and gave me a thank-you smile.

I was twice blessed.

And could ask, "Mrs. Astor, may I leave you now?" She nodded. "But I do hope we can continue this conversation later this evening."

"Yes. There will come a moment when all the social-hopeful-hostesses here will *surround* Mr. McAllister. He will become a total loss to me."

"I don't blame them. I find the same pursuit is true for my husband."

"What do they want out of him — railroad advice?"

"At least!"

"It's nice to have two such handsome men around, but I suppose, Mrs. Vanderbilt, we *should* grab the moment. Just tap me on the shoulder."

I bowed, then began to make my way to my husband, to tell him all.

As I nodded at guests, in passing, I was quite aware that William Backhouse Astor was not among them. His powerful wife was right when she told people that he seldom attended a party, or a concert, or the opera, unless she absolutely insisted. And then he looked very uncomfortable.

W. B. Astor preferred to give his own "selective" soirees, on his own yacht, *Nourmahal* ("Light of the Harem"), safely offshore — with his sporty male friends and gambling cronies aboard, augmented by the showgirls in town who happened to not be on stage that night, and by "ladies", it was said, from the better brothels.

I realized what a powerful and staunch woman Caroline Astor must be to offset all this. But I felt there was a reason for her husband's waywardness. The same potential reason occurred in my own marriage. I saw "Caroline and Alva" as two plumed horses with the same harness around our necks. This is what I wanted to discuss with her. I felt we could not continue the daily parade unless we had talked it over. Our husbands were two different men, but they had been born into the same confining problem.

I felt if Mrs. Astor understood all this, perhaps it would draw us closer. And that this closeness might finally open the door for Vanderbilt recognition ....

6

TWO-PARTY SHOWDOWN

WORKING MY WAY THROUGH OUR GUESTS was a great pleasure. And not just because I was always noticing a new costume — something Chinese, Greek, or Egyptian. Even a bird out of Audubon. But participation level of the party was very high, and so was the noise. They were exclaiming across each room to total strangers to let them know their reaction to individual costumes. If two people came dressed remotely alike, it was a bond.

Some of the guests were already making their way up to the third floor. The children's gymnasium had been converted into a dining bower. Hundreds of plants and flowers, including orchids and roses, formed backgrounds for intimate arrangements of dining tables. The guests could either dine buffet or sit down to an eight-course dinner. The post midnight repast had all been prepared by our own chefs and servants with professional assistance from Delmonico's Restaurant. And the waiters would *not* be on bicycles!

Wending my way through a cluster of appealingly costumed ladies in the salon, I finally spotted my husband. He responded to my beckoning, and we stood aside to exchange comments. "Yes, Alva? I think you want to tell me about the great lady. I saw you talking to her."

"And you know what impresses me most, Willie K.?"

"That costume and her hair down her back. Why isn't there any gray in it? She's a lot older than you."

"It's a very fine wig, my sweet. But no, that isn't it. I am still amazed this woman is here without her husband. But even more, at the absolute paradox that she is commanding the social scene in a city which *only* allows recognition of a woman through the name and prominence of her *spouse*."

"Quite a statement, my dear wife. And you're right. But there is enigma afoot. Caroline Astor *has* to be a strict manager of this city's social hierarchy. And why? *One* abomination, such as her William Backhouse Astor, could topple the whole structure!"

I turned my head away to laugh. I wanted to really let go, but I knew people were watching the host and hostess. We had to maintain our status. After all, we were halfway there.[4]

I pulled Willie K. into a cloistered corner and put his hand against my cheek. "Thank you for letting me have this party. For being patient through all the planning. Enduring my moods. Approving the menu. Selecting the wines. And —"

"— wondering *who* we are going to ask to pay for it all!"

I leaned my forehead against his. "Have you seen your father for the last half hour? He is surrounded by important men. Including General Grant."

"Oh? So by now he is fully aware of the price of recognition?"

"Fully."

We exchanged a murmuring moment. But I knew, somehow, my William K. Vanderbilt would find the money. He was the brains of his father's railroad business. Cornelius was the conservative and dependable one. But it was my W. K. who was the adventurous and progressive genius.

At that moment, I felt I loved my husband more than any other time since we were married. I wanted our party to go on forever, but I was already dreaming of the hour when we two could wearily climb in bed together, probably at dawn, to whisper over the night's triumphs, surprises, and flukes. To admit chances we had to take that somehow came out *right*. To gossip over the costumes — the brilliant ones and the dull. To whisper over the discarded love affairs we observed, plus the new ones forming. Over just plain joy until sleep was bound to overtake us.

In order to make this a reality, I could not waiver for the upcoming other half of the evening. Sighting my adversary did not mean I had won any sort of confrontation.

So I enticed Willie K. to go with me and watch the finale of the "Go-As-You-Please" Quadrille. We could soon see it had worked its way to an overflow of gaiety. There were back-to-back bumpings, toes stepped on, arms stretched by partners who refused to relinquish them, and costumes twisted to a ludicrous angle. When the music finally stopped, the uproar of realization that it was over raised into the air through the two stories of the ballroom to the gymnasium above. Waiters came down the stairway and found excuses to peek in to see if a small riot would interrupt their preparations to continue the flow of late night dining.

It would not. In fact they could see the guests would be only more hungry. So they hurriedly returned to inform Delmonico's.

The Opera Bouffe terpsichore was forming next. Willie K. and I used the time to recount the diversity of costumes we had seen up until now.

"How'd you like Mr. Hunt and Mrs. Potter leading that other Quadrille?"

"Fine, Alva. Almost as good as Bo-Peep dancing with Daniel Boone."

I knew he meant his sister, Mrs. W. D. Sloane and Senator Wagstaff. "But how about that Sioux Indian chief and Puss?"

This time, W. K. knew I meant one of the Oelrichs and one of the Welmans.

So he protested, "But why does she need the word 'Pussy' spelled out in rhinestones on her neckband?"

"So you can tell her from Mrs. Buchanan Winthrop's 'Pride'."

"But 'Pride' is a peacock!"

"And Puss is a dead cat. Alva, are all those heads around her waist real?"

"Yes, plus those white cats' tails — her skirt is made of them!"

He choked, but, for my sake, did not treat the observation with male candor. Instead, he noticed there was an unbelievable couple passing by. "Alva, look. The Goddess of Ice is cooling off Miss Electric Light." He nudged me. "Hard to believe it is only Mrs. Theron Strong and Mrs. Cornelius Vanderbilt.

"Only? Never speak of Alice Vanderbilt as 'only'!"

"When are you and Alice going to stop your game of trying to out-hostess each other?"

"Tonight. She'll never top this one!"

"But she'll try."

"We'll wait and see what the social commentators have to say."

"Why?"

"Because then we'll have it in print!"

And comment they did. I can even quote them. The next day the *New York Herald* carried the headline: "Like an Oriental Dream — the Scene in Mr. W. K. Vanderbilt's House Last Evening .... The Wealth and the Grace of New York in Varied and Brilliant Array." Then went on to say our fancy-dress ball presented a scene "probably never rivalled in Republican America and never outdone by the gayest court of Europe." It was "a gladsome night of such merrymaking as all the resources of the world, easily commanded, could afford."

Later, the Wall Street broker, Henry Clews, was forced to admit, "Aside from the entertainments of Alexander the Great, Cleopatra, and Louis XIV"— of which he could only speak from hearsay — "nothing more grandiose has ever confronted me than Mrs. Vanderbilt's bal masque. "

Mrs. Vanderbilt's? I was honored. Mr. Clews said it was my bal masque!

So did four newspapers, including the *New York World*. Furthermore, the *World* sent out reporters to interview costumers, dressmakers, florists, photographers, and livery stable men to find out how much money our fete generated "among working people". The paper totaled it up to the sum of $250,000, and headlined the column "The Ball Makes Money Roll".

William K., Cornelius, and W. H. Vanderbilt, himself, were very impressed. I think they might even have considered — for one wild moment — hiring me as a promoter in their railroad business.[5]

But at this point in our bal masque Willie K. wished to divert me from pondering. And he did. "Look at Cornelius. Garbed as Louis XVI. I'm proud of him. It must be torture!"

"Nonsense. Look at his brocade. It's trimmed with point de Espagne lace." I waited while my husband took note. "And that waistcoat — those pointings are of real silver, if I ever saw it!"

"While you are at it, Alva, don't forget his sword. The hilt is trimmed with diamonds."

"Yes. Never underestimate your elder brother. And have you noticed one *more* thing? Regardless of the debut of this house, Cornelius has been walking around, all alone, examining every detail of it, planning a bigger and better one for himself and Alice. Within ten years, I predict they will double the size of their house by buying the rest of that block between 57th and 58th."

"It may become bigger, but not better. You have superb taste, Alva. Alice can never surpass that."

"Thank you, darling. It is nice for a woman to know that her husband stands solidly behind her."

"And every Vanderbilt should stand behind you, too. Even Cornelius will have to admit that tonight you are raising the status of the family from being overlooked to being reckoned with."

60

"Not yet. I still have to hear it from the horse's mouth."

"I agree. Just as long as you don't try to *overtake* her."

"I have no interest in doing that. Ever."

"Good. Let *Alice* try. She has more experience at being a nag ...."

I was convulsed. But I tried to cover it with a mawkish grin. W. K. appreciated the control, excused himself, and went over to talk with Chauncey Depew as Father Knickerbocker. And why not? Depew was soon to become vice-president of the New York Central.

I, in turn, sought out his wife. She stood among a cluster of admiring women. Mrs. Depew had come as Ondine. The costume was worth a total description.

Her dress, of course, was of sea-green satin. There were clusters sewn all over it of velvet moons, water lilies, and long grasses. The literal crowning touch was her hair, powdered with silver dust and coiled under a cap of white tulle. All this was spangled with silver stars. Her pins and bracelets represented dew drops. As if all this were not enough, she was the diamond queen of the evening. Who could miss the range? All the way from diamond lizard and turtle pins to a diamond star necklace. Mrs. Chauncey Depew was a zodiac zoo of brilliance!

I told her so, until I felt I would unavoidably blush. It was the impending Quadrille which saved me. I said, "You will excuse me? I must attend the Opera Bouffe, you know. It is my sister's creation."

"Mrs. Fernando Yznaga's?" She watched me eagerly nod. "Then, by all means, go, Mrs. Vanderbilt."

I did. I found my Mary Virginia, gave her assurance, and then stood back to watch. Critically, of course. And she knew it.[6]

When the Quadrille was finally over, my sister came directly to me. I pronounced it "more eccentric than pretty." I considered this a compliment. Mary Virginia did not.

"Alva, I always have to make allowances for you. Your opinion is generally something I *cannot* pass on. So would you mind telling my dancers that the Opera Bouffe was at least neatly done?"

"It was!" And I told them so — furthermore, how graceful they were and what a talented director they had. They were satisfied. But not Mrs. Fernando Yznaga.

I decided, when her dancers left, later in the party, that I would give them special favors to take home. Perhaps that would help.

In the midst of all this gaiety, I wondered if I would spend the rest of my life being misinterpreted.

But right now it was time for the guests to take over the entire dance floor. Willie K. announced this, and the waltzes began. To be alternated with gavottes. And accented with the popular Ticklish Water Polka. Our dance floor was to be current indeed. And the Landers Orchestra was to be spelled off by a military band!

My husband moved over to me. "Now, should the two of us lead the dining procession?"

"The guests are already ahead of us."

He smiled. "I have a feeling Alva Vanderbilt is only going to ascend those stairs when Caroline Astor is *with* her."

"Am I that obvious?"

"Yes!"

I blew him a kiss and went to look for Mrs. Astor.

As I circled the edge of the dance floor, I was amazed to find her, looking out of the corner of her eye. For me? I approached her with all the casualness I could perform. "Mrs. Astor."

"Oh, there you are, Mrs. Vanderbilt." She pointed. "Look, my Carrie is in the center of the floor again."

"Ah yes, and waltzing with Mr. McAllister. Very clever of her to do that *before* the would-be hostesses find him."

"Indeed. So this signals complete freedom for me. And for us, my dear — I see your husband has found the huntress, Amy La Farge."

"Could it be because of the tiger skin she is wearing?"

"If not its red satin lining. But I think she is quite safe. She has a bow and quiver of arrows on her back."

"Let us hope she does not wish to play Cupid...."

Mrs. Astor thought this was accumulatively amusing, and the two of us ascended the stairs in growing good humor.

Needless to say, we were observed. I took the chance of glancing back to see if even a huntress could not divert my husband from noticing. She could not.

As we reached the dining room, my maitre d'hotel of the evening bowed. "Mrs. Vanderbilt. Mrs. Astor. May I escort you to a table? ... Which would you prefer?"

Finally we chose one — not only behind a stand of palms but a bower of flowers. After all, I had ordered 10,000 blossoms for the occasion. Why not use them?

He seated us with professional care and handed us each a menu. Not that there was any choice. But I felt that my guests should know what they were eating and also have one of the several souvenirs of the party to take home.

Though I knew some guests probably preferred to take home one of our footmen in his new Vanderbilt maroon livery!

Mrs. Astor pulled her lorgnette from a bag, which carefully matched her gown, and studied the evening's fare. "My dear, what an excellent menu-planner you are."

The remark was a little direct, but it pleased me immensely. Most women would have exclaimed, "My dear, what a lot of trouble you have gone to!" I would have hated that observation. I wanted my guests to feel it was a pleasure, and I had done it for them — effortlessly. Caroline Astor had just given me the benefit of the doubt. Here was a true hostess!

As she continued to study the menu, I had a chance to really enjoy her costume. The gold roses on her velvet gown were embroidered with pearls. But it was the subtlety of her long, flowing sleeves that amazed me. The *inside* of each sleeve glittered with jewels. And, just as I had observed at her arrival, ropes of diamonds and pearls girdled her neck. Even her cap was fastened to her flowing hair with plumes and aigrettes of diamonds. I concluded she and her designer must have gone to an enormous amount of research to dress a Venetian lady so correctly.

"Mrs. Vanderbilt, before I order, I want to thank you for rescuing my daughter's Quadrille. It was very considerate of you, and also very clever, may I say? I think you have made a friend of Carrie for life."

"I find her very remarkable. And her mother also, Mrs. Astor."

"In that case — having just given me a compliment — would you be informed that I was fully aware you *withheld* both my invitation and Carrie's for this ball?" She could see me visibly gulp. "And that I know *why*, Mrs. Vanderbilt? But never mind, I admire you for it. It certainly brought etiquette to my attention. And definitely caused me to straighten up and send over my calling card posthaste!"

I said nothing and tried to gaze at her without emotion. But I was aware she was in no hurry to eat the appetizer the waiter had set before her. So I expected another dressing-down. And got it.

"Furthermore, Mrs. Vanderbilt, I am wondering if you deliberately chose Monday night for your costume ball? Surely you are aware that Monday night has always been reserved for my weekly at-homes!"

"Yes, Mrs. Astor, I realized that. But I must also assure you this particular night has been of no consequence in the Vanderbilt social calendar. None of us has ever attended."

"That is your oversight, not mine. These evenings were designed by me to give an opportunity for the new families in the city to attend."

"The Vanderbilts are not a new family."

"But they were. And they never attended."

"Possibly, Mrs. Astor, that is because the manners of the Commodore were so bad that he could never make an appearance at the same house more than once."

She gasped, gazed at me, and then began to chuckle. "The same was true of old John Jacob Astor!" She noticed I was careful not to nod. "And I hope you have also observed, Mrs. Vanderbilt, that neither of us could have made our ascent into the social world until those respective gentlemen had passed on."

"But madam, you have the advantage of 1848 as compared with *my* terminal date of 1877!"

Mrs. Astor tilted back her head and performed what was very close to a guffaw.

Finally she quieted down and eyed me closely. "Ah hah, my dear young woman. Every female leader of society has a successor. Perhaps you will be mine."

"Thank you. But that position will no doubt be taken over by the wife of your eldest son."

"Not as long as this Mrs. Astor is hale and hearty!"

"Then please, at least, be assured that I have only one ambition. To be a hostess."

"And a splendid one, my dear, splendid. I *know* all the hours this preparation takes." She finally eyed the appetizer and murmured an approval. Then continued with, "But the difference is that you have Mr. William Kissam Vanderbilt to assist you. I do not have Mr. William B. Astor in the same capacity."

I was aware she always preferred the initial "B" to his family middle name, Backhouse …. Understandably.

My own plate had long since arrived, but I was pleased to see that my waiter had been careful to serve her first. I rewarded him with a glance. Mrs. Astor took her first bite, then another, and another before she nodded it was delicious. I was delighted to see the quality of the food was making her more friendly toward me.

The arrival of our best wines was soon to make her more confidential. She drank a half goblet without stopping. "No doubt you are aware that my William prefers his social life elsewhere?"

She waited until she received a nod from me. "Very well. Then I may proceed to the cause of this. Mrs. Vanderbilt, you and I are both married to *second* sons."

"Exactly!" I was caught off guard. Hadn't I intended to make this the focus of our conversation? But not for another half hour!

Mrs. Astor was getting right to the point. "My William is not acccepted into the family real estate business. His older brother, the noisy John Jacob Astor III, feels it is all his — that he is head of the family. Well, he is. But this does not mean that my husband is not just as intelligent and capable. He certainly has managed the real estate we have inherited. He knows every inch of it. And he is *not* going back into the family's old fur business—not when the Astors had to get into real estate to become respectable!" She waited for me to smile. I did. "True, my William is a 'trapper' of sorts, but he confines it to tarts, actresses, and socially wayward males who like to bet on the horses."

This time I was the one who had to swallow a large amount of wine. I knew she *never* referred to him as being any more than "at sea."

"Ehhhh — yes — Mrs. Astor."

"Your William is different?"

"As far as I know."

"Well, don't be sure. If he's had a European education, he thinks nothing of it."

"But I have also had a European education."

"Then are you intending to make it 'a game *two* can play'?"

"I don't know … Should I?"

"Please do. And accept my compliments. I, myself, am too old to go man-hunting. Ward McAllister is quite enough for me." She leaned forward. "Mrs. Vanderbilt, in what year were you born?"

"1853."

"I was born in 1831. If my mind for figures serves me, there are twenty-two years between our ages. Is that right?"

"Yes. But I do not find that it really matters."

"You mean the wife of a second son is the wife of a second son?"

"Yes!" We laughed and shook hands across the table. I felt I could continue. "Mrs. Astor, at this point, I must tell you my concern is financial."

"Hmmm. And it will reach its height when the great William H. Vanderbilt dies?" She waited for my nod. "I see. But before we go on, you are no doubt fully aware of why I have never liked him or his father?" She received a shake of the head from me. "No? ... Because of ungentlemanly manipulation of railroad stock."

"By the old Commodore or by my father-in-law?"

"I'm not sure. And I don't even know what manipulation means, but I've heard the Astors talk about it."

"You are a Schermerhorn, Mrs. Astor."

"I know, my dear. And I shouldn't let them make up my mind. Particularly when they never let me forget it. The Schermerhorns were, and are, great administrators. Sometimes I think that is why my husband married me. So that he wouldn't have to do it." She gave a rueful laugh ...."But back to the Vanderbilts. I suppose you are speaking of the *will* made by W. H.?"

"Yes."

"Then you are aware that the eldest son gets all of the money? All. And he doles it out as he wishes!"

"Yes, my dear Mrs. Astor. And I am determined to avoid that."

"May I wish you the best of luck?" She finished her appetizer, leaned back in her chair, and gave a long sigh. "My husband has managed what we received very well. And I am eternally grateful to him. I just wish he would drop around at the house more often so I could tell him."

"My husband is also a good manager, though we, as well, don't see him as often as we'd like."

"Then he must be doing a very good job of running the family's railroad business."

"Yes. He is the enterprising one."

"More than his older brother, Cornelius?"

"Corneel spends more of his time keeping the wheels rolling."

"So you feel your William should inherit the same amount as Cornelius?"

"Yes. Or very close to that amount."

"A couple of million less won't disturb you?"

"No."

"Then I hope you will be successful, Mrs. Vanderbilt. Since your father-in-law has already written his will, make him write another."

"I have."

"Then a third!"

"Ah, yes, I will try."

"Until he gets it written to *your* satisfaction — even if it takes ten tries!"

"Thank you, Mrs. Astor." I finished the last of my wine, and she raised her empty glass to me. The waiter took the cue and was quick to refill both our goblets. Ordinarily he would have done it when he saw the level go down an inch and a half, but apparently he recognized that a tête-à-tête with Mrs. Astor was not to be routinely disturbed.

I made a mental note to reward him later.

As he brought the next course, she inspected it with favor, and tasted it with approval. Then continued. "My dear Mrs. William Kissam Vanderbilt. If you accomplish this, it will be something of a *first*, you know."

"I know."

"But I daresay you will accomplish others in your life. Perhaps many firsts."

"I do hope so."

"And I would like to think I have laid something of a social foundation for you."

"Oh you have, believe me!"

"But that responsibility is not easy. There will be times when you think you cannot keep up the pace ...." She received a look of humility from me. "However, competition from a rival will keep you in the running."

Rival? Did she know?

She did. And continued, "But the wife of Cornelius can only threaten you. Never overtake you."

"I am not so sure. It is said Alice runs without a bridle."

"And you run without a whip. *That* is important."

I drank, and blessed my husband's choice of wines. "Thank you, Mrs. Astor."

She, again, was finishing everything on her plate, with great relish. "Not at all. I observe these things constantly here in New York. And in Newport, as well. My dear, sometime you and your husband must sail up and visit us at Beechwood."

"Mr. Vanderbilt and I would *like* to see your house." I leaned forward confidentially. "He is having a yacht designed for us right now."

"But not built?"

"No. We don't have the money."

"You will! And tell him to name it after you."

"That is his choice."

"The *Alva* would be such a pretty name. What does it mean?"

"Dawn of day."

"See?"[7]

Mrs. Astor gave her final shot on the subject. "Do it — so that when W. K. Vanderbilt is on board his yacht, it will remind him of his *wife!*"

I laughed. And then attempted to divert. "Mrs. Astor, did you know I spent one or two of my childhood summers in Newport?"

"No I didn't."

"My daily companion was a little Cuban boy."

"Cubans again."

"Yes. We climbed down those cliffs and played on the rocks below."

"Below Cliff Walk? How dangerous. I would have spanked any daughter who did that!"

"That is exactly what my mother did."

"And you went right back the next day?"

"Yes."

"And she spanked you again?"

"She did."

"Mrs. Vanderbilt, I can see your childhood determination has carried over." She watched me smile self-consciously. "And I can see that what you still want is recognition."

"Yes." I took a deep breath.

"After tonight you and your husband will certainly receive it."

"From you, Mrs. Astor?"

"From everyone."

"But I want recognition for the entire Vanderbilt family!"

"Very well. I will see to it that you all receive the proper invitations."

"Both here and in Newport?"

"Yes."

I was relieved — so relieved. But I decided to chat on as though it didn't matter quite that much.

"Mrs. Astor, I would love to have Richard Morris Hunt build a house for Mr. Vanderbilt and me there."

"I have a feeling you will. And that it will be bigger and grander than Beechwood."

"But I would like to locate it near you."

"There is a house next door to me. Buy it and tear it down."

"Bellevue *is* my favorite avenue."

"Of course. It will soon be everyone's. So tell your husband to buy in and build early. Make those twenty-two years between you and me count!"

"I will."

"Tell *all* the Vanderbilts this." She gave a wry laugh. "Even if I am cutting my own throat."

"Oh no. That can never happen between the wives of two second sons. I can never rival you. Neither can Alice. You will always be *The* Mrs. Astor."

"I will remember what you say twenty years from now. Twenty years from today?   Very well. Let's sit down at a table on that occasion. And eat. And talk …   You will be a wiser woman, Mrs. Vanderbilt. And so will I …."

7

T HE LUNCHEON CAROLINE ASTOR WANTED THE
two of us to have would have been on a day in the year 1903.
And for a long time, I thought it would take place.
At the Metropolitan Opera, she had Box Seven and Willie
K. and I had Box Six. We smiled at each other often and had small chats
in the balcony foyer during the intermissions.

Caroline seemed genuinely interested in the completion of our yacht
and that it was called Alva. Also in our many travels aboard it. She
wished a progress report on the house we were planning, and eventually
built, in Newport. True, it was located next to her Beechwood. And she
was always very interested in our children and what they were doing.

But her life changed, and so did mine. My own had turned to politics
and social work. Caroline's still revolved around entertainment, especially observing other New York hostesses who were now in competition.

Though her annual ball was still the most important event of the year,
the new generation was complaining that cotillions were boring.

Caroline Astor's second "lord chamberlain", Harry Lehr, encouraged
other hostesses, when he was hired by them, to pursue diversions.

A baby elephant, distributing peanuts, wandered around the ballroom
of Mrs. Stuyvesant Fish.

Another time, Mrs. Fish's guests all arrived dressed as dolls, and spent
the evening in competitive baby-talk.

On yet another evening, she gave a dinner for one hundred dogs and
their owners, with the bitch of the evening receiving a jeweled collar!

Other hosts and hostesses transformed their ballrooms into a forest or
a lake. Or had their guests arrive on horseback. Or had them smoke cigars
wrapped in $100 bills because of the delicious taste of a bank-note!

But Caroline Astor refused to lower her standards. "These are entertainments that belong under a circus tent," she said.

However, she broadened her guest list by inviting 1200 to her 1904 ball.

She then promptly narrowed it to seventy-nine for a dinner she gave to honor Prince Louis Mountbatten. With herself making a total of eighty, she stated that was the exact number her dining room would accommodate!

Her last ball was, again, selective, and was held in 1905. But by the end of the year, she unfortunately had a stroke.

In those intervening years before Caroline Astor died in 1908, I heard whispered rumors that she dressed in her usual elegance and descended her famous staircase, then moved into her gold and white reception room to "greet" guests already departed from this world.

I thought this was a great idea. She again was an innovator. As a good Episcopalian, I felt it was fine to get in practice to talk with people Mrs. Astor liked and wanted to chat with "on the other side"!

So, as I dictate this next chapter, I show how much I honored this lady, by doing exactly what she asked me to do earlier during our amazing and memorable conversation at the party.

A REAL BUGGY RIDE

It was true. Mrs. Astor did what she said.

From the night of the 1883 party, no member of the Vanderbilt family ever again *had* to fear he or she would be excluded from the guest list of any major social event.

It took a little longer to obtain membership in some of the more exclusive clubs, but in time it was always accomplished.

Our bal masque had apparently become the party of the century. And for more reasons than one.

People said no party was ever given to equal it. Needless to say, I clipped all the newspaper and social accounts and put them into a scrapbook. It was amusing to see how the write-ups differed, but I never blamed the reporters. With that many guests, they had to contact individuals beforehand to find out what the more important would be wearing and also be told what the entertainment procedure of the evening would be. Otherwise their newspapers could never have come out on the stands the next day. I found they were usually right about the costumes, but the quadrille order was always incorrect. And understandably so! That story would be left to the historians, and I could predict they would lean heavily on the news account. So the real facts about the Star Quadrille would probably never be straightened out.

I could see Mrs. Astor quietly smiling.

With the building of the Metropolitan Opera House, then our home at 660 Fifth Avenue, and finally the giving of our party, I was sure my critics were asking, "What will Alva Vanderbilt do next?"

And indeed, I was asking myself that. But I decided to let all of them believe it was the constuction of our yacht which preoccupied me, and not our financial future. Harlan and Hillingsworth yards in Wilmington, Delaware, were in charge of the construction of our yacht. The blueprints called for a vessel extending 285 feet from stem to stern. That was fifteen feet longer than the Commodore's

North Star. J. P. Morgan's *Corsair* was only 165 feet. Jay Gould's *Atlanta* ran to 250. And William Astor's *Nourmahal* to 233.

So what about the ship of William H. Vanderbilt? There was none. This family head was totally uninterested in such falderal. He didn't even own a rowboat.

It was again on this gentleman that my interests were centered. Little did he know I would take him literally when he said, at the time of my marriage, that he would like to be my substitute father. Father! More like godfather, grandfather, and what women eventually would call their sugar-daddy.

But it was really horses this marvelous man liked. Horses. As he told reporters, "No yachts for me, no, sir! They are easy to buy, but they are hard to sell. When I want to go to Europe, the *Britannic* and the *Georgic* are good enough for me." So good that he was known to sail all the way to a European port, stay on board, and sail all the way back on that ship's very next voyage!

Trotters were his passion. Also his father's, and the Commodore saw to it that this son, Billy, would inherit his favorite trotter, Small Hopes. W. H. began eyeing the horses of other owners at DuBois's half mile track on Jerome Avenue near Macomb's Dam in the Bronx. As a mate to Small Hopes, he purchased Lady Mac, and together the two trotters could cover the mile course at Fleetwood Park in 2:23¼.

To defeat such competitors as Frank Work, his Wall Street broker, W. H. then acquired trotters Aldine and Early Rose. This team was soon capable of a mile in 2:16½. After a defeat by Mr. Work, W. H. paired Aldine with Maud S. and gained the world's record of a mile in 2:15½ at Fleetwood Park on June 14, 1883. His broker never forgave him.

In 1884, on one bright afternoon in September, it was with this pair that I wanted to climb into a carriage and go trotting. I knew approximately the time my father-in-law would leave his stable at Madison Avenue and 52nd Street and come over to Fifth Avenue. So he could be *seen*. Oh, yes, everyone knew the maroon rig of William Henry Vanderbilt.

I was purposely dressed as though I had come back from a session with architect Richard Morris Hunt. Actually, we were planning a remodeling of Idlehour. This Long Island house was to be a new and more liveable palace for ourselves and our three children. But there was more.

I must pause here and explain. That is correct — I said three children. On a Sunday morning in July of 1884, Consuelo and little

Willie were sent out for a walk. When they returned, I was in bed with our new son, Harold Stirling Vanderbilt, in my arms. He was explained to the children by their nurse, Boya, as "a gift from God." He was a beautiful baby, and I let it go at that.

The dresses that we wore in those days were enough to cover up any indiscretions. And this is exactly what our friends considered it. We already had an eight-year-old daughter and a seven-year-old son. Obviously, we were going to stop at that. After all, we were Episcopalians, not Catholics.

So we simply let our new Harold be an afterthought. And though he grew up to be the world's most famous yachtsman, we were not yet prone to deference. He was accepted into the family as a new and elegant live toy.

I think it was this fact that I was a new mother which made my father-in-law notice me more quickly that afternoon. He slowed down, then tipped his hat. I waved back with a semi- hailing hand. W. H. let his team know my probable wishes, and they stopped, whereupon I admired those two trotters to distraction. The great Mr. Vanderbilt could do nothing except invite me to join him. A passerby was quick to help me ascend. I blessed him lavishly. W. H. made sure I was safely seated, and the two of us were off to astound Fifth Avenue.

"Alva, my dear, everyone is looking at you. Perhaps it is the new bloom on your face."

"If they are, they are laughing."

"True, Harold Stirling was a surprise to *me*. But not to Maria. Women have a way of noticing these things. She nudged me at church one Sunday and said, 'Billy, I think Willie K. and Alva have an announcement to make'."

"And you whispered back, 'Good heavens, are they building another house?'"

W. H. roared until it frightened the horses. Then he asked, "Is that where you've been this afternoon, down to that Studio Building of Richard Morris Hunt?"

He had played directly into my hands, but I did not say no or yes. I simply stated, "Mr. Hunt says Fifth Avenue is becoming Vanderbilt Lane."

"It is! Let me show you." With that, he turned his mares around and headed for his former house at 459, now occupied by his third son. "Frederick William says our old home is holding up very well. But I bet it doesn't please his Louise Anthony Torrance!"

"She has been Mrs. Frederick William Vanderbilt for enough years to be able to talk back."

Again he roared. "But I don't enjoy this daughter-in-law the way I do you when *you* talk back."

I patted his hand. "Then let us head for your house at 640 immediately."

"My house? It's what *your* Mrs. Astor would call a Vanderbilt blight."

Nevertheless, he turned us around and we headed north.

"*My* Mrs. Astor? At least she never again has let Ward McAllister invite us to a Patriarch's Ball and then make a point of not allowing us to be presented to her!"

"Indeed. But your lady lives in a brownstone, herself."

"And have you listened to *her* talk? She always refers to brownstones as 'our answer to all those people in Greenwich Village who built those ostentatious Georgian mansions!'"

"And she knows good and well she is speaking of my father and mother."

"The Commodore only. Your mother never wanted it."

"Well, he didn't have to put her in an insane asylum because she didn't!"

"Sophia was no fool. But I always thought she should have divorced your father and married the superintendent who declared her sane!"

This time, W. H. hooted so long, he simply nodded at his house as we passed, and let me point at the Sloane's and the Shepard's house at 642, as belonging to Vanderbilts — his Emily and Margaret, of course. Then I pointed to 660. "Guess who's house *that* is."

"It's the best one in town. So it could only belong to a Vanderbilt."

"You are right." And little did either of us know it would soon be declared the third best architectural structure in the United States. The first one being Boston's Trinity Church. And the second one being the United States Capitol! Since this was a selection by the architects themselves of 175 U. S. buildings, it was a great honor to be recognized as number three.

My father-in-law gave a snap of the whip into the air. "So I suppose we had better go past the Webbs and the Twomblys."

Eliza was at 680, and Florence Adele was at 684 — again both Vanderbilt girls.

"And we would never be forgiven, Alva, if we did not trot past 1 West 57th Street."

"Cornelius and Alice should have put their entrance on Fifth Avenue."

"If they had hired your smart Mr. Hunt, instead of Mr. Post, they *would* have."

"Really? Especially since Mr. Hunt designed the pedestal of the Statue of Liberty, and New York just made a big event out of laying the cornerstone?"

"Yes, Corneel would have liked *that*."

I appreciated the implication and again gave my father-in-law's hand a pat. It was now time to approach what I had come along to make certain was true. I cleared my throat and began. "Mr. Vanderbilt." I never called him W. H. to his face, never Billy, and certainly never father! "As we passed this house of your eldest son, may I once again inquire if you intend to pass *on* the railroad business in the same way your father did?"

"Ho ho, my dear daughter-in-law. You did not come along for the ride?"

"I did not. However, I am enjoying it."

"But you would enjoy it more if you knew I had made out a new will?"

"Precisely."

He cracked his whip louder this time. I decided, at this point, I should appear chatty. "Sir, I've always wanted to ask you, 'Don't you think, Mr. Vanderbilt, it is dangerous to race against your *broker*?'"

"Not as dangerous as against my undertaker!"

I granted him the point. Aldine and Maud S. had alerted to the sound of the whip and were now starting their trip alongside Central Park. The rich colors of fall were beginning to appear in the leaves of the trees. And I was telling my father-in-law, even at this critical moment, that Richard Morris Hunt had done remarkable aerial drawings of these walled areas whenever he submitted his designs of new entrances to the Park. I said, "These drawings now make it possible to see all this as if you were a bird in the air, Mr. Vanderbilt. I think the brilliant Mr. Hunt is perhaps anticipating an era of flight."

W. H. was impressed with my casualness, but he returned to the subject at hand. "A new will, eh? Alva, are you telling me you are worried that I can't see through my right eye, that my lower lip twitches, and that I have high blood pressure?"

"I am. So is your wife." I leaned close to him. "And so are you."

He thought this over for several moments, then tipped his hat to a couple strolling besides the Lenox Library. He was expecting me to point out this structure as another Hunt achievement. But I was now willing to listen to what very definitely needed to be said. "Alva, my dear," he finally began. "You want me to do what my father would never allow. Split the control. Yes?"

"Yes. But it does not need to split the business."

"Only the wives?"

"Alice and I are already split. Asunder. She wants you to declare her husband as head of the family."

"I will."

"I know. But not as head of your railroad empire."

"I realize your Willie K. has done as much as Alice's Cornelius. And you are perfectly aware that I have turned over most of the running of the business to them. Of course, we talk every morning but essentially —"

"My dear Mr. Vanderbilt, that is all well and good — until you are gone and your will has to be interpreted. Then everything may break down!"

"But you don't care as long as it breaks down, Alva, into an equal share for my first and second sons?"

I could not speak for several minutes. We trotted along. I had a feeling that the two mares were listening. But weren't *they* women too? And weren't they aware of what one decision could do to their own status? I felt they were not trotting champions for nothing!

W. H. was still waiting for my reply. I was about to make it when he reached over and patted my *own* hand. "Alva, my dear, as a young wife, you truly have the interests of your husband at heart. I am convinced you are the only female member of the family who is *not* totally interested in money."

"I am more interested in a railroad that runs up both sides of the Hudson River. And then west to Chicago."

"Just like the new telephone lines?"

"Yes. And both north and south of Detroit — even coursing Michigan and Indiana — to Minneapolis and St. Paul."

"And don't forget as far south as St. Louis!"

We both laughed. The horses seemed relieved.

"Alva. You are a wonder. Grover Cleveland is running for President. Perhaps we should put *you* in as Vice President."

"Of your railroads *only*, sir."

I wonder what he would have thought if he knew some day I

would have a position as president of various divisions of the National Woman's Suffrage Movement? With, I must say, about as much merging and railroading going on!

But I replied, "Mr. William Kissam Vanderbilt, as head of some of those railroads, is good enough for me."

"And Corneel, as head, is good enough for Alice. So I have made both of you ladies happy?"

"Never. Not until you write it out and make it perfectly clear. So it will be very plain to everyone in that room when your will is read. It is *your* word that will settle all arguments."

"Yes. God knows I don't want any of you to endure what I have been through all these years over *my* father's will!"

"Then prevent it."

"How do I know you won't *still* sue each other?"

"There are no Cornelius Jeremiahs in this generation."

"Not even a Frederick?"

"Frederick is a very wise man. In fifty years, he will probably end up with more money than *any* of your children."

"That's because he married a woman so much older than he is."

I had to laugh. "Yes, that may help. My dear sir, it is age that counts."

"And you want *me* to use it."

"I do. I do."

This time he put his arm around me. "My dear child — just like the Mugwumps — let me go home and think about it." And with that, he turned his prize pair, bless them, around, and all four of us headed south. I was sure he would at least go as far as his gift to Central Park, Cleopatra's Needle. But no.

"Aldine and Maud S. are spirited horses. Why are they so obedient in turning around?"

"They know I have sugar cubes in my pocket as their reward!"

"Always?"

"Always ...."

Nothing was said all the way back to our château. Except about the trees. "Aren't they beautiful, those colors?"

I wanted to reply, "Yes, the leaves know when to turn."

But I didn't need to. W. H. Vanderbilt was thinking.

And in the year following, he continued to rewrite his will until he felt he had it fair and just. I could only *trust* that the urging Mrs. Astor had given me was going to pay off.

A month and four days after Grover Cleveland was elected

Painting of Cornelius (Commodore) Vanderbilt by Jared B. Flagg, c. 1876.

Painting of Sophia Johnson Vanderbilt. Artist and date unknown.

Painting of William Henry Vanderbilt by Jared B. Flagg, c. 1877.

Painting of Maria Louisa Kissam Vanderbilt (Mrs. W. H.) by George A. Baker, 1867.

William Kissam Vanderbilt.

The very young Alva Smith
Vanderbilt (Mrs. W. K.), c. 1875.

The young Alva Smith Vanderbilt
(Mrs. W. K.).

Richard Morris Hunt, Architect.

The Studio Building, designed by Richard Morris Hunt.

Idlehour, designed by Richard Morris Hunt.

The W. H. Vanderbilt twin mansions. The W. K. Vanderbilt chateau at 660 Fifth Avenue.

The White and Gold Salon of the W. K. Vanderbilt chateau
at 660 Fifth Avenue.

Alva in her Venetian costume for
her 1883 Ball. Photograph by Jose
Maria Mora.

Alice Vanderbilt (Mrs. Cornelius II)
in her "Electric Light"
costume. Photo also by J. M. Mora.

Caroline Astor (Mrs. William B.), known as THE Mrs. Astor. Painting by Carolus Duran, Metropolitan Museum of Art.

Alva Vanderbilt, c. 1885

Cornelius Vanderbilt II.

Alva, Harold Stirling (in front), William Kissam, Jr., and Consuelo, c. 1888.

The W. K. Vanderbilt yacht *Alva I.*

The second W. K. Vanderbilt yacht *Valiant.*

Marble House, Newport, R.I., home of the W. K. Vanderbilts.

The Numidian marble dining room of
Marble House.

The famous Gold Room ballroom at Marble House.

The Gothic Room of Marble House.

The magnificent bedroom of Alva Vanderbilt at Marble House.

The Breakers, the Newport residence of Mr. and Mrs. Cornelius Vanderbilt II.

Consuelo Vanderbilt, the Duchess of Marlborough, as Lady in Waiting for Princess Alexandra.

Cameo photo of Winthrop Rutherfurd with "Newport Stars in 1892."

Blenheim Palace, Woodstock, Oxford, England; south front, aerial view.

The Great Hall.

The Long Library.

The Saloon.

The Red Drawing Room.

Painting by John Singer Sargent of the Ninth Duke and Duchess of Marlborough and their sons Blandford and Ivor.

The Ninth Duke of
Marlborough and his two
sons, Ivor and Blandford
(right), at Blenheim Palace

Consuelo Vanderbilt, the Ninth Duchess of Marlborough and her sons Ivor
and Blandford (right).

Colonel Jacques Balsan during World War I.

Portrait of William Kissam Vanderbilt, Jr. by Earl Milchiss.

The Vanderbilt Cup for automobile racing. Front left, reverse right.

The 1906 addition (right) for Mr. and Mrs. W. K. Vanderbilt, Jr. to the original Vanderbilt chateau.

Alva II, the global circumnavigation yacht of W. K. Vanderbilt, Jr.

Afterguard of Harold Stirling Vanderbilt's winning yacht *Ranger*.

Harold Stirling Vanderbilt, three-time
winner of the America's Cup.

August Belmont.

Drawing of Caroline Belmont
(Mrs. August), 1854

Oliver Hazard Perry Belmont

Present entrance to Belcourt Castle.

Original carriage entrance to Belcourt, then home of Oliver Hazard Perry Belmont.

Carriage entrance after 1906 remodeling.

Original promenade court of Belcourt.

Rare print of open Belcourt loggia, for viewing
promenade court below.

Rare photo of Belcourt baronial hall showing favorite Belmont
horses and armor.

President, William Henry Vanderbilt died. On December 8, 1885. Of a family malady — the same thing which had killed his mother years earlier — apoplexy. Their arterial systems had simply ceased to function.

Though we all had been aware that the end might come, it was a terrible shock.

And it was a great blow to Wall Street. There were instant conjectures. Would there be quantities of New York Central stock thrown into the market to cover indiscreet Vanderbilt speculations? Would the whole railroad system collapse the next day?

By morning, although everyone was aware of the death of W. H. Vanderbilt, everything was serene. He had no margin accounts in the market. W. H. *owned* all his stocks outright. He held $70,000,000 in government bonds, plus $22,000,000 in railroad bonds, $3,200,000 in state and city bonds, and $2,000,000 in mortgages and other paper.

This complete estate totaled around $200,000,000. And out of that, he made it very clear he was leaving $67,000,000 to his eldest son, Cornelius.

And $65,000,000 to his *second* son, William Kissam Vanderbilt.

It was in the will. And, ah yes, I was present at the reading.

When Cornelius was declared head of the family, Alice glanced over at me and her eyes said, "Ah hah!" But when the amount of money my husband was to receive was announced, she did not glance over. I have a feeling she was too shocked to do very much of anything.

But not *this* lady. I decided, after this reading of the will of my father-in-law was over, I would walk to 52nd and Madison Avenues and enter the Vanderbilt stables. I would go to the stalls of Aldine and Maud S. and put my arms around the neck of each mare. Then I would reach into my pocket and pull out what I had brought. Sugar cubes. Which they expected. Always ....

8

D O YOU KNOW WHAT HAS BEEN ON MY MIND
lately?
Bowling alleys. It seems I find a great deal of pleasure in
providing recreation.

Having furnished and maintained a recreation hostel for the use of
nurses from the American Hospital in Paris, I decided, "Why not do it at
home here?"

So I made arrangements to install a bowling alley for the use of the
nurses who cared for me. It would be located in the garden of my chateau.

I asked my donkey about it. He said, "Fine with me. Just don't locate
it along any of the paths you and I take. That route is ours. Don't interfere
with it."

I agreed and planned for such threatening recreation to be located
elsewhere.

I sent all the way to the United States for it. A complete bowling alley.
My Consuelo thought it "was a little late in the day" to be doing all that.
But I was happy and excited.

In due time it arrived, and I had it installed.

My nurses were very pleased and began to use the bowling alley for
many hours of amusement.

So did my children and grandchildren when they came to visit. Even
Consuelo.

And townspeople, whenever they cared to have a little divertissement.

At this point, in dictating my memoirs, I wish to tell you about a second
bowling alley. At Idlehour. One which had been converted, this time. And
again, one which had an influence on me and my children.

Now that the will of W. H. Vanderbilt had been read and implemented,
the money which this dear man left my Willie K. had made my life much
easier. I could postpone competing. I could devote my time to our three

children. To the running of both our Long Island house and our château in New York. And to the further support of the railroad career of my husband.

FOUR CHILDHOODS

My thirties *were* devoted to our three children — Consuelo, Willie K., Jr., and Harold Stirling.

In a family, I don't care whether there is a nurse, governess, tutor, and sufficient provided servants or not. It is the *mother* who becomes a manager of their time — her own, and that of her children. I find it is an all-consuming occupation.

There were periods, during my thirties, when I worked so hard that no one could have convinced me that any mother of children ever *lived* to be forty! I absolutely believed that all women died at thirty-nine. And those who were walking around who *looked* older, were heavily "gotten up" with a lavish use of wigs and cosmetics.

I was so fully prepared to die at thirty-nine that, at the end of those ten years, when I actually *did* turn forty, I was not depressed. Not the way women usually are. I was overjoyed that I had made it!

I have talked about Consuelo and little Willie, but not Harold Stirling. He *was* a wonderful baby and a great toy for our two older children. However, he put Willie K. and me right back in the role of new parents — again, to the amusement of our friends.

I had insisted that Harold's middle name be Stirling. My father, Murray Forbes Smith, was of Scottish descent. His grandmother was a Stirling from Edinburgh, and she was brought up entirely by her aunt, Lady Alva. This was where I got my first name and also the playful title "Lady", which some of my friends used, the *same* ones who were amused by my late pregnancy.

Apparently this great-grandmother of mine was also the source of some of my independence. Against the will of her family, and against her "station in life", she married a physician, a Dr. Forbes of Edinburgh. Escaping the antagonism of the entire family, the two came to America and settled in Virginia. They had a daughter named Margaret, and she married a Smith. It was the child of this union who was my father.

He, in turn, married Phoebe Desha, daughter of General Robert Desha of Kentucky. Trained as a lawyer, my father abandoned this career to move to Mobile, Alabama, and attend to the General's cotton shipping business.

Here, in the heart of the feudal South, I was born, the seventh of nine children. (Unfortunately only five survived.)

Nine. So you could say I was a piker, having only three. But if you raise those three properly, that can be quite enough!

The children and I spent most of their early years at Idlehour, our home on Long Island. Male or female, I wanted each of them to learn how to be "domestic". With Willie K.'s permission, I converted a bowling alley on the grounds of our home into a playhouse. This playhouse had a kitchen. On a *real* stove, they were taught to cook. Though their specialty was homemade caramels, they could turn out a fairly good meal, and often we all four sat down at lunchtime and consumed it with murmurs of delight. Afterwards, I saw to it that all three of them became very efficient at cleaning up.

In the late spring and summer, they left their playhouse and waded together in the Great River that trickled along our property. They learned to fish and to probe under the rocks for crayfish.

A servant or two assisted them in learning how to handle a sailboat. Little did those servants know they were training a very young boy, named Harold Stirling, to become not only one of the world's great yachtsmen, but the man who was to defeat T.O.M Sopwith and Sir Thomas Lipton consistently in the America's Cup Races, and the Queen's Cup. He also won the trophy in the International Challenge Cup.

Previously, when Harold was still in the arms of his adoring nurse, Bridget, Willie K. was insistent that Consuelo and little Willie should learn as much as they could about horses. So they were given ponies to ride. Consuelo was dismayed that she had to learn properly to ride sidesaddle. Particularly so, because she had wheedled out of me stories about my own youth, when I, too, played with a boy, though this boy did not happen to be my brother. There was a family who lived near named Forbes — not related to us. It was their son, Charles, who would join me in going to their stable and getting out their most spirited horses, so we could ride them around the stable yard. Needless to say, I did not ride sidesaddle. I rode spread out, and I held on for dear life.

My mother heard about it, knew it was very dangerous, and forbade me to do it again. But the joy of the enterprise was too great for consequences. Again and again I slipped away to the Forbes' stable and, for a glorious moment, relieved my soul to a risky excitement. I was whipped each time I did it, but I considered that as only secondary.

Consuelo shared this information with little Willie, and I had a lot of explaining and convincing to do to prevent them from repeating my venture. Instead, I harnessed their ponies to a trap and let them ride around. The two children were still not convinced that they should not be riding bareback, until one day when Consuelo was out in the trap, and the skittery pony became frightened and bolted straight toward a water hydrant. Little Willie was watching, horrified. He turned to me. Already aware, and afraid my daughter would be thrown out, I ran and grabbed hold of the pony's bridle and dragged it to a halt.

On the next weekend visit from their father, Consuelo and little Willie told him how brave I had been. I was grateful, but I was more grateful that the experience had been such an example to them!

Little Willie had his father's charm and sweet temper, but he was mischievous and recklessly daring. Forecasting one of his careers as an automobile racer and the founder, financed by his father, of the Vanderbilt Cup Races, he loved to ride one of those high-wheeled bicycles at such a speed that he was tossed off several times. I finally declared that I would confiscate the bicycle at the next fall. So, when this fall occurred, he did *not* tell me. Instead, he sat through a whole lesson before his tutor discovered little Willie had broken his arm.

I felt terrible about it, but the injury was enough to convince him. I did not need to confiscate the bicycle. After that, he did not especially slow down, but he became more skilled and cautious.

Consuelo would often join in the mischief. One day she and her brother were sailing their boat on a pond. Their governess, who wished to be called Fraulein Wedekind, gazed out on the pond and thought it was time for them to come home. With Fraulein, they were learning to speak German, just as others in the household were helping them to learn French and Italian. But Fraulein's pleas in German did not help on this day. The more she called, the slower they neared the bank. Finally she caught hold of the boat and tried to straddle the water with one leg on shore, but even this didn't stop them. They bowed to the impulse of giving a sudden shove with one of the oars. Fraulein landed in the water. In her Middle High German fury, she held out her wet skirts all the way home and came straight to me. I listened.

As was my custom, I, personally and in private, switched Consuelo's and little Willie's legs with my riding crop. But it was the last punishment I ever hoped to give them. They were now old enough to ask if I had received the same type of punishment in my childhood. And I was bound to answer!

"Yes, children, I did."

"With a riding crop?" asked Consuelo.

"Sometimes. But also with a willow branch, cut green."

"Did it hurt as much?" Little Willie wanted to know.

"More. And more often."

"How often?" They both asked.

I personally believed, from much experience, that punishment did not deter a person from what he or she *really* wanted to do. But I could *not* tell them this, though they were certainly demonstrating it. I simply adhered to the facts. "Well, my dears, I have to say there was one terrible year in my family's history in which I received a whipping every single day."

"Every day?" they echoed.

"Every day. All 365."

Consuelo's eyes grew wide. "Didn't it make you sick?"

"More sick in mind than body."

Little Willie asked the more telling question. "Did you still love your mother?"

I dodged this query. "How did you know it was my mother who did the whipping?"

"Because our father — our father —"

And he could not continue. I knew why. Willie K. never disciplined the children. It was all left to me to do.

My husband's activities with the children, as contrast, were mostly confined to amusement — solving the puzzles and playing the manufactured games popular at the time. Many of these he would buy in New York and bring out to us as surprises on weekends.

Little Willie was particularly good at detecting the secret openings of the beautiful turned-ebony balls my husband would seek out for him.

Consuelo loved the Chinese-made "Sunday Boxes" and puzzles he would bring her. She reveled in their scenes and symbols so deftly carved in ivory.

As contrasted with these puzzles, games were usually played with some kinds of cards, many of them intricate and exotic, or with board games, such as "Castle", played with dice, which the children loved to shake up in a small carved-letter open tube.

That was my husband's contribution. And mine? I was skilled in the reading of books to them.

I had kept an 1870 copy of Richard Doyle's *A Series of Pictures from the Elf World*. This book had poems by William Allingham, which the children liked almost as much as the remarkable drawings. Consuelo and little Willie also liked to hear me read Ralph Caldecott's *Ride-a-Cock Horse to Banbury*. And they would sing out "Cross!" Our Harold preferred *Hey Diddle* and *Baby Bunting*. And he personally felt George Routledge had written it for *him*, and that I had developed my voice to have a Southern accent, especially for the nightly reading.

It was obvious, in all this, that my husband wanted to be loved by everybody. And he was! But this was one of the things which began to gnaw at me. I was hearing stories about his having lunch with various ladies in New York. I refused to believe this until I could find out for myself, and I could not do this until such time as we were all housed at 660 Fifth Avenue. In the meantime, I had the responsibility of the children. I did not want this daily task to make me excel as a mother but fail as a wife. This was a very precarious tightrope to walk, and I felt I had not developed the skill.

However, I knew I must stop thinking about these things. Even at this moment two of our children were asking me very penetrating questions. Little Willie had asked the last question, and I knew that I must very carefully answer it. Our first son had already started to stammer, and I had to constantly slow myself down to match a pace that was comfortable for him. So I carefully said, "Yes, Willie, it was the same in my own family. My mother was always the one who had to do the disciplining."

This brought on a natural question from Consuelo. "Did you still love her?"

This query hit me hard, and I knew I could not ask in return, "Do you still love *me*?" But I wanted to — I certainly wanted to.

"Yes, I did," I replied. "Until the day she died."

"Why?"

"Because I felt it was her duty to discipline me."

I knew this answer would not satisfy the generation to which our children belonged.

So little Willie was able to ask what he most wanted to. "Were you *that* naughty a little girl?"

"Well, let me tell you two about the time I was the most naughty. Then *you* can decide." And I began. "When I was a little younger than you, Consuelo, I decided I was too old to continue sleeping in the nursery with the younger children. I wanted a room all to myself. I asked for the little room right next to the nursery. I was refused. I tried to argue with everyone about it, but to no avail. So I decided to become so hateful and disagreeable that the nurse and governess would put me out of the nursery — forever. Then I might have a chance."

I saw the children cover an anticipating snicker. I continued. "One night, my sister and I were hitting each other with bath towels. On the mantel was an assortment of little china animals — artistic and valuable. Over them hung a large picture. I took my towel and decided here was my chance. I knocked down and smashed every one of the china ornaments. Then I attacked the glass in the picture and shattered it. I turned to my horrified sister and said, 'There now, I've seen the last of this nursery!' And I went to bed. When my mother came home from a dinner party that evening she saw what I had done."

"What happened?" They both asked.

I found I was not anxious to tell them. "She grabbed up her riding whip and gave me one of the worst lashings I have ever received."

Consuelo leaned forward. "But did you get the *room*?"

"Yes, I did."

Both of them gave a long sigh, stared at each other, and asked to be excused.

I granted their request and watched them go, but I wondered if either one of them cared about the whipping I received.

It bothered me.

Late that night I passed by Consuelo's room on my way to my own. I heard the sound of soft weeping, was alarmed, and went in.

Little Willie had crept into her room, and the two of them were sitting on the side of the bed. They were whispering about what I had told them.

I was touched.

Willie's beautiful green eyes were moist, but it was his sister who was doing the weeping.

She looked up. "Mother, that was a terrible price to pay for having your own room!"

"My *mother* felt the same way."

Willie tried to speak for Consuelo. "But she whipped you every day!"

"Not with a riding whip. But, my dears, she was really trying to guard me — save my life — from all those dangerous things I was doing."

"Even having your own room?"

"Yes. She did not think it was a good idea to give me special privileges."

Consuelo reached over and put her hand on mine. "But couldn't she *talk* to you?"

"Apparently it did no good."

Consuelo could no longer weep silently. She let forth real sobs. I held her in my arms and tried to comfort her. And I reached over and patted Willie.

As all three of us sat there, I felt I certainly had my answer to their feelings about the whipping.

Perhaps they would understand my own resorting to the riding crop to discipline them. And I hoped all this was now committed to the past.

The tears began to flow down my own cheeks.

But the one assurance I *did* have was that my children really loved me ....

9

I AM CONTINUING TO ENJOY TELLING MY STORY IN
period. I'm remembering the dialogue of the time — the florid
words, expressions, puns and catch-phrases. It all comes back.
    There is something else that comes back. The first time I met
certain people.

Oliver Hazard Perry Belmont, for instance. I had heard about him long
before. I had been told tales about how flamboyant he was and how
elaborate and precise his taste was, in both horses and people!

He was being seen at all the best places. I was eventually being seen
there, too. By him.

The formal meeting took place at the races in Central Park. He had a box
near ours. Willie K. could seldom go. There is nothing more lonely in the
whole world than sitting in a box alone at the horse races. There is no one
to mark your card with, to ask questions of, to predict the next race with,
to join you in anticipating your winnings, and especially to cheer and yell
with during each race.

That day I did choose the right horse to win on the third race. Oliver H.
P. Belmont noticed my elation and asked if he could go collect for me. I said,
"Yes, thank you, sir."

When he returned with my winnings, I invited him into our box.
Oliver introduced himself as a fellow member of the clubs to which my
husband belonged. I said I was delighted to finally have a chance to meet
him.

Oliver then reminded me that the New York Times said he and his
former wife had attended our gala ball of 1883. I immediately confessed
to him that it was a grave oversight on my part, having greeted 1200
guests that evening, I certainly should have remembered him above all!

He grinned and stated he would not have stood out — his "height was
too short". I said mine was too. Hadn't he noticed? In fact, that was why

I was standing on a dais when I met him. He knew I understood perfectly. That similarity was enough to begin a friendship. Except that he finally confessed the Times *was wrong — he and his wife were not there.*

I gasped, then began to laugh I realized this man was adept at what they now call double-talk. And I found that I liked it. We "chattered" for the rest of the afternoon. He even had sherry and cakes sent to the box.

I was no longer alone. For the rest of the season, he was either in our box or I was in his.

In dictating these memoirs, I take into account Oliver Hazard Perry Belmont was usually called Oliver. Also O.H.P. Sometimes Ollie or Harry. It was his brothers who occasionally used the name Ollie. And, because one of his brothers was named Perry, the name Harry coupled with Perry sounded like "the mercantile twins". So in reciting this story of my life, I will call him Oliver, and now and then refer to him as O.H.P.

When I begin dictating this episode, now, I have a feeling my donkey will cock his ears. He might even slow down his pace, so he won't miss a word. My bath chair cart may travel a minimum of distance during these next few days!

CRUISING WITH THE YACHT *ALVA*

When it came time for little Willie to enter school and for Consuelo to continue with her tutoring, dancing, and elocution lessons, we moved back to our château at 660 Fifth Avenue.

I was glad.

Not just to ground those rumors about my husband, but to counter them. If other women proved interesting to him, I felt his wife must at least try to be as pretty, fetchingly dressed, and socially adroit.

Furthermore, Alva Vanderbilt must bring her problem home. If the involvement with her three children was too great for her to be in the daily New York luncheon swirl, she must become the creator of a late-night supper whirl. Right in her own dining room.

And that is exactly what I did.

I instructed my servants that the table must always be set. And food and wine ready. Food could consist of cheeses, beautiful breads, and rich cakes — something which I could set on the table myself. The cook and maids need not be present. Not even the butler. When people dropped in on their way home after a concert, opera, or the theater, I could greet them at the door. I would chatter liltingly and show them to the dining room. My husband could then be summoned from his desk, from the facts-and-figures work he had brought home. And the party would begin!

It worked. The parties did begin and they did continue.

Inevitably the conversation would get around to railroads. Then I would carefully steer it to yachts. We would discuss who had been where on whose ship on what cruise. I would deftly drop a progress report on the construction of our yacht, *Alva*. Willie K. would then take over and relate the engineering data and forecast completion. We were well predicted!

To my husband's and our children's delight, and especially to mine, it was finally announced our yacht was completed.

The christening was scheduled for October 14, 1886. I chose my sister, Mrs. Fernando Yznaga to do the honors. We were to travel down to Wilmington to the shipyards of Harlan and Hillingsworth for the occasion. W. K. insisted that our entire family ride there in our private New York Central Wagner palace car. He felt the ship would match the railroad car in elegance, and it would be "only a simple transition to go aboard!"

Amazingly, it was. Everyone was impressed, including the children. I was given credit for "the refinement which the lavish furnishings showed." Having worked hard on the planning, I smiled gratefully, was relieved, and accepted the credit.

I not only wanted the United States to know what a yacht could be, I wanted people overseas to know. We would start with a cruise down to the West Indies. And then plan to steam across the Atlantic. After all, we were not the first Vanderbilts to start this tradition. But love for sailing had skipped a whole generation because W. H. had hated even the thought of it. It was time to rekindle the Vanderbilt name on the seas. And I intended to do it.

Little did I know at this time that the next generation was going to take over where I left off.

As planned by Willie K., the christening went off on schedule. Mary Virginia swung a bottle of champagne against its bow, and our yacht *Alva* slid down the ways into Christiana Creek. We were launched!

The next few years would determine the seaworthiness of our ship. But more that of the Vanderbilts themselves. I wanted *Alva* to be a re-creation of *North Star*. Except for one thing. I did not intend for my husband to be severely snubbed in any port. Not as the old Commodore had been snubbed in London on June 3, 1853, when he graciously extended a formal invitation to entertain the British dignitaries "at a dejeuner" elegantly planned aboard his *North Star*. Not a single dignitary appeared. I, as a Vanderbilt wife, was determined such a marine disaster should never happen again!

So for the next few years, I got in practice. We entertained, on board *Alva*, on both our cruises at home and abroad. I am happy to say all guests honored our invitations at all times.

Willie K. and I included our children in on as many of these cruises as possible. I told them their boating experience, which we had started at Idlehour, was thus continued.

All three would laughingly point out, "Yes, Mother, but on a much grander scale!"

In fact, certain aspects of *Alva* they felt were designed especially for *their* pleasure. The principal one was our ship's ability "to roll like a tub in a storm." The children would race from side to side to balance it. I prayed to my Episcopal God for *small* storms. I did not mind that they felt the three of them were truly assisting the Divinity in righting our yacht, but I felt in time God might be impressed with their seamanship and offer them stronger storms!

This was something I did *not* want. I also predicted this rolling deficiency might finally do in my beloved namesake vessel. But not before, I hoped, we could at times leave the children safely at home and take some longer "cruises for adults". Complete with a select guest list, of course.

Which we did. One of the most frequent guests on these trips was Oliver Hazard Perry Belmont. I was never sorry. Willie K. was frequently in the chart room or allowed to take a turn at the wheel, or even stand watch. During those long hours, Oliver was always good for charming conversation. He would expand any loneliness or confinement of quarters — with Belmont family anecdotes, or his knowledge of horse breeding and racing, his awareness of function in architecture, his growing collection of medieval armor, or the endless extending of his acquisition of European art. But more immediately what to see and do when we made port and went ashore tomorrow.

He was often needed to augment the occasion with innovative impishness. Willie K. was frequently tied up with going into the port city with the captain, to obtain marine parts, maps, or supplies with which to continue the voyage. He was also to be received by maritime figures as "that second Vanderbilt with the big yacht". In other countries except England, the 1853 cruise of *North Star* had *not* been forgotten. Certain officials wanted to be invited aboard immediately to see if our yacht was as splendid as Grandfather's had been. So W. K. did exactly this. And I must say they were seldom disappointed.

I did not want to spend precious time shaking hands. After all, I was still in my thirties!

As Oliver would facetiously say, "This lady on my arm wants to escape her many duties and see some of the wonders of the world. And she wants to do it in as pleasant company as possible. With me. So stand aside."

Oliver and I had already been noted in the New York papers as "a duo" at the horse races in Central Park. I asked myself, "Who else was going to accompany me?" Willie K., as chairman of the board of the Lake Shore & Michigan Southern Railway, was still usually tied up in a meeting. Of course, Oliver, too, had an obligation to further the family business — in his case, banking. Regardless of the fact it *was* the business of the Belmont family, Oliver had announced to August, Sr., his father, early in the game, that horses would become *his* business — his only business. Oliver hoped to continue Belmont Park and the Stakes, on their Long Island property at Oakdale. What better way to develop a breeding farm? But, also, Oliver stated that he would take over the family real estate in Newport, Rhode Island, eventually to build some sort of a dwelling to show off the favorites of his own breed. He stated he did not consider all this as a side interest. To him, it was a full-time business. And he privately knew, after his father's death, that he would inherit enough money to carry it off. And make a good profit.

Oliver's older brother, August, Jr., already had taken over many of the family responsibilities. Oliver did not wish to fritter away his own life in board meetings.

In 1889, we decided to have one of our select-guest-list cruises. We had left the children safely at home with their governess and tutor. On this cruise into the open Atlantic, Oliver was a favorite guest, and certainly mine. Our trip began pleasantly. But soon a storm had come up, and, as predicted, the Alva converted into a "rolling tub". Oliver and I isolated ourselves in two deck chairs, to ride out the gale.

We had been talking at length about the beginning years of his young manhood. I reminded him there was an early origin for his feelings that he "must have his own business".

"Alva, are you referring to my hardy halcyon days as a young banker in Bremen?"

"Exactly. Your assignment abroad. It was given to you the day your parents learned that you wanted to marry Sara Whiting."

"Assignment abroad!" Oliver was hooting at my designation. "My dear little Mo thought Sallie Whiting was a flirt."

"And your mother was right."

This is what was so satisfying about the dialogue that went on between us. We fed each other outrageously true concepts and each of us quickly responded to the humor without ever needing to be "filled in". Thus our conversations could go at a great pace because neither of us had to backtrack for information. Oliver and I *were* a pair.

Oliver continued. "Assignment, indeed. That kept my parents

from calling it by its real name — a sentence. Two years in Bremen. Really!"

"Come, come, they only wanted you to prove yourself as a capable young banker. So you could follow in papa's footsteps, of course, and support a wife."

"Ah, yes. The great August Belmont would not have to do it!"

"*And* support a child."

"True, my dear. When I did return that Christmas of '82, I got 'Flirtatious Sara' into bed as soon as possible. *But* I married her first ... and at Swanhurst, no less .... Then what happened? We went to Paris for our honeymoon, and that cursed mother of hers and Sallie's two unmarried sisters followed us. Very soon we were all living in the same apartment. I couldn't get rid of them, and I couldn't get Sallie to let me rent the two of us a place of our own. So finally I left. But when I got back, Sallie and her mother had written letters to my parents. Now everybody was taking sides. I was ready to fight them all, but Sallie felt it was no use. And pretty soon it was all over. If they had just left us alone .... What did my parents and those Whitings expect?"

"I don't know what they expected, but they got a beautiful granddaughter."

"Natica was more than my revenge. What a gorgeous, divine child. With her mother's good look and, of course, mine."

"Fortunately she had *your* disposition."

"Whatever she had, Natica is now a granddaughter whose Grandmother Whiting will never let her see me."

"And never let you see *her.*"

"It's a solid front. It seems both Milly and Sallie warn Natica against her father. I have become Absent Absinthe Oliver!"

"Absinthe? That only happened in Bremen. To kill your passion during that long waiting period, no doubt?"

"It doesn't matter now. The Whitings have given Natica the image. If I try to see her, it's because I am crazed — crazed!"

"Oliver, someday she is going to be a young lady with a mind of her own. Then they can't stop her."

"I hope you're right. But the Whitings are terrible people. Mama Milly is the worst. She never wanted her daughter to grow up and be a wife. Let alone mine. Plus a mother. So she has kept Sallie at *home.* Can't bear to let her go. And now she has done the same thing with my daughter!"

"But remember, Oliver, darling, Natica is also your child — not just Sallie's. And she must have *some* of your spunk, some of your good taste. She will recognize you for the absolutely elegant man that you are."

"It's my elegance they're afraid of. When I drive down Bellevue Avenue in one of my phaetons, I slow up when I get to Swanhurst. They always know it. I glance into all the curtained windows of that house. I keep hoping Natica will dash out on the porch and say, 'Daddy, Daddy! Can I have a ride?'"

"More like, 'Father, may I accompany you in your carriage?'"

"Oh, yes. I am sure they have completely ruined her."

"Doesn't she ever pull one of those curtains aside and wave to you?"

"I've never seen her do it. And I *wait* for it. I have even staged a breakdown or two in front of their house. But there is never a sign of recognition."

"You're sure they're all inside Swanhurst, watching?"

"I am sure of it!" Then Oliver grew quiet. He shook his head. "I still regret the divorce, but the situation was intolerable for everyone, including my dear Natica…. Sometimes I wonder — if I died, if they would even let her visit my grave?"

I stood up and took his face between my hands. "Oliver. You are indestructible. You are not going to die."

"No?" He shrugged. "No, I'm not. And it serves them right!"

I laughed. The rolling motion of the ship was continuing. I moved my deck chair closer to his. But he rose and insisted both chairs should be moved as close to the center of the ship as possible.

"Alva, my dear, I swear your husband causes these storms on purpose."

"Why?"

"It makes us all loll about. We seem drunk. That way, it saves him a considerable sum on his whiskey bills!"

I liked the observation and laughed hard enough for my husband to hear and inquire, "What's so funny?" I told him. He chuckled, in turn, punched Oliver a glancing retort on the shoulder, and returned to his many duties.

I continued. "It may also save on his food bills, Oliver. Seasickness tends to cut down on all activities in the galley."

"Haven't the Vanderbilts ever been able to find a chef who never gets seasick?"

"Never. And the crew all stay below out of choice. It is only the footloose ones who can make it up the gangway to the dining room."

"Do you give battle pay?"

"I've even suggested bribery. It's no use. A churning stomach is a churning stomach."

"Let alone a rolling Vanderbilt yacht. Shall we give up on this deck and move inside?"

"Yes."

And we did. Oliver and I then chose a conversation chair I had selected in New York for the salon.

"Are you choosing this chair because it has two seats but only one body?"

"Indeed. If you and I are going to go down on this yacht, I feel we might as well go down together."

"Still talking."

"To the bottom — never missing a word."

So we sat down and went on with our conversation, face-to-face. Oliver was such a devilishly handsome man, I never minded. That mustache, that smooth skin, those brown eyes, which usually met my own. Together we brown-visioned our way through the world. We saw it all in a tinted way. Oliver also gave this fact credit for our sometimes off-color observations.

To me, it was Episcopal irreverence. But to Oliver, who had always preferred to be raised in no church at all, it was healthy blasphemy.

I decided to bring it up as a topic of conversation. "Oliver. You're really not a non-Christian."

"I'm not a Jew either."

"Because your mother was not a Jew?"

"That's right, Alva, my darling little Mo was not."

Contemplating this contrast in our upbringing, at this very moment, I ask, "Oliver, if we sink, do you realize whose fault it will be?"

"Mine. For not being a true Jew."

"Nonsense. How can you be, if your *mother* is not Jewish?"

"I realize that. But people still say I am."

"Never fear, Oliver. If we sink, the fault will be *mine* — for not praying harder as a good Episcopalian."

"Well. It's the first time you've ever admitted it."

"You're right."

"But Alva Vanderbilt only *knows* one way to pray. Hard!"

"Like everything else I do?"

"Yes, my dear — if allowed, I would have added that next."
I sighed. "I seem to have only one pace. Full speed ahead."

"I'm sorry the captain feels the same way about this yacht *Alva*."

"Shall I order him to slow down?"

"No. He's riding out the storm."

"But, Oliver, he doesn't realize that with *me* aboard, the storm will never stop!"

"Very well. Then I will go tell him!"

Oliver jumped up and pretended to head for the passageway. I began laughing and was still at it when the ship gave a giant roll. Oliver had to return and sit again.

This time I was the one who pointed the finger. "Are you aware there is another hazard on board? Oliver Hazard Perry Belmont. Tell them who you are."

"The Newport shipping family or merely a graduate of the United States Naval Academy?"

"Both!" I watched him again mock an exit, then waited for him to expect me to hold him back. I did so, then pretended to change my mind. "Wait. This captain only recognizes heroism. Tell him your grand uncle, Oliver Hazard Perry, won the battle of Lake Erie by yelling —"

"—'We have met the enemy and they are ours'!"

"Glad you remembered it …."

Oliver eyed me. "It was embroidered on all our family sheets." Then he stood up and purposely circled our double chair twice. "Alva. What are you saying? Do you think this captain is intending to *abandon* ship?"

"Yes! So now you have to go tell him who your *grandfather* was."

"Who?"

Oliver looked so intentionally puzzled that I whacked him to attention and pronounced, "Matthew Calbraith Perry."

Oliver struggled to his feet, now playing the game. "Who is *he*?"

I stood up and recited, "This man's daring and diplomacy opened the gates of trade with Japan!"

"Remarkable. Where did you read *that*?"

"In a travel brochure!"

With that, we both collapsed back into our chairs.

One of the stewards, sent by Willie K., came by to peek in and check on our safety.

I waved to him. "How are the other passengers doing?"

"Madam, they are all in their staterooms."

"And Mr. Vanderbilt?"

"Very busy, ma'am."

"Oh. Well. And the captain?"

"Very concerned."

"If he gets sick, let us know. Mr. Belmont, here, is connected with an admiral!"

"I see. I will, Mrs. Vanderbilt, I will. Thank you."

The steward's eyes grew larger as he backed away.

Oliver was in hysterics. He pointed at me as though I were an actress on stage who had just abandoned the script and spoken her own lines.

An impressive roll of *Alva* made us simmer down. Oliver asked, with concern, "Shall I close the door?"

"No, no. If this salon fills, we are sunk in more ways than one."

"Salon, indeed," disparaged Oliver. "This is a *wardroom*, if I ever saw one."

"Oh, no, it never becomes a wardroom until it is totally immersed."

"In seawater or fresh?"

"In alcohol …. And I wish we had some right now."

"I don't think we really need it."

"I'll ring the steward."

"Alva! You'll never get him back — not with the two of us in here. He'll go overboard first!"

I took time to have a nice, long chortle. "What makes you think we're already drunk?"

"The expression on his face …."

I decided to get up and stretch my sea legs while I could!

Oliver watched me for several moments. "Are you staggering on purpose?"

"I'm not sure."

"I would rise up from this chair and outdo you, except for your age."

I bounced my palm off his head. "My age? You can *never* forget that I am all of five years older than you are?"

"Never."

"Then I get the first drink. Because I need it more!"

"Oh, damn. I knew I could never carry this off. For the rest of my life, you will have the advantage on me."

"For the rest of your life? *Our* lives?"

"Why not? As you get older, you may need me around. In fact, the older you get, the more you may require my attention."

"I hope so!"

We both laughed but gave a look at each other. Our eyes seemed to wonder if this would ever really be true.

At that point, Willie K. came in, on the report of the steward, to see if we were out of our minds.

"You two. Imbibing during a storm?"

Oliver stood up very straight. "Neither one of us has had a thing to drink, except this morning when we were served that blasted pink lemonade your cook thinks is his specialty. He even had the audacity to add a few sprigs of mint he brought aboard."

"I'm sure it was meant for juleps for Alva."

"And I don't drink them."

Oliver put his hand on W. K.'s shoulder. "In fact, as I said, 'This whole storm will save you a mint!'"

Getting the point, Willie K. shrugged and appeared to be amused. But he was actually impatient and peered uncertainly around the room. "At this moment I am more concerned about a rumor. One of the stewards tells me Mr. Belmont has advice from an *admiral*. Do you two have a telegraphy system in here that I don't know about?"

"Telegraphy?!" Oliver blinked. "No, sir. Tell him it is a *direct line* ...."

Willie K. soon caught the reference, savored the idea, and eyed Oliver. Then he began to chuckle. But still with uneasiness.

I knew W. K. didn't like facetiousness. So I tried to assure him. "Not all the way, dear. Let's give Oliver's ancestors a rest!"

Willie K. then relaxed and enjoyed the joke without overtones. I knew my husband well. I had to ....

He excused himself and hurried out. "Sorry. I'm still making sure all deck equipment is secured."

In turn, Oliver and I decided we would try to secure the furnishings of our salon-wardroom. We turned chairs on their sides, pushed tables to the wall, put lamps on the floor, and placed prints and paintings flat in safe corners. I had never intentionally dismantled anything since my naughty childhood. Neither had Oliver. It gave both of us a sense of power.

We began to discuss our childhoods. We both had mothers and fathers who included us into all their social activities. We were not children who were "trotted out on occasion". Oliver was once again wishing he had a daughter with whom he could do that same thing. He deferred to my children. "Look at your three. You are performing a function called mothering, and you're doing a good job of it, Alva. You love them, and they love you. And I, also, love them."

"We may be dealing in good Southern molasses, Oliver, but they love you too." As he beamed at me, the ship gave another roll, and I had to touch the wall to steady myself. But I went right on. "Sometimes I feel I have overdone it. Perhaps I have been confined too long to staying on Long Island and raising the children. My own advancement as the wife of Mr. William Kissam Vanderbilt has apparently suffered."

Oliver took my hands, stood alongside, and looked straight at me. "Alva, I know it is different for a woman. Tell me, what were your feelings when *Town Topics* began decorating its pages with comments on Willie K.?"

"You sure you want to know?" He nodded. So I began. "At first I didn't believe it. I knew Colonel William D'Alton Mann took bribes to keep people's names out of the gossip sheet. So I decided all news he printed was highly suspect. I knew he had his informants and that he even kept some people's servants on his payroll for precious tidbits. Or kept musicians who played for their dances and observed romances budding."

"Don't forget the snubbed, disgruntled social climbers as another source."

"Yes, Oliver, I knew all this, but I still didn't want to believe it. Willie K. — a womanizer?"

"That's why he chose you to marry, Alva, no doubt. You are beautiful, and more than that, you are really a woman!"

I gazed my appreciation. "Just as you were the young husband, I was the young wife. I believed in our marriage. I felt W. K. and I were a team, a partnership, a corporation for raising our children, running our home, and conducting our social life. I thought we were successful and could show people that all three functions could actually be done at the same time and done well."

"Exactly. Originally, Sallie and I hoped for the same thing."

"But, Oliver, when I really began to doubt, the world started to look different to me. I walked around our Idlehour house and looked at our family mementos in a new way. They somehow mocked me. They were not something we were all doing together. These memories now appeared to be *my* idea — things I had arranged for the family, events I had made happen."

"I know. They hit me the same way. 'All *Oliver's* doing.' Yes, yes."

"I felt isolated, as though I were imposing my entire will on the family. It was no longer the two of us. When Willie K. arrived at Idlehour to spend the weekend with us, it was as if he were a spectator. He became very patronizing. 'Isn't that nice? Isn't it jolly fun? My, my, how clever your mother is.'"

"I know. I accompanied him, you remember, to Idlehour for a couple of those performances."

"That's what they were! Good acting. And I got tired of it. I began to feel sick whenever he left for the city. I felt he was pulling down the curtain on us. On all four of us."

"Yes, Alva. But I hope I never gave you that feeling."

"No. You really cared, Oliver, about what we were *all* doing."

"I tried."

"Except for one thing."

"What's that?"

"I realized you were my husband's best friend …."

Oliver did not want to discuss this. He paced the floor for several moments. Then he diverted. "Alva, you are also the kind of a woman who should have a career."

"Me?"

"This seems to be a year for women. I hear some federation has just been founded."

"Oh, yes, you mean the General Federation of Women's Clubs."

"Something like that. And there's a woman named Jane Addams in Chicago who has just established a place called Hull House."

"Yes. Bless her heart. I'll get to those things in time. But right now I must work out my life with Willie K." I paced the deck, myself. Finally I had to ask, "Oliver? Are you shielding your best friend?"

He did not dodge the question. "I am really shielding you. I don't want my Alva to get hurt."

"Your Alva can never be anything more, Oliver, than your *female* best friend. Face the truth. This is 1889."

"You have done a few 'firsts' in society. You wouldn't consider another one?"

"The wrath of the Vanderbilt family would know no bounds."

"Why?"

"Because you can only get a divorce in the state of New York on grounds of adultery."

"But you *may* have your grounds."

"Ah, hah. You are not shielding W. K. You are admitting what has been going on!"

"Well — the gossip sheets accuse you and me of the same thing."

"It's not true."

"Alva. It might be better if it were …."

I leaned against an overturned chair for several moments and thought. He was right. I should admit I was beginning to really love this man. In truth, I wanted to be with him all the time.

Oliver took both my hands. "Look, I have talked about *my* marriage. There is no reason why you shouldn't talk about *yours*. I only feel it isn't quite fair without Willie K. here to defend himself."

"Sara is not here to defend *herself*."

"Thank God."

"I feel the same way about Willie K."

"But as you said, I am his best friend."

"All right. I'll make a bargain with you — if he comes in here in the next few minutes, all three of us will discuss my crumbling marriage."

"During a storm?"

"What better time?"

Oliver laughed, and then suggested we sit on the floor, both for stability and for the maintenance of our stomachs and their marine tolerance. So we did.

"Alva, what about your friends? Are you still intimate with Lady Mandeville?"

"How can I be at such a distance?"

"What about your sister?"

"She is busy being Mrs. Frederico Yznaga."

"So you have no one to talk to? No one. Except possibly your husband's mother?"

"Maria is still in grief. Besides, dear George Washington Vanderbilt, no less, is living in the big house with her now."

"I thought he was in his 14th Street library most of the time!"

I smiled. "But this leaves Maria even more alone. No, I am not going to add to her troubles. Cornelius and W. K. manage her funds. Her first obligation would be to her son."

"But as far as Willie K. is concerned, you don't know *Maria*. She has a mind of her own. And she has always loved you. I predict that, even if the whole family deserts you, she never will."

"Desert me?"

Oliver made my eyes meet his. "In case of a divorce."

It was the second time the word had actually been spoken.

"She would put up with a divorce?"

"If she thought *you* wanted it, yes."

I crossed my legs, redistributed my skirts over my ankles, and thought. Was this the road ahead for Oliver and me?

But I did not have long to ask. Willie K. slid the door across and came in to see if we were both still all right. He was amused at the state of the salon plus the fact that we were both now on the floor.

Oliver waved a casual hand. "Pardon me for not getting up, W. K. I thought if *this Alva* is going down, I would keep your wife entertained."

"You may have to. This storm has more wind than water."

Oliver blinked. "I think there's plenty of water out there — if you want more."

My husband grinned.

In spite of my claim, I knew this would be no time to start a personal examination of a marital relationship. The two men were in the middle of their usual bantering. And that was that.

Oliver continued. "I have an eerie feeling, Willie K., that if this yacht rolls over, you won't bother to tell us."

"I'll muster all hands on deck and have the word passed along." He gave Oliver a searching look. "Eerie, did you say? Wasn't that the horse that won the Belmont Stakes this year?"

"You never *could* spell. No, that was Erie who won."

"Ah hah. The same as your granduncle's lake?"

"Exactly. Now I suppose you would like to know the time?"

"I would."

"It was 2:47."

"And the jockey?"

"W. Hayward. It was a good track, and so were the winnings."

My husband pointed a finger. "Alva, you should have bet more of our money."

"Next time get Oliver to do it. I'm saving my money for the Derby and the Preakness next year!"

Both men roared. But suddenly they had to stop.

Our yacht gave a double roll. Oliver quickly stretched out on the floor, folded his hands, closed his eyes, and gave up the ghost.

Willie K. staggered, then ended up on the floor beside him. "Alva, my wife, look at this man. Shall we lay him out like this, as if he were on top of his sarcophagus in a cathedral?"

"No. Put him inside. Otherwise, he will continue to make jokes — especially during the service — and disturb all the worshipers."

Willie K. leaned over to Oliver's ear. "It's inside for you, my good man!" Then he managed to stand up. "Now, if you will excuse me again. I have to go assure the captain that he will receive double pay for this voyage."

"Whatever happened to battle pay and bribery?" Oliver waited for an answer. W. K. nudged him with his foot, then made a serious but meandering path into the passageway.

As I watched him go, I knew it was somehow symbolic.

Though we all survived that particular fate and the state of the weather, I was apparently right.

In the late summer of 1892, *Alva* sank when she was struck by another ship, in a storm off the coast of Martha's Vineyard.

Fortunately there were no casualties, but it was a terrible shock. To all of us. And certainly to me.

Because I knew that was not the only cherished thing in our lives which, at that moment, was going under ....

10

I SHALL STATE AGAIN AND AGAIN IN DICTATING THESE *memoirs, the responsibility that I believe wealth brings to those who possess it.*

Money presents an opportunity — one which is there to be realized. If money is not used properly, it can only become a huge waste. The banknotes might just as well literally be burned.

But I sincerely feel wealth can build its own monument, whether that monument is for private enjoyment or public. If the monument endures, it can become a source of enjoyment for both.

A well-designed house is indeed a monument. The greater Vanderbilt family seemed to realize this. And I am proud that I was the instigator. Why? Because I began by choosing Richard Morris Hunt as my architect.

Not all the great Vanderbilt houses which were subsequently built were designed by Mr. Hunt, but I always felt the best ones were. Even though Idlehour burned in 1899, Hunt's sons rebuilt it immediately and in a different and charming style.

The point is, these houses were built. And I am now going to tell you about one that turned out to be what I honestly felt was the best of them all. Mr. Hunt always said the same thing. The two of us could not have been wrong!

But, right now, I wish to offer a salute. Regardless of the architect, most of the great Vanderbilt houses endure today, and endure well. May they continue.

So, I say, all hail to the Vanderbilts for being the family that made the greatest contribution to American architecture! I think you now understand what I am doing in dictating these memoirs — why I am doing it — and how I am doing it.

So there should be no more occasion for my introductory remarks.

I will tell my story straight on.

BUILDING A HOUSE OF MARBLE

After the sinking of *Alva*, I was tempted to contact her designer. He was Mr. St. Clair Byrne of Liverpool, England. I wanted to ask him if he had any advice about how to save my marriage. I felt, if he had learned anything from the sinking of the yacht named after me, he might be able to profit from the loss and prevent a second occurrence!

I proposed the idea to Richard Morris Hunt. He thought it was very amusing and very typical of me. Our heads were already together again as we were launched on a new project. The year we began was 1888.

I had acquired a disease. My idol-in-the-arts, Louis XIV, had it before me. It was called *La Manie de Batir*, the fury to build beautiful houses. R. M. Hunt said I obviously had a kingly case of it. But he was not sorry. He enjoyed working with me and by now felt that we had become a team.

As the founder of the American Institute of Architects, in 1857, he would soon want me to become a member. But I would decline. I felt I was not a trained architect, only a self- taught one. And it was *not* the same.

However, on this new house, we were working together even more than we had on our chateau at 660 Fifth Avenue. Almost five days a week. He was saying, "Mrs. Vanderbilt, apparently you like self-expression along constructive lines!"

Mr. Hunt always made me smile, but this time he was dead right. Whenever my family returned from their visits to Europe, I was struck with the uniform ugliness of American architecture. I would ask him, "Why can't the Vanderbilts be like the de Medici family? They made their money among the people, and they gave it back. What would the city of Florence be without them?"

"Do you want the Vanderbilts to do the same thing for New York?"

"Of course — and we are, but I also want more houses built on Long Island. And perhaps some day in France. But right now at my beloved Newport in Rhode Island."

This time I had come to the familiar office in the Studio Building to ask for a classic house along Greek lines. Mr. Hunt was combing his walls, files, and shelves for photos, sketches, travel books, and prints. I had brought a few myself. After all, you can't visit the Acropolis as many times as I had without wanting to re-create the Parthenon, even if you have to bring along photographs of the *family* in front of this structure to do it.

Right away, Mr. Hunt asked, "Mrs. Vanderbilt, are you sure your Southern background isn't showing?"

"I'm sure it is — all those pillars in front of all of those houses?"

"You also may be speaking from a pulpit of the Greek revival."

"Oh, yes. And loudly. With even a revival of my Southern accent."

"But, madam, I remind you the Medicis were of humble origin."

"So were the Vanderbilts. I consider *any* grandfather, who began by raising vegetables on Staten Island, and sailing them in his scow across to Manhattan and Brooklyn to sell, was a humble man."

"Indeed. How well did you know the old Commodore?"

"W. K. and I visited him on Sunday afternoons. He apparently liked me. He told my husband I never talked patronizingly to him the way everybody else did. I was simply open and argumentative."

"And so you are. Now, how many arguments do you think we're going to have over a Greek temple?"

"How many? I don't know, but at least an argument as good as the one we had over a particular detail of measurement. I don't even remember what it *was* now, but it caused you to say, 'Damn it, Mrs. Vanderbilt, who is building this house?'"

"And you came back with, 'Damn it, Mr. Hunt, who is to live in this house?'"

We both had a good laugh. And decided to go to a first name basis — preferably only in times of crisis. Professionally it was rare. But at least, after that, we decided we were Alva and Richard *if* the occasion demanded.

I also needed someone to whom I could bare my daily doubts as to whether my husband and I could stay married.

I told him, "I'm sure Willie K. is wondering the same thing. So much so that he has literally given me a blank check for a new house."

But, for me, the questions didn't stop. Was he doing it to divert me? Was he keeping me busy so that he could pursue interests elsewhere? Especially feminine?

Mr. Hunt and I knew we would never know the answers. We felt the only thing for me to do was to march straight ahead.

The children were either in school or with their tutors, and whenever possible, as was my custom, we all gathered at home for lunch.

By now I was relaxing my discipline of them. Little Willie's stammer was better but still existed. And our Consuelo had become extremely petulant. It was time. But nothing had as yet happened to our young Harold. He had profited from the experience of both. I had to now let all three show more self-expression. And I did. In other words, I let our children talk back to me. This was not the custom of the day. Children truly were to be seen and not heard.

Inevitably, this relaxation of so-called duty backfired on me. At times, they would become over-insistent, and I would have to put my foot down. Usually loudly, which always gave every-one who overheard us the impression that I yelled at our children and they spoke back audibly to me. It was not quite true, but I felt what was said was healthy. As long as there was basic love between us, I was not worried. And why should I? Little Willie and Consuelo showed great improvement.

So R. M. Hunt and I were domestically free to dream and plan. Onto those drawing boards would go realities. But the first must be the location.

He had already made this point very clear to me. "My dear, you must have very good reasons for choosing Newport. Is it because of some childhood memories of being there?"

"Mainly. But I must remind you that at my costume ball ... is it five years ago already?.... Mrs. Astor suggested I buy the house next door to her Beechwood mansion and tear it down."

"And you didn't hesitate. But I want to make sure it isn't just Bellevue Avenue, in turn, that beckons Mrs. W. K. Vanderbilt."

"I am certain neither of us can find any spot on the Atlantic Coast more 'favored of Nature'. It has both the ocean and bay, with good and safe harbors. And enough high ground along this avenue to allow long, sloping lawns and uninterrupted views."

"Are you listening to the same siren wave that sang to Sappho and Sophocles?"

"Of course."

"Then it really is natural to you to build a Greek temple?"

"It is, Mr. Hunt. Absolutely."

He sighed. "Very well. We shall proceed."

It took two years of hard study, plus travel, and my in-person searching for furnishings.

The facade of the building — this was to be much more than a house — *was* of classical design, and its materials were to be just as carefully selected. Charles E. Clarke, of Boston, was our general contractor. When construction finally began, we had chosen white Tuckahoe marble from a quarry on the Hudson River. We chose it for its durability, but it also had the quality of being especially impressive in the moonlight. This appealed to me because I intended to give a lot of night parties.

"But, Mrs. Vanderbilt, your exterior will be well lighted with those many bronze lamp fixtures we have chosen. Moonlight will fade away."

"I will begin the parties anywhere from ten o'clock until midnight. And, as our guests dance, eat, and murmur the night away, I will have all the lights turned off on the ocean side of the house, and they may stroll across the lawn to the cliffs —then turn back and view the lovely whiteness of the moonlit marble."

"Please, my dear, be rigorously sure to invite my wife and me to all of your parties."

"I will. Every party."

And I did. Catherine Howland Hunt and Richard fortunately summered in Newport at their own residence, so it was not difficult to see them often.

The interior of the building took various directions, according to its function and to the art objects that I had collected in Europe. Decorators were called in to assist on professional consistency.

Willie K. was seldom around to consult. He was building a new yacht and forming a new stable of horses. All my groundwork was defying me because he was caught up now in a whirl of high society yacht and hunt clubs.

My good and dear friend, Oliver, was busy doing the same thing I was, building a mansion. Further east on Bellevue Avenue, it was called Belcourt. Since Mr. Hunt was also the architect for Oliver's mansion, which was still very much in the design stage, he sometimes brought the two of us together, usually to compare our projects. Otherwise, I saw Oliver only socially. It was not like being aboard ship!

As you might imagine, Oliver was building, by 1892, his own future domicile in his own individual way. It was becoming sumptuous and it would actually show off his favorite horses and also his collection of armor and art objects from Europe. But it would be three more years before he would move in.

So circumstances decided for me, at this juncture, that "other men" were to be my salvation. A hundred of them, as a matter of fact, all Italian! And again it was all related to our construction materials. The white marble we had chosen for the facade itself would have been impossible to carve for the making of pillars, friezes, reliefs, and other exterior decoration. So the familiar Carrara marble was brought from Italy — all under the supervision of Batterson, See, and Eisele, with John Eisele, himself, in charge. This necessitated bringing a small army of Italian craftsmen to do the carving. These hundred men were skilled artisans, in the traditional and colorful shirts and smocks, with bandannas around their necks or folded and tied around their heads. It was possible to think of them as American-Italian workmen, except for their shoes. You can always tell that a man is European by his shoes. Immediately I had a studio built for these skilled gentlemen in Newport. I was proud of each one of them. For example, at the end of their two years of hard work, the model which they used for the marble capitals was so exquisite in its execution as well as design that the directors of the Metropolitan Museum in New York asked that they might have it to put on display.

Neither Mr. Hunt nor I wanted a mausoleum effect by continuing the white marble inside the mansion. The workmen agreed — in fact, they were thrilled. So, from Monte Arenti, the Siena marble was shipped over in all its yellow-veined splendor for the entrance and terrace and for the great stairway. The variations of this marble, shading from golden brown to delicate cream, would catch the sunlight in the daytime and the lights by night, always reminding the workmen that my architect was truly alive and so was I! Because this Siena marble was brought over in huge blocks, the artisans did not "have their work cut out for them". There was much to do. For instance, each tread of the staircase, with its entire two-story rise, was one solid piece of marble. I found my one hundred Italian lovers were kept too busy to notice me.

Therefore, I kept making myself evident. I wanted the dining room to be all red marble. Red. Even if we had to go all the way to

Nubia in Northeastern Africa to get it, which we did. Marble, like genius, seems to have no exclusive habitation.

Naturally, my Italians thought I had done it for them so as to keep them around as long as possible. I let them think so, and continued to visit them often. Though I could speak very little Italian, I knew the cadence of their speech and the intensity of their glances. I believe they wanted me to know they were very grateful that I treated each one of them as a distinguished craftsman. To exchange these thoughts, we used sign language, much pointing, and many exclamations. Each time I left the studio, I vowed to make them feel I had just attended a gallery show at which every artist had been present!

Naturally, there were other workers involved, in distant places. The great rompe in the hallway was made of gun metal combined with plain and gilded bronze. It was the work of craftsmen chosen in Paris. After it was completed, it was on exhibition there for several months and received the highest praise for its correct conception and perfect execution.

There was one room I had built to the specifications of one collection. It was the Gothic room. I had purchased the entire life searchings of one man to find the best survivals of Gothic art in carved doors and stained glass windows. The latter were from old cathedrals built in France at that high point of artistic accomplishment. This was the collection of Monsieur Emile Gavet. Because he had spent all his money on these treasures, he was very reluctant to part with them, but he definitely needed the money. The loss was still too great for him and he, unfortunately, died soon after. To make sure I would do what he, himself, would wish, I had already asked him to appoint a director. When the room was finally completed, it was this gentleman I brought over to place the entire collection. He was delighted the room had been built around the atmosphere of these rare treasures, rather than forcing them into an inharmonious, ready-made place. He recognized that the ceiling, stone mantel, and even the wood for the floor were imported to enhance Monsieur Gavet's collection.

Having started our study for this mansion in 1888, Mr. Hunt and I could never have predicted that it would be the summer of 1892 before my husband and I could give our lavish opening for what people were calling the marble palace, later to become simply Marble House. All three of us had been very private about all this construction, hiding it with high fences and requiring secrecy from our artisans. So the opening was to be exactly that, a giant burst of initial splendor.

We chose the night of August 19. Invitations were engraved and precise, as was the guest list.

I had carefully selected what I would wear. Tones of gold, warm brown, and cream — to not only reflect the interior marble but my hair, of course, now dyed to fit the occasion. And I had brought my best jewels, chosen for these tones, from New York. On one of the last days before the opening, I was making an inspection to see that every detail was in order and especially that the appropriate giant floral arrangements would have places reserved for them.

As I came through the huge wrought iron entrance doors and turned to watch them swing perfectly on their special pivots, I was once more amazed at the John Williams Bronze Foundry who had designed these. Plain hinges wouldn't do!

Suddenly Mr. Hunt came running to me and grabbed my arm. "Alva! Don't stop here. Come upstairs. Quick!"

Alva? He was calling me by my first name. It must be an emergency.

"The men have just put out a fire!"

"A fire? Oh, dear God."

"They ignited some wax or something — it burned the floor and blackened that marble."

"You mean by Willie K.'s bedroom?"

"How did you know?"

"That's the biggest expanse."

By that time we were on the mezzanine. We both paused to pant for breath. I gazed up and could see smoke stains and could smell the steam from the blackened floor.

We each grabbed a railing and made our way finally to the second floor.

There it was. I stared at the damage. All the workmen had disappeared, afraid of what I might say, no doubt. My Italians should have known me better than that. I might be furious, but I would understand.

"Richard. What can we do?"

Richard? He looked at me. I was calling him Richard? It *must* be an emergency.

"I'm depending on you, Alva. Can we put off the opening?"

"It will do no good. We can't replace that marble in less than a year, can we?"

"No. We must invent something. We can replace the floor, but we have to really use our heads to duplicate this marble."

So I thought hard and fast. "Richard how about trying wallpaper?"

"Wallpaper? There are no good printed imitations."

"Then let's think about *faux marbre*. Listen. There's a terrible house near ours on Fifth Avenue. It has what looked to me to be fake marble on the walls of the foyer. One day I was curious and touched it to find out. It was wallpaper! They had an artist duplicate the exact grains of their exterior marble entrance. They even told me the whole story — in fact, they were proud of it."

"Find him. Find that artist!"

"I will call Maria. She can ask her George. He knows every house on the block."

"*Now*, Alva. Right now!"

Our telephones were not in yet, so I went next door to Mrs. Astor's. The dear lady was out shopping, but I was welcomed in. I thought this was amazing — considering all the disruption, noise, and dust they must have encountered during the two years of our construction.

I rang up Maria. She listened, and, in her usual way, said, "Yes, Alva dear, I will take care of it."

And she did.

The artist came. George Washington Vanderbilt sent him at his own expense, as a housewarming gift to us, no less.

The entire burned area was cleaned up. The new floor was fitted in. The wallpaper was glued on. And our life-saving marbleizer took over. I watched him work. It all began to look marvelous. I felt it was much harder to detect than the wallpaper in my neighbor's foyer. Of course it was. *Here*, he had better marble to duplicate!

Even my Italian artisans said so. They were delighted I was pleased and would not blame them forever for the fire. Indeed not. Apparently it was an accident. Our relationship could endure. I even hoped that someday I might visit some of them and their work in Italy.

So now the opening of our marble palace could proceed on schedule.

But I left that wallpaper exactly where it was. I even became fond of it. The deception amused me. I would tap it as I walked by. And I considered that it might even endure for the life of the house!

11

THE OPENING ARGUMENTS

KEEPING OUR DATE OF AUGUST 19, 1892, FOR THE opening of our mansion, Willie K. and I were bedecked and stationed at the great front entrance to greet our first guests as their carriages drew up. Even though a dense fog had moved in from the Atlantic, we had repelled it by turning on all our lights. Both gas and electric, outside and inside. They lit up the night and reflected against that fog. It could not compete!

At the gate, our first couple was being admitted by a gatekeeper. He was clad in our Vanderbilt maroon livery. During the evening, footmen in the same livery were to line our staircase and dot themselves about the interior to give an atmosphere we wanted.

I could now see that the carriage of Mr. and Mrs. Richard Morris Hunt was coming up our half-moon driveway. I had asked them to come a bit early, so that they could do a last-minute expert inspection of each room. Particularly of the flowers and their placement. In their honor, I had arranged for a special order of lillies — of the Danube, Nile, and Lotus varieties. They were everywhere. Thinking of the Hunts tonight as Catherine and Richard, I knew they trusted me with this floral assignment. I was as fond of the beautiful and gracious Catherine as I always had been of Richard. But I considered this to be something of another emergency. After all, I felt in many ways this was *their* evening.

Willie K. and I had been so impressed with the completion of the house—a completion not only on time but *ahead* of time. It had been a complicated coordinating of carpenters and craftsmen, orders and shipments, arrivals and transference from the dock, installations and operational testing. A daily and hourly supervision for three long years, plus the pleas to the workmen that they *not* discuss the projects on which they worked, either to other workmen or to the Newport townspeople. Not only did Mr. Hunt and I want everyone to be completely surprised, we wanted them to be downright astonished.

Willie K. was less instructive. In fact, he was noncommittal. In "Gossip of the Racegoers", the *New York Times* had recently profiled him as First Vice-President, principal owner, and member of the Board of Governors of the Coney Island Jockey Club. They said, "Mr. Vanderbilt is as quiet and modest in his dress as he is in demeanor. There is so little of the 'howling swell' about him that people are disappointed quite a little when he is pointed out to them, and are loath to believe that he is one of the richest men in the world."

William Kissam Vanderbilt did not want to spoil his reputation! He would be at the debut of his mansion as though it were routine, as if he *always* did openings with quiet precision.

It was only his *wife* who was noisy.

But, loud or soft, each of us had agreed on one thing: We wanted our entire structure to honor Richard Morris Hunt. So we began by placing a bust of Louis XIV between the windows on the mezzanine. This marble bust, placed high on the wall, was a copy of one done in 1665 by the great artist Giovanni Lorenzo Bernini. Even higher, above the windows, we ordered the placement of a pair of gold figures in relief, holding white medallions. The one on the right was of Jules Hardouin-Mansart, architect of Versailles and chief architect of Louis XIV. On the left, was one of Richard Morris Hunt, architect of this mansion but also chief architect of the Vanderbilt family! Both of these medallions were the work of the sculptor, Karl Bitter, no less. The Hunts descended from their carriage. As they came through our great, bronze, initialed, grille-entrance, one of our butlers took their wraps. It was a joyous welcoming by Willie K. and me. As a matter of fact, all *four* of us were cheering completion.

After an exchange of amused compliments about our attire — theirs also chosen to match our interior, of course, we let the Hunts wend their way through the gold room, the Gothic room, across the terrace hall to the library, back into the great hall and on to the dining room. They returned, smiling. Apparently all was well. I pinched Willie K.'s arm as they ascended the stairs to the mezzanine. We wanted them to have their private moment. Richard showed Catherine the bust and the two medallions. She gazed, and then turned and beamed down at us. So did he. We were convinced we had done the right thing.

Richard proceeded to point out the incredible J. Allard et Fils chandelier that filled the great forty-foot stairwell space. The Hunts then went on up the stairway, made a quick inspection of the second floor, and soon returned to pronounce it also ready for viewing. I was glad, because the carriages of the next guests were already coming up our ramped drive. As they alighted, these guests were pausing to stare at the facade and admire the lighting on the tall, classic columns.

I invited the Hunts to stand in the receiving line along with us. As the butlers took their wraps, the guests could hardly wait to approach all four of us. As they shook our hands, compliments began gushing. They gazed around, gasped, gaped, and went on staring. As waiters offered them champagne, I noticed they took glasses from the tray and held them a long time before sipping. Evidently, the doors, the fountain, the tapestries, the lamps, the chandeliers, and especially the grand stairway were too much to take in at once. Our guests had to have time. Even if they were not allowed, as yet, to peek into the gold room or the dining room. Doors prevented it. That would come later. No need to flood the artistic palate.

The opening would later be referred to in the *New York Times* as "a dinner party and musicale". I am certain the newspaper wags were sure, in writing about the dinner, that I wanted to show off the fact my dining room chairs were of solid bronze and weighed so much that it took a separate footman to lift each one when seating an individual guest!

Mrs. Stuyvesant Fish later accused me of buying those chairs to keep my dinner guests prisoners. Indeed, they would have to summon a footman if they wished to leave the table! This Mamie Fish and I had become great friends. She could say anything she wanted to, and usually did. I was known to society as being daringly innovative, but she was known as being downright audacious. So we were often a team.

At this moment, I needed a good laugh. W. K. and I had had our first argument of the evening, over whether I should be at the door to greet guests or dramatically arrive later, down the staircase. I have always been firmly convinced that there is no greater compliment to a hostess than to have a grand staircase on which she may descend at the proper moment. Whether she is on the arm of her husband or not, the act will show off her gown to perfection. Her coiffure. Her jewels. And, I hope, the joy within her decolleté neckline.

My husband and I both had won the argument. This was unusual. It was decided I must greet guests at the door, then he would personally escort them through the rooms on the first floor. I would ascend the staircase and show them through my sitting room and his office on the mezzanine, then lead them on up the staircase to the second floor to see my bedroom, his own, Consuelo's, little Willie's, Harold's, and the guest room.

Because we had only invited eighteen of our family and friends that evening, it would not be hard. After they all had seen the second floor and had admired my bedroom, of course, I could request that they all descend the stairway and refill their glasses. Then I would remain upstairs and check my gown and hair. When dinner was announced, all guests could be asked to come into the great hallway. At that proper moment, I would come down the staircase.

Ah, lovely. Willie K. would meet me on the last steps, I would make my final descent, and the two of us would lead the way into the dining room.

I could hardly wait for our guests to have the first sight of my red, Nubian marble dining room with the mantel at the far end, patterned after the one in the hall of Hercules in Versailles. Appropriately, over it hung the portrait, attributed to Pierre Mignard, of the young Louis XIV, given by the king to the city of Ypres, Belgium. Louis XIV would be honored throughout our entire scheme of decoration. Also Louis XV and Louis XVI. Our Gilded Age mansion was, after all, a tribute to the Petit Trianon at Versailles. I could not be choosy!

At this moment, after welcoming all the guests and doing our separate tours, I was still aware I was a mother. I knew that little Willie and Harold must be up on the third floor, a floor designed for house guests and for our staff and servants. The two would be watching what was going on by peeking between the bannisters — preferring to be two Peeping Toms than to join their family. When we were all downstairs, I knew they would creep to the second floor railing of the stairway and peer through to the floor below.

But not Consuelo. She was now a member of the party. At fifteen, she was dressed charmingly. Her dark hair flowed gracefully down her back, and she curtsied and spoke with the guests in her usual responsive way. She was also developing a sense of humor. As a mother, I was most happy to listen and revel in this.

From tonight on, I was certainly looking forward to *all* of our family's being together for the entire six or seven weeks of the summer season. And in this, our new dwelling! It was a livable house in spite of all its intentional splendor. Because Newport had meant so much to me, I wanted it to mean as much to our children.

As we waited to be last, I stole a moment away from the guests to ask, "Willie K., can't we start planning tomorrow? How about a picnic on the lawn? Let the children choose where, even if they prefer the cliffs."

"Alva. Please. I have to go to Birkenhead to contract for our new yacht. It is an old and very proper shipbuilding firm, and they are insistent I leave here immediately after our opening."

"They are that fussy? Do the Americans know you are going to have the *British* build you a yacht?"

"I don't know. But it will be better and larger than *Alva*."

"To you, everything is 'better than *Alva*'— meaning me."

"Oh come, come. You will have plenty to do to get this house under good, smooth management. And only you can do it."

"I can do that with my eyes shut. If you don't want to go on a picnic, then let's do something else the children also like such as go down the street and see how Oliver's new house is coming along. Furthermore, they know he has his two favorite horses stabled nearby."

"No doubt. Until his house is completed, he probably *sleeps* with Rockingham and Hurlingham."[8]

"Well, I offered our own stables. But he says those two favorite leaders of his heard about the party you and I gave to celebrate the completion of it."

"Right in the stables, of course."

"Yes. And now those two horses will not be satisfied with anything less in their own. They're waiting!"

"Offer them Belmont Park."

"They know Oliver has also raised them to trot him around in his cabriolet or his curricle or his new spider Phaeton — not just to race."

"I must tell him he'll never get rich that way."

"He already is. I don't think he cares."

"Alva, are you seating him on your right tonight?"

"No, I'm seating him on *your* left."

"Undoubtedly because he's a democrat."

"No. Because Oliver Belmont is charming!"

Fortunately, it was the proper time to sit. We could not keep our footmen waiting. At opposite ends of the dining table, the chairs were slipped beneath our respective bottoms, and we bent our knees and sat. I noticed each of us hit the chair firmly, but smiled as though it were the most natural way to sit!

This room, lit by candlelight, showed off the red marble to perfection. It was an all-pervading glow that I hoped would lead off conversation and promote glass-clinking. As Mamie Fish preferred, I also liked to start off dinner with champagne instead of wine. We both found that the older guests, later, tended to nod off during the musicale if they'd had too much wine. And, on occasion, snore. None of that!

Dinner was served. It was excellent. I had planned and built a spacious, well-equipped, basement kitchen, then had hired four French chefs to run it. So dinner should have been excellent. The waiters wore white gloves and served each course *on the minute*. The entire dinner was planned that way to assist the chefs to prepare and send everything upstairs hot. Even the puddings and pies. It worked. The guest who turned to his or her companion and got lost in conversation, found, on the dot, that his or her unfinished plate was missing. At other dinner parties, I had seen men grab hold of the plate and refuse to give it up! But *my* waiters always won.

Everyone was "oh-ing and ah-ing" over this glowing dining room. But this didn't last long. By now, my husband had received enough praise. He wanted to talk horses. Down at the other end of the table, I knew that he had made Oliver already start talking. From his draw-rein gestures, and from what words I could hear, my husband was re-creating the day the Coaching Club opened its season by driving out to our Idlehour.

Very well. Even I remembered the beginning of that day. Gathering at nine that morning at New York's Hotel Brunswick, all of us wives were planning to give our husbands a great send-off. Our spouses were clad in bright-colored coaching coats or more informal attire, complete with scarves and innovative, jeweled pins to match the day. Plus a blossom in each buttonhole. I noticed their hats were of an even wilder variety — from caps to wide-brimmed soft straws.

Everything stopped as the coach rolled up to the portico. What an impressive vehicle! It had a body, beautifully primrose in color, enhanced by a border of ebony black at either end. Atop were four seats, long enough to seat fourteen persons. In harness were four sleek and well trained horses, their reins held smartly by coachman Ben Woodington. Mr. F. K. Sturgis was on the box. Fownes, the guard, was at the wheel, with the shining horn in hand.

I was right. W. K. began recounting the story — and very audibly, because some of the participants were present. Further down the dining table, my dear friend, Mrs. Jay, had poked her husband that he should listen.

He did. Then sang out, "Don't forget who was on time that morning and who stepped out to begin the drive!"

Oliver decided to have a good time with this reminder. "But you're a little late entering the conversation. I believe it was Colonel William Jay."

"That's me!"

"Oh. I thought it was the president of the Coaching Club."

"That's who I *was*!"

"Good heavens, really? Colonel, this is confusing."

"I'll prove it. I'll tell you the route!"

"Of course. Do tell."

"All right. First, the ladies waved goodbye to us, and then our entire equipage started rolling up Fifth Avenue. Sturgis tooled us to 86th Street, over to Southern Boulevard, then across 92nd Street to the Astoria Ferry. J. R. Roosevelt took the reins from Astoria to Flushing. We changed our horses, and J. V. Parker drove us to Lakeville, remember?"

"Where you changed again?"

"Correct."

Willie K., jealous of Oliver's caricature, spoke out. "But good old T. A. Havemeyer was the whip to Garden City. I'll never forget it. He knew that the sooner we got there, the sooner we'd have lunch."

"So he could sit up on top of the coach and nod for two hours afterwards?"

"Yes!"

The colonel charged on. "I took it over to Smithville, and we changed horses. Then Hugo Fritsch mounted the box and drove to Amityville."

Oliver inquired with an eyebrow only he could raise, "And you changed horses again?"

"We did. Schermerhorn drove that next team to Bayshore."

W. K. tried to finish off with, "Frederick Bronson took us to my Idlehour. We arrived precisely at six o'clock."

"W. K., that was only because those villagers had laid the dust all along the route."

Oliver rolled his eyes. "Dust? They laid it? Bless their hearts. They were probably without water for the next month!"

The colonel was impervious. "Well, at least the villagers didn't complain, and they all cheered and waved."

W. K. reminded, "Except at Babylon. We were too pressed for time to stop."

Oliver flapped a limp hand, "Oh, well, what's one *more* biblical hassle?"

I raised my napkin to cover my amusement. His remark summed up exactly how I was still feeling. What's one more? I was really annoyed that, if each man at the table was not buzzing with compliments about our new home, he should at least be asking questions about construction, the source of materials, the lease of a wharf and a warehouse, quarters for the work force — all these things I had been sure Willie K. would discuss. But no.

Apparently only underwriting the entire cost was eventually what really interested all of our male guests. When they finally asked and learned it was $11,000,000 for this Newport "cottage", as they were called, the men seemed satisfied. But of course, both Henry and W. D. Sloane were prompted by their wives to inquire, "Does this include the furnishings?" They heard me answer a firm yes.

My husband added, "I hope so, but not the cost of the overseas trips which she made to *choose* everything."

"It would have cost you more if J. Allard had done it!", I reminded him.

"He did."

"But not all the seeking out, Willie K. That takes unpaid hours."

Oliver cleared his throat. "It is marvelous how we gentlemen never work without being paid, but you ladies will work tirelessly for nothing."

I glanced my gratitude. W. K. backed off.

But the colonel was still remembering the Coaching Club day. "When we all climbed down from the top of that coach, our dear Willie K., here, took over and we were met with he-man drinks. And real food that didn't stop until we all fell into bed at midnight!" Everyone thought he was through, but the colonel could not stop. "I even spent one whole day admiring your flower beds, your livery — of the highest order, I must say — your sheep ranch and your stables too. I even enjoyed your hennery."

"More than the piggery?" W. K. asked.

The point died without a salute. "Let alone the cattle, all good butter-makers. And his majesty, 'Saumerez', must be the most valuable animal of his breed."

I could not resist. "Wait a moment. Go back. If you liked the flower beds, colonel, then you must have adored the peach house, the orchid house, the tropical house, the palm house, the rose house, the tomato house, and even our three graperies!"

Desperate to change the subject, Mrs. Jay eyed me. "Speaking of houses, Alva, my husband came home and told me 'We've got to have one of those stick-style houses like Idlehour'!"

Across the table, R. M. H. bowed his head. "Tell your husband that Mr. Hunt is ready at any time."

I smiled.

In all fairness, the ladies at the table then took up the architecture talk. Returning to Newport, they began exclaiming over each room of our new house. They were adroit at referring to individual ceilings, mantels, lighting fixtures, specific art objects, and even the stair railing. I nodded approval at all statements and proudly answered all questions.

Next to me, I had seated my husband's brother, Frederick and his wife, Louise. For three reasons. Frederick and George W. had always resented the fact that they did not inherit as much money as my husband. They each knew I was the force behind it. But this was not entirely true. I had simply told W. H., who was, after all, the father of *each* of them, that he must remember Willie K. in his will proportionate to Willie's worth. W. H. had done so. But Frederick and George W., in reaction, were each determined to "make up the difference". I was aware of this.[9]

Though George W. was not at our opening, I spent most of my time at dinner being pleasant to Frederick and his wife. This was the second reason I had seated them next to me: they had had an opening of their *own* new house on Bellevue only the year before. This great house was called "Rough Point". On that night, Frederick had proudly burned 10,000 candlepower in lights, for an opening that rivaled ours. The third reason was Frederick's marriage to Louise Anthony Torrance. The family called her Aunt Lulu. She had divorced her husband and married Frederick, very aware she was twelve years older than he. Also aware of the five years I was older than *Oliver*, I liked to observe these two, my relatives by marriage, to see how it was working out. Apparently well. She was shrewd, and he appreciated her advice. In spite of the age difference, they were two minds working as one.

Was there hope for Oliver and me? If my own marital relations continued to grow worse, I had to think ahead. In case of a divorce, I wanted custody of the children. But I also wanted a new husband. I was attracted to men, and they apparently were attracted to me. Living alone, at my age, was out of the question — for my sake and the sake of the children. If Oliver would *have* me, I would try to begin thinking about becoming Mrs. O. H. P. Belmont.

These were not the kinds of thoughts a wife should have on this occasion, especially when her husband just told our dinner guests, "At the end of this opening, tonight, I have an announcement to make."

I supposed this announcement had something to do with railroads, the present economic condition, or, better yet, his multiple special interests. My husband now belonged to every important men's club in New York. I had only myself to thank for that. Along with his yachting interests, he was now not only raising horses but also setting up races on both Aquidneck Island and Long Island for his new automobiles, domestic and foreign. Let alone managing his Lake Shore or Nickel Plate railroad lines!

Back in 1888, knowing he would be this busy, he had turned to Mr. Hunt and requested that he design for us "the very best living accommodations that money could buy." My husband meant accommodations for *me*. He knew I would take it seriously. When I did, it meant I would not be around our New York château to bother him as often. And neither would he be there to bother me. Our classic arguments would have less frequency. He knew these always disturbed the children — no matter how confined we tried to make them. All three children could read our moods.

At the moment, I gazed around at our guests — those with children and those without. Plus the seven of them who were single. And I thought, "What a lot of surprises time has in store for you."

After dessert and a lingering coffee period, I announced we would retire to the gold room for our liqueurs. I knew the musicians and our one soloist were waiting. They had insisted on eating only *after* their performance, so I was sure they must all be starving. I would have a complete supper ready for them the moment when they made their last bow.

Willie K. requested that the gentlemen go, first, to the Gothic room to again admire my collection of stained glass windows. Just as I had arranged, these were all beautifully lighted from the outside. The rich colors gave a dramatic atmosphere. But I knew what our male guests really wanted was to lounge about and smoke their cigars and cigarettes. Requesting, out of deference to the musicians and the singer, that they wait until after the musicale, I received their polite promise. W. K. would not hear of it and demanded that there at least be an intermission. "And from that moment on, Alva, they can listen to the music from the Gothic room. This is *my* house, too!"

I agreed. But this was the last time he ever referred to our marble palace as "my house, too." From that very night onward he took no responsibility.

Except to pay the bills. I was grateful for that financial care, heaven knows. But, to me, this was not enough. Not what I really wanted.

As I sat in my chair in the gold room, sipping my Cointreau and listening to the music, I gazed around. It was my desire that this room be a triumph of decoration. Everything I had learned from my white and gold salon at 660 Fifth Avenue, I wished to apply here. Better use of materials, better lighting, and better acoustics. Sitting here, looking and listening, told me I had been successful.

The image was as marvelous as the sound. The mirrors doubled every gold design Mr. Hunt and I had created. And each one was paying off. The two chandeliers alone were worth repeating into infinity. They were modeled after those of Château Maison-Lafitte outside of Paris.

In the four corners of the room, we had provided additional illuminations — lamp standards with candelabra, and in this case, held by marine urchins seated on pedestals of Fleur de Peche marble.[10]

The vocal soloist had now taken over. This singer seemed to lift his tones to the ceiling and loved the sound it sent back to him. As I listened, my eyes also wandered to the top of my gold windows and doors. There were large masks of satyrs. The mirror over the mantel was crowned by a mask of Apollo with two cherubs in relief. They were repeated in panels along the wall. As I gazed, I felt how appropriate masks were to my mood.

But Oliver caught my eye and the mask had to fall. This man was reading my mind. Evidently, he decided to lift my spirits. He nodded toward the marble mantel and raised his brows. From Oliver, this meant he was not only impressed, he approved!

Allard had indeed performed a great design wonder. The large bronze figures at the corners held candelabras. Between them was another mask, that of Bacchus with garlands of ormolu flowers. Below, inside the fireplace was a fireback as an appropriate place for the figure of Hades. Far above, was a glass globe of the world, actually encircling a ball of the heavens — the globe telling the hour, the day, and the month, as it revolved around the ball once every twenty-four hours. All this was backed by the great mirror and my Apollo. An assemblage designed to give this room a magnificent focal point.

For a next gaze of appreciation, I was not gauche enough to peer up at the ceiling. But I caught Richard Morris Hunt doing so. He was first admiring the panels that continued the gold near the room's entrance, one with a centaur, the other with Herakles. Then his eyes went up to the mural where Pallas Athena, while adorned with the head of Medusa, was carrying aloft a youth who was bidding fairwell to his love, impeded by Cupid grasping his ankle.

With a theme like this, I thought it was just as well I was not looking! So I feasted my eyes on the work of Karl Bitter in the gilded wood panels in carved relief along the walls. He was soon to rank first among America's architectural sculptors, thanks to R. M. Hunt. The theme figures were again lavishly classical — Aphrodite, Demeter, Herakles, Poseidon, and Thetis. If a guest at my musicale were given only one piece of art to view in the entire room, he or she could have chosen any one of Karl Bitter's panels and been completely fulfilled.

When the musicians and the soloist came to their intermission period, I applauded my pleasure at their competence, then arose to open the doors to the Gothic room, myself. I wanted my husband to know I had not forgotten.

Prompted by him, in turn, the gentlemen flowed into the room, seated themselves, and our footmen began offering them cigars and cigarettes. Unfortunately, I had gone to order other footmen to bring ash containers. Too late, I saw the ladies follow the men! I must do something or W. K. would be so furious with me he would never make his announcement later, whatever it was!

As something of a maneuver, I rescued and guided the ladies across the terrace hall to the library, by promising them more liqueurs when they got there.

126

The intermission ended with my throwing open all the arched bay windows possible in the gold room, to diminish the smoke. Then, enticing my ladies back from the library, I steered them directly into the great hall and straight into the gold room. Otherwise, I was afraid they would again join the men, and my musicians and singer would be completely left without an audience!

As it was, the performers wondered. But I saw that the ladies were all seated and then explained to everyone that the gentlemen were fine. They could hear perfectly well from the Gothic room.

The concert continued. Consuelo had long since retired upstairs, but I wondered if she, little Willie, and Harold were still observing the party, or had even crept down to the mezzanine and were listening. If so, they must be very amused. I would recount it all in the morning, and somehow account for the circumstances!

As I sat again in this precious room, I had stationed myself near its three entrance doors. For some reason I began studying the locks. Complete to the last detail, they were lock boxes in the form of a scallop shell and stalactites. Was this typical of my debut as mistress of this house? As the lady who must make this dwelling a happy and livable home, I now knew I would not have my husband by my side. I could not be a shell who longed for a stalactite.

Nor would Willie K. begin to love every inch of our house the way I did. From this moment on, I must move alone. If I needed something, I had to arrange for it. If I adored this mansion, I had to do so on my own.

My "bringing gifts to the Temple of Apollo" had apparently demanded its price. I had tried to pay my tribute to the glory that was Greece and the grandeur that was Rome. And, even as a good Episcopalian, I felt, "Man declares the glory of God and art showeth His handiwork." If I had gone *this* far, I must, certainly, not turn back now!

The musicale was finally over. All performers were duly applauded. Then I saw to it they happily went off to enjoy their waiting supper.

Appreciation had wended its way from the Gothic room, but I also felt the applause might have awakened some of the gentlemen.

W. K. was now on his feet and graciously inviting the ladies to join them. By this time, they were most willing and most aware of my husband. They went in, murmuring, "What is he going to say? What is this announcement?"

Willie K. drew me over in front of the fireplace and put his arm around my shoulders. Everyone grew quiet.

He began by bowing. "My family and friends. My Alva. I feel this house deserves a presentation. As a recognition for its beauty. And for its achievement. Students of architecture will, no doubt, begin to come here to study what our Richard Morris Hunt and my wife have accomplished. And, as has happened in Europe, I hope that it is a structure which will last for centuries. I can only tell you, as a railroad builder, that I think it will!"

Everyone was amused. And agreed with applause.

"So I, therefore, make the presentation of this mansion to the lady of the house. My Alva Smith Vanderbilt." He turned. "And I would like to give it to you, Alva, as your thirty-ninth birthday present!"

Then he kissed me. I kissed him back in appreciation, but also in surprise.

Everyone applauded. Everyone except Oliver.

As the butlers began holding the coats and evening wraps for the guests to put on, and the carriages began arriving, Oliver stole a moment to pull me aside. "Is he crazy? Your birthday isn't in August, it's in January!"

"I know."

"Did he forget to *give* you something?"

"No."

"Then what in blazes is he talking about?"

"Willie K. has said all along he wanted to give me something big for my fortieth birthday. But this house was finished seven months early. So I said, 'If it was the *house* you wanted to give me, let's forget about it, shall we'?"

"But he didn't!"

"If William K. Vanderbilt is going to do something, he's going to do it."

"Even if he doesn't have a reason?"

"In this case, he really had to reach for one."

"He certainly did." Oliver groaned. "What a gift."

"What a responsibility."

"He's dumped this whole place in your lap!"

"That is precisely what W. K. would do — just out and out *do* .... Oliver. You've known him as many years as I have."

"In that case, I would like to go over and ask him a question."

"Ask him what?"

"I'll say, 'Willie K., if you really are giving Alva this place for her thirty-ninth birthday, just what in thunder are you planning to give her for her fortieth?'"

12

CRUISING OUT OF CHAOS AND INTO TROUBLE

THE FINANCIAL PANIC OF 1893 HAD WORN OUT Willie K. His competitors had done too much reckless railway financing. The failure of seventy-three railroads started with the Philadelphia and Reading Railroad. This had been followed by the failure of 600 banks and 1500 commercial firms. My husband wanted to get away from all this tragedy. He felt some of his family and friends just might like to get away from it also. So he began making arrangements.

On November 23, 1893, we all began a cruise to India on our new yacht, *Valiant*. Willie K. had decided not to call it *Alva II*. He wanted this new creation to have a name of its own. Besides, the relationship between my husband and me was not strong enough for a renewal. Not even for starting all over again.[11]

Our new *Valiant* was a 2,000-ton, full rigged, sail-and-steam private ocean liner, with a crew of sixty-two. Willie K. was right, *Valiant* was twenty-seven feet longer than *Alva*, and it was big enough and fast enough to cross the Atlantic in seven days. Mr. St. Clair Byrne designed it, and it was built by Laird's Shipyards in Birkenhead, England.

In May of 1893, Lady Alva Montagu christened *Valiant* at Birkenhead. She was the daughter of my good friend Consuelo Yznaga. As is obvious, by this time, I had named my daughter after her, and she had named her daughter after me.

The trip which Willie K. and Captain Henry Morrison had planned was an ambitious one. Leaving New York Harbor, they wanted to touch St. Michael's and the Azores, then on to Gibraltar, to Alexandria, the Suez Canal, Aden, the Red Sea to Bombay, and then overland to Calcutta, to Rangoon, Madras, Ceylon, and possibly back to visit Southern France.

Again, on this cruise we had invited guests. Oliver Hazard Perry Belmont and Winthrop Rutherfurd were to prove the two most crucial gentlemen aboard.

As far as family was concerned, we had Consuelo and Harold with us. Young Willie was at home attending school. And of course we took along a doctor, a tutor, and one woman, a governess. I felt *one* other woman aboard was trouble enough. In spite of the size of *Valiant*, a yacht was still a confining area. I had learned from previous voyages to Europe that any mistake made in choosing a female guest was an expanding one. We were literally stuck with her for the rest of the trip. Let alone her wardrobe. And I decided not to take the risk. Merely the governess, Consuelo, and I would be quite enough!

Willie K., in his usual infinite wisdom concerning people, had decided these voyages were boring for Consuelo. So this time he had invited along one of New York's most handsome and eligible bachelors, a man thirteen years older than our daughter. But I was not sure whether this Winthrop Rutherfurd was invited as a companion for her or a guardian. As the voyage progressed, he obviously became a companion — to the delight of our inexperienced Consuelo, of course.

Winthrop was a descendant of Peter Stuyvesant, through the line of his very attractive mother, Margaret. She was a prominent and self-appointed critic of the society to which she belonged. Winthrop could also bask in the recent success of his father, Lewis, known for taking some remarkable photographs of the moon. I, myself, had been seen at tennis matches at the Newport Casino with Margaret, and I admired Lewis for using his wife's money for so lofty a purpose! But I was not impressed with their son.

Winty, as our daughter was soon calling him, was trained to be a lawyer. But horses and hounds overtook him. He preferred to do fox-hunting on Long Island. As a gentlemanly diversion, this pursuit was a cut above even coaching. Winty was a friend of the Roosevelts of Oyster Bay, which included Theodore, not yet on his way to becoming President. Winty also rode to the hounds with Elliott Roosevelt, the reckless Elliott who had a plain but bright daughter named Eleanor, then nine years old. Amazingly, on only their third time out, Winty and Elliott rode so hard they each broke their collarbones.

Now obviously recovered, Winthrop Rutherfurd was out to run a race for our daughter's hand.

But not while I was around. As the cruise progressed, I found him too worldly and too worthless for my taste. Willie K. did *not* find him so. He pointed out Winty was making Consuelo happy, and it was the first time she had shown any pleasure in any of our voyages — or in going ashore to appreciate, more than academically, any of the wonders of the world. My husband could see our daughter was indeed blossoming. So could I. And I was determined she should not waste this initial feminine bloom on Winthrop.

Unfortunately, I was not as careful as I might have been. Their romance could proceed at a pace because they would often observe that I was in the company of Oliver Belmont. Just as their father was often in the company of his good friend, Winfield Hoyt. As far as Oliver was concerned, I'm afraid Consuelo and Winty were asking themselves questions. Wasn't my relationship with my husband so precarious that I must be looking elsewhere for a new one? Wasn't the handsome and charming Oliver the desirable choice? Weren't they, therefore, really assisting in my transition?

As we continued our cruise, all this came to a head one day in a conversation — not between the three of us, but between Willie K. and Oliver.

It took place in W. K.'s and my stateroom. I overheard all of it inadvertently. They did not know I was even on board.

Everyone was going ashore in Alexandria to spend two days there while *Valiant* went through the Suez Canal. Then we were to reboard for the crossing of the Red Sea and the Indian Ocean to Bombay. My husband and Oliver delayed to make sure all papers were in order for the Canal procedure. They were contacting Captain Morrison when I returned aboard. After sending Consuelo and Harold ahead with the tutor and governess, I stayed behind to supervise getting the luggage to the hotel. With all the fuss of making this transfer, I suddenly had some significant stomach pains from a too-quick breakfast. I was obliged to return to the certainty of marine plumbing.

Moments later, having blessedly relieved myself, I did the usual amount of noisy flushing. I was now tidying my hair so I could return my hat to my head and secure it with the new jeweled hatpins I had purchased on our last spring stay in Paris. They were complicated and had screw-guards at the points. So I was taking my time.

All of a sudden I heard the door to our stateroom open and was startled to recognize the voices of Willie K. and Oliver.

"For a man who hates bookwork, Oliver, you are some stickler. I don't see why you think I should copy all these numbers. Why not just hand it over?"

"You should have your own copy, W. K."

"The Captain has it!"

"That's the point. You don't. Suppose they delay *Valiant* going through the Canal? You're the one who is going to have to unsnarl it. There will be no way to get back on board, to this stateroom because this yacht will be en route."

"They can't do that!"

"Oh yes. And then they will charge you for the delay time. Be smart, Willie K. Copy down those permit numbers, then fold up the paper and stick it in your vest pocket."

"But our party won't wait for you and me, they'll go on to the hotel."

"And Alva will see that they each get there safely, plus all the luggage."

"You have such faith in my wife."

"Any woman who is married to a casual gentleman will develop a great sense of responsibility."

"If you ask me, it's *over*developed."

"That's because she is called upon to use it so often."

Trapped in the bathroom, I was amused at Oliver's defending me. Ah, ah — bathroom, did I say? I was also conscious that my husband would have been screaming at me to learn finally that, nautically speaking, I must call this room "the head." So, literally, I was trapped in the head.

What could I do? I was already involved as the subject of conversation. If I suddenly opened the door and came out, they would not only be shocked, they would be embarrassed, to say the least.

Better to stay where I was. Why not just wait until W. K. had jotted down his information, returned the copy to the Captain, and he and Oliver were on their way to the hotel? Then I would be free to leave on my own. When I saw them again, I could make up some excuse as to why I was delayed.

So I continued to stand in front of the mirror and weave my hatpin through the straw crown of my broad-brimmed hat, into my hair and safely past my trapped head.

I heard Willie K.'s pen begin scratching away. Also his words. "Oliver, speaking of responsibility, it is perfectly obvious you spend the bulk of your time on deck with my wife."

"On deck? Would you prefer that the two of us climb into one of your lifeboats?"

"Consuelo and Harold are beginning to think of you as their second father — their lifeboat, indeed."

"What? All *three* of your children are remarkable. I am terribly grateful that at least two of them have let me into their lives. And perhaps Willie already feels that way."

"You have a daughter of your own."

"Which her mother and her stepfather never allow me to see."

"I find Mr. Rives isn't such a bad sort."

"But Sara is. And I don't want to get Natica into trouble."

"Very well …. You and Alva are a little obvious about your attraction to each other. Not only my family, but everyone else seems to know."

"You mean all New York and all Newport?"

"And all Long Island. They say the two of you were recently seen together at a concert *and* at one of the races."

"Why aren't they more specific? The premiere of `The New World Symphony' by a young man named Dvorak. And the winning of the Belmont stakes by a horse named Comanche."

"They will."

"But as yet, my dear William, I have not had to pay a bribe to *Town Topics*."

"I wish Colonel Mann would just talk about simple things such as the new `hootchy-kootchy' dance at the Columbian Exposition!"

"Chicago is not his beat. His business is gossip in New York. Did you pay him enough to let you alone?"

"I did."

"Must have been a fair penny. Did he tell you that you were only one of a dozen fancy-free millionaires with a taste for women?"

"In which case, he should give me a *rate*?"

Oliver hooted, and I thought I heard him slap his knee …. "You are not that far away from your grandfather's bargaining powers."

"The Commodore had a few women of his own to cover up."

"But sometimes I think you have feelings of guilt that it was *Alva* who put the Vanderbilts on the social map."

"Oh? And now I am trying to assert my independence?"

"Well, what else would you say belonging to the Metropolitan, Knickerbocker, Union, Racquet and Tennis, Turf and Field, and the New York Yacht Clubs *is*?"

"I am grateful to her for all that."

"Your gratitude is more than the other Vanderbilts show."

"Except for my mother. Also my father certainly expressed it to her before he died."

"In many ways! But to you both."

"True. So how long do I have to be grateful?"

"Well, Alva just gave you a marble mansion."

"I gave it to *her!*"

"You unloaded it on her."

"Unloaded? I paid for it, Oliver, don't forget."

"But she was the one who worked with Hunt day after day. Sloshed around with the contractor in terrible weather. And scrambled all over Europe to search for and bring back your furnishings."

"I was busy."

There in the confinement of the head, I gulped and wanted to scream out, "You certainly were. Time after time I went to you to approve something, but you were either out of the office or out at sea!"

I could not utter a sound. Instead, I had to simply push a second hatpin on through my hair until it came out the other side of the brim. Then I screwed on the pin-guard, very tightly.

Oliver sensed it was time to change the subject. "By the way, why weren't Cornelius and Alice there at your opening?"

"I don't remember. Maybe they were out of town. But I can assure you they are now at work building the Breakers. And that house will be more than an answer to the fire which burned down their former one."

"You can bet your life, W. K., the Breakers will be bigger. But it will not be better!"

"Alice will do her damnedest. And Corneel will underwrite it."

"And after he underwrites it, you think he will unload that house on *Alice*?"

"You saw what happened last season, Oliver. Alva did nothing but entertain. When the Breakers is finished, Alice will do the same thing. About all Corneel and I can do is get out of the way!"

"That's *your* interpretation. But there was a time when Alva had to get out of the way. Do you remember what you put on the registry at Saratoga when the two of you were on your honeymoon?"

"Were *you* at that United States Hotel?"

"No, but it is legend by now. You wrote 'William K. Vanderbilt, wife, two maids, two dogs, and fifteen horses'."

I could hear Willie K. laugh, but I could also realize from the great pause which followed that Oliver was *not* making his point. Shifting responsibility was not something my husband wanted to talk about, except where it concerned personalities. And he was doing it right now.

"Corneel has always blamed this rivalry between my Alva and his Alice as the *real* reason for this trouble that keeps growing between Alva and me."

"He doesn't blame it on other women?"

"Corneel doesn't know about that."

"You told me everybody knows."

"Corneel never listens. He hates that kind of information."

"Does he feel this rivalry is killing off both *husbands*, too?"

"Killing off? You're probably right. But it will hurt Corneel emotionally long before it does me."

"Because he's such a righteous man?"

"And a supporter of the church."

Oliver slurred, "You mean that man tithes *religiously*?"

I started to chortle in appreciation, but I stopped and had to put my hands over my mouth. Instead, I listened for W. K.'s "haw haw." There was none.

Oliver went on enjoying himself. "Corneel will no doubt become a recluse first."

"You know my family better than I do."

"But what about you?"

"Never. I'd rather turn to other women. '*Obviously*,' as you would say."

I leaned against the washbowl and stared at myself. Why, at this moment, was I dressing Alva Vanderbilt to please William K. Vanderbilt? Why was I wearing rouge? Fixing my hair — still true or untrue auburn — the way he liked it? Pinning my hat on at an angle he fancied?

I must be holding on to the hope that we could stay together, because we had once been in love, because we still appreciated many things about each other.

Or was it because of the children? Did I want them to grow up with the same father with whom they *began* their life?

At that moment, I felt it must be *all* these things.

But I had trouble picking up the next hatpin. Somehow I felt it was a mockery of my own efforts as a wife of one of the most important men in the industrial and financial life of America. A man whose efforts I thought I was constantly trying to support by strengthening my own.

Oliver threw the dart. "Listen, W. K., I realize that I am not immune. Those same gossipers are saying that I prefer another man's wife — yours. And I do."

"All right. But the point is, my friend, I think Alva prefers you."

"There have been many times when I have hoped so. But, Willie K., everyone knows you are my friend."

"They're *that* intelligent? Good. Well, you are. And I am yours. But I am beginning to feel Alva deserves to be loved by someone who understands her."

"Maybe you're right. Alva and I are both outrageously willful people. We appreciate this in each other." A break was obviously wanted. "Willie, are you copying those figures as fast as you can?"

"You know I can't do two things at once!"

"Yes. I've noticed you at a dinner party."

"Oh? When?"

"When you're supposed to pass something, and at that moment the person next to you strikes up a conversation. Everything stops. We poor guests at the other end of the table never get the wine or the bonbons or even the salt sent down to us."

"Yes. Alva says it drives her crazy."

"She glares."

"But I never know what she's trying to tell me. My wife likes a man who can read her mind."

"She does."

"And it seems to me you are the man who can do it."

Great silence.

"She also likes a man with taste, extravagant tastes such as yours, Oliver."

"True. I'm a very florid fellow. But, Willie K., you're pretty splendid yourself!"

"Oliver. Sometimes I ask myself: when did this all begin? Why wasn't I looking?"

"Well, actually, Sara and I were not present at your grand ball in 1883. So none of the newspapers mentioned what we were wearing. I was not so sure that even you and Alva would have noticed."

"Apparently we wouldn't."

"Even if Sara and I were at the Patriarch's Ball at Delmonico's, in December of that year?"

"If she wouldn't, it was because Alice and Cornelius were present. She probably spent all evening letting Alice know the W. K. Vanderbilts were there, too."

"The point is, my friend, that Alva is now aware of both of us."

Still more trapped in that bathroom than ever, I gave up. Here were two men who were very aware of the same *woman*. But their friendship came first.

Just as I had always predicted, certainly. So why was I upset? No doubt because we were so terribly attracted to each other that I felt, over the years, the first loyalty of each must naturally be to me.

I had to give up that idea. This was a century in which men were loyal to *men*. Above all. In fact, they actually felt it was their basis for love of a *woman*. Also a solid foundation on which to choose a mate. Male concurrence. But not so for us ladies. A lady was always loyal to her gentleman. Very, very seldom to a woman, first.

Looking straight into the mirror, my eyes said that, as long as I carried this understanding through the rest of my life, I might keep some kind of a relationship with each of these men. I might stay sane. I might even realize my boundaries in this game of love.

Already I heard Oliver laughing about another matter. "Better let me proofread those Canal procedures."

"And check my figures?"

"Don't you remember? My father was a banker."

"But you are a horse dealer."

"Is there any difference? He preferred to write his gains into a ledger, and I —"

"— you prefer to ride yours into a stable!"

I heard both men stop and do a snorting titter. Once again, I gave a hatpin a journey through one side of the crown and into my hair. I began to wonder if I was not being walked around the paddock as if I were a horse. To be appraised. Admired. Assessed.

At the moment, my husband was even continuing to do it. "Oliver, I feel Alva has turned the children against me."

"Impossible. They all three adore you."

"I told you they also adore O. H. P. Belmont. But Alva may *welcome* a second father. Right now, she says I am never home, that she has to perform all the supervision and all the discipline."

"Again? What about their governess?"

"Haven't you heard what Willie and Consuelo did to Fraulein Wedeking? Those two rascals were late for their lunch. They had been out boating. So when they came into the dock, Fraulein put one foot on board to make them hurry."

"And her other foot was on the dock?"

"Correct. So you know what happened."

"Marvelous. Consuelo and I said Fraulein smelled of sauerkraut anyway. It washed her off."

"Alva switched their legs with a riding crop."

"She told me. She said it was the last time, ever, to both — Consuelo was getting to be too much of a young lady and Willie too much of a young man."

"She should never have done that to either one of them in the first place."

"But she was the only one at home to do anything at all. And don't forget, Alva's dear mother sometimes used a horsewhip on her."

"But it didn't stop her!"

"Good."

"No excuse. Does she feel justified because she says I spoil the children?"

"You spoil everybody, W. K. You're a much loved man."

"I think Alva would be suspicious of a man 'who wants to be loved by everybody.'"

"Can you help it if you are the Vanderbilt son who is more handsome and charming than Cornelius, Frederick, or George?"

"Be serious, Oliver. I think Alva and I may be headed for the divorce court."

"Divorce! In the state of New York?"

"I know, yes, I know the grounds are —"

"— adultery. Only!"

"Arranged by a trumped-up night with some woman you've never seen before."

"Positively."

"No wonder people think twice."

"And while you are thinking twice, how can you consider getting a divorce from a woman who saw to it that you inherited 65 million?"

"My father made out *nine* wills before he died."

"Until he got the amount right."

"Cornelius received his *rightful* 67 million."

"But if it weren't for Alva, your inheritance amount would have been lumped in, with your other brothers and sisters, to divide and *divide*. After that, all of you would have had to be satisfied with what you could get from a trust fund!"

"I suppose so."

"You know so. Alva broke the mold!"

Inside my marine confinement, I threw a kiss at the walls and hoped it would make its way through to Oliver. The mold he was talking about was "the hard one" I had brought up in conversation with Mrs. Astor, and later with W. H. on our "buggy ride". Now things were changing. The eldest son did not always inherit all the money and then dole it out to his brothers and sisters as he saw fit. New things were happening in family after family. Perhaps these people were also remembering that the old Commodore was disappointed in his "eldest" sons, one by one, down to William Henry, whom he finally began to trust. It was this fact about which I continually reminded W. H. Vanderbilt when he was doing those nine wills. He was *not* the eldest son.

At this point, I simply secured the guard on my last hatpin. With a new skill.

When the next question came from my husband, I had a feeling he might have stood up. "Oliver. What if I divorce Alva?"

"You could. On what *real* grounds?"

"Ambition."

"Ambition? You mean, by any chance, influence?"

"All right, influence."

"Sound off, W. K."

"Well, she has established the Vanderbilts by building Idlehour, the Metropolitan Opera, our Fifth Avenue house, the Newport mansion —"

"So what is she going to build next?"

"No. What is she going to do next? What influence does she want now?"

"Alva has conquered America. Why not try for Europe?"

He sighed. "Exactly."

"You haven't done so badly yourself. How? As owner of *Alva* and now *Valiant*. All those dinners for dignitaries on board, and all their soirées for all of *you* on shore."

"But I'm not using one of our children as bargaining power."

At this moment, still in my prison, I imagined that Oliver Belmont also stood up.

I heard him now ask, "Who? Consuelo?"

"Yes!"

"Is this any surprise? Family after family in these United States are letting their daughters marry Europeans."

"In exchange for money!"

"In exchange for *titles*."

"And Alva is after one for our daughter!"

"That's the only chance Alva has. Your two sons will marry whomever they wish. It is only a *daughter* who can bring a title into a family." Oliver let Willie K. absorb this, then went on. "Look at Maria Theresa. She married her daughters off to all the crowned heads, until she had a finger in every court in Europe. What could it mean for Consuelo? Perhaps that she could be royally happy."

"Or unhappy! Oliver. You know what I'm saying."

"Of course I know, W. K. But what makes you so sure?"

"We are sailing to India in two days. We will be entertained by the British. We anchor in the Hooghly River and are even invited to stay at Government House. Alva is delighted. She will be asking questions."

"About what titles are available?"

"About what young men are still negotiable."

"So she can pick and choose."

"I don't want Consuelo to marry *any* of them. I want her to marry a man she *loves*."

"So, on this cruise, you have brought along a young man named Winthrop Rutherfurd."

I heard him, I heard him. Again, I wanted to kiss Oliver. What a nice observation. He saw through everything, that man! I knew once more why I was so attracted to O. H. P. Belmont. It was *impossible* to fool him.

My husband asked innocently, "Oh? Winty? He was simply the most handsome and charming young man I know. Should be great company for Consuelo."

"So I notice."

"I think she feels the same way about him."

"Does it occur to you, W. K., that is why you and Alva are having more battles lately?"

"Are we that vocal?"

"A yacht is no place for a private conversation."

"I do not want Alva to run Consuelo's life."

"I think she's run it pretty well. Consuelo is a beautifully educated young lady. Her demeanor and manners are natural. And she keeps those two lustrous eyes of hers very open."

"Oliver, *I* would like to take a little credit."

"Certainly. But look what an accomplishment the *two* of you have in this daughter of yours. She is no ordinary creature."

"And the man who marries her will be a lucky fellow."

"That's the whole point Alva is trying to make. Your wife does not want to *waste* Consuelo."

"Well, she doesn't have to make a search that is worldwide!"

"That is exactly what she is going to do. After all, the two of you were both educated in France. You know the difference in a European marriage."

"But I came home to choose an American. And so did you."

"Because they are more *interesting*. Just like Consuelo!"

"So our daughter should turn around and marry a European husband?"

"Yes. European wives have a greater position in the world."

"Oliver, you are talking about a *title*."

"I think that's what Alva has in mind, yes. She feels that Consuelo's talents would be more appreciated and better used in a titled marriage."

"What? Than in a plain old American marriage?"

"Yes!"

"Balderdash!"

At that moment, I could imagine Oliver leveling a gaze at my husband. "Willie K. Right now, I don't think the Balderdash family has anyone available ...."

I tried to stifle the laugh that began to shake me. Oliver always made the most of this type of opening. I admit I loved hearing him do it. It released me, it made a mockery of my own pretenses. And Oliver would then wait for my laugh to boom out. We always ended up as two relaxed wags having a wonderful time.

In trying to control myself, I was literally choking. I could not get a drink from the tap — it would make noise. So I had only one alternative. To get it from the toilet. After all, it was converted sea water. So I did. As I scooped it into the palm of my hand, I must say it was the most choke-quenching thing I have ever tasted. If this water killed me, for the moment it was worth it.

Suddenly I heard someone stomp out of the room and onto the deck. I knew it was my husband. Hearing a calculated and sophisticated step slowly follow, I was sure it was Oliver. He was letting his friend vent his wrath, alone. Willie K. had little guile in his personality, and he hated being made uncomfortable by any man who used it, particularly to perfection.

I now knew it was the use and enjoyment of guile which separated these two men in my affections. And I felt that I would
probably have to realize and weigh that for the rest of my life. But
there would never be any question of which one I would choose. It
was just that I hoped I would *never* have to make the choice.

I waited. And waited. Until I was sure I could hear their voices
again, as their footsteps hit the measured rounds of the gangplank.

I came forth in relief. Great relief. And moved to a porthole. As I
saw the two men hail a carriage, get into it, and pull away, I picked
up my handbag and followed. At a safe distance.

As I hailed a second carriage, and it pulled *me* away, I knew I
might have to keep a safe distance—from the relationship of these
two men — for the rest of my life ....

13

THE DRESSING DOWN

W HEN WE FINALLY ARRIVED IN INDIA, THINGS did begin to happen. I listened with open ears to what was being said by our British hosts about the campaign ahead for the W. K. Vanderbilts in marrying off an eligible daughter. To these, our advisers, it was commonplace that American families were being coveted for their wealth and that deals were being made every day by European royalty to exchange their titles for badly needed financing. And why? The world was getting smaller. It seemed Americans could take a cultural short-cut to quickly obtain what it had taken European families centuries to acquire. And, in turn, these much older countries could use the acceleration and assistance from the new world toward maintaining what they already possessed. So my British hosts lost no time in pointing out the eligible young European gentlemen that W. K. and I must consider for our daughter.

This did not interest my William Kissam Vanderbilt in the least. In fact, it backed him off. He was, at the moment, more aware than I that India was a steaming, dusty, desperate country which tended to throw tourists closer together — mainly for self- protection. Such tourists as Consuelo and Winty. While we were being entertained, those two could be protecting each other beyond belief. Sixteen years of inexperience was being assured by twenty-nine years of "knowing the ropes". I should have anticipated and prevented this. But too late. The attachment between our daughter and this country club swain was now cemented.

Willie K. had let it go unabated. So much so that by the time we left India and proceeded on our route, my husband and I were at each others throats about it. Finally, we decided to take Consuelo and Harold, abandon the cruise, and head for Paris.

I, for one, hated to leave Oliver to return without me, let alone all the rest of our guests, but I knew he would not waste a single moment aboard or ashore on the return voyage. When I would see him again in New York he would have a pocket full of stories and a table laden with purchases to show me. Very well. I could wait.

Right now, he knew the differences between Willie K. and me were mainly over our daughter and her future attachment, so Oliver wished me well in the problems of selecting a husband for Consuelo. I needed that assurance. Oliver was the only one who believed I could not only do it but could do it well.

Arriving in Paris, we four W. K. Vanderbilts settled at the Hotel Continental for a parental period of cooling off. This city was the best location in the world for me. I loved Paris. I was more at home here than I was in New York or Newport. But, by now, I had one great concern. How much had Consuelo and her father talked to each other since we left India?

Even though Winthrop was on his way home to Long Island, how many things had he said to Consuelo about my plans?

Was I being "ganged up on"? Was this going to become a battle of two against one — with Winty sending commands and promises over the Atlantic? Could I fight off all three of them? And probably at the same time?

As I lay there in the spacious bed of our hotel suite, I had time during the night to think. I was often alone. Willie K. would return to our bedroom at any hour of the night he chose, and I could only imagine where he had been. We still occupied the same bed to keep up appearances for the sake of the children, but I did not respond to his footstep. And I did not argue or make scenes at that hour. I simply gave him the impression that I was sound asleep.

Having plenty of time to wonder did no good. His female contacts were now multiple, and Paris had become his playground. Again, I could try to explain it all on a basis that he had had a European education and was therefore much more cosmopolitan than if he had been educated in the United States. But it did not help.

Whenever I talked this over with Richard Morris Hunt when we were planning Marble House, working side by side, day after day, we both tried to figure it out. But no matter how much this great man tried to soften the blow to my domestic stability, it never worked and it never made sense. R. M. H. *also* had had a European education, but the reaction was not the same. Richard and Catharine,

I know, had remained faithful to each other all their married lives and were still doing so.

Because this popular man and I were together so much professionally, I know there were whispers about an alliance of our own. But no such "affair" ever occurred. He was a one woman's man, and it was very natural for us to respect each other and very apparent that we did. So why was my husband so different? I was quite aware that Willie K. had not been unfaithful to me for many years after we were married. And that it, indeed, had all gradually begun when I was busy with the children at Idlehour. Eventually I, also, found myself occupied with running the elaborate layout of that estate — so that each time he came home for a weekend, he would not be immediately faced with maintenance problems. I tried to shield him.

Right now, I was asking myself, "Was I so occupied that he had to look elsewhere? Had he become so difficult that I had to look elsewhere?"

No amount of closing my eyes did any good. Whether he was finally lying in bed beside me or not. Whatever the cause, it was very apparent that it was *my* problem, and *I* would have to solve it.

And soon. I was waking up every morning to a restless Consuelo and a complaining Harold. I could always arrange recreation for Harold, but Consuelo was quite a different challenge. I had to, first of all, regain her confidence in me.

So I decided to begin in a small way, in dealing with them both, by telling them of my French background. What better way than to know about their ancestors, their heritage?

I began with the story of one of my male Protestant ancestors, who, starting with Louis XIV's reign, knew and enjoyed religious liberty under the Edict of Nantes. Then, when the king revoked the law and Catholics resumed persecution of the Huguenots, this male relative of mine crossed the Atlantic, in 1685, and and settled in New France.

Consuelo and Harold seemed to be listening.

So I also told them of my own memories of living at 120 Champs Elysee, of being educated in France in the doomed days of glory under Napolean III. Fortunately, before the Prussian siege drove Parisians to fight off starvation by eating rats.

To divert from their reaction, I reported that my oldest sister, Armide, had been a debutante at a ball in the Palace of the Tuileries. Again, fortunately, before the Communards scarred it with their torches.

Somehow I was always present at an opportune time in Paris, and fortunately, again, way ahead — by twenty years — of the devastation of World War I.

"But, Mother," said Harold, "Consuelo has the advantage —she has been here before. She told me about building castles in the sandpiles of the Champs Elysees."

"Very good pronounciation," complimented Consuelo, very fluent in French by now. "I also rode the carrousels and watched the puppet shows."

Harold turned to me, "I only want to buy a toy boat and sail it in the pools here. May I?"

"In the Tuileries?" I received a quick nod. "But don't forget you can also tramp the Bois de Boulogne."

"Good. But my boat comes first."

Consuelo smiled. "However, Harold, you won't have May Wilson or Waldorf Astor as your playmates, the way I did."

"I just want to sail my boat. Alone."

I grinned. "Someday, my son, you even may have a yacht of your own."

"Do I have to sail it to the West Indies first?"

"Why?"

"Because that is what *we* did with *Alva*."

"What do you have in mind?"

"I would prefer the South Pacific."

Consuelo clapped her hands. "Jolly good. Don't you think so, Maman?"

Consuelo had become so adjusted to our requiring her to speak French at home that she had long since tried to always address me as Maman. But was I losing their interest? "I thought you all enjoyed seeing Havana and walking around the streets and parks in Jamaica. Especially Haiti. No? Then what about Nassau?"

"We *did* enjoy all those places. But Harold just wants to try new waters."

"What about the world tour we all did in '87? Did your father and I throw away our money?"

"No, no. But we still had to go to school every day."

"Yes! So you wouldn't *miss* an entire year!"

"But we wanted to learn by looking, not from those horrid *books*."

I had to laugh. It was exactly the same thing I wanted to do when I was each of their ages. I only wished to read history and talk to people. Talk, talk, talk. Mind to mind, that's the way I wanted to learn.

Consuelo was all too aware of what I was thinking. "You said, one time, Maman, that you wanted to learn to draw all those things you saw in the museums here in Paris."

"Yes. Let alone the buildings themselves. I did try. But my mother and father would never encourage me or allow me to take a single lesson."

"Why?"

"In those days it was better to have a girl learn to play the piano. *That* was something everyone could listen to. Furthermore, it was a far better way to eventually trap a husband."

Harold stared. "But, Mother, *you* don't play the piano. How did you trap — get — father?"

"With my long auburn hair, and my soft southern accent."

"You don't have an accent."

"Only when I get mad." Consuelo nodded all too knowingly. She remembered, no doubt, the back-brace I had designed for her. Twenty times a day I would have to say, "Consuelo, stand up straight, don't hunch over, you are getting round-shouldered." So I finally did something about it.

Harold pursued. "But did father feel cheated because his wife couldn't play the piano?"

"I told him I had tried. Practice, practice. But I never seemed to know my lesson when that man came to the house."

"Who?"

"My Italian teacher. One day he had had enough. He put my fingers on the *correct* keys. Hard. Very hard."

"What happened?"

"I slapped him!"

"You did?" Harold seemed pleased.

"Then I ran out of the room, screaming that I would never take another piano lesson as long as I lived!"

"And did you?"

"No!"

"Good. Can we slap *our* tutors?"

"Of course not."

"If we screamed about the lessons we have to do with our tutors, would it do any good?"

"That is very different."

They both chimed out together, "It is still a *lesson!*"

Again I was caught. I granted them their point and suggested that we all three go out to walk up and down the Tuileries to find a stall where we could buy a boat.

Harold ran ahead. Consuelo stayed close to me. "Did *you* have a tutor when you lived here?"

"No. I was sent to a private school for one year."

"Oh, was that the time when you sat up in the top of a tree and refused to come down?"

"Yes, not even the gardener could coax me. And I made sure that nobody else could climb that tree as long as I was up there blocking the way!"

"Were you naughty at other times?"

"Yes, I was. The school had formal evenings when we were allowed to dress up and have the privilege of behaving ourselves in the drawing room. I thought the whole thing was a sham. So on one of those boring nights, I loosely piled my long hair up on top of my head. When I made my proper entrance, I let the whole mass down. It fell all the way to the floor. Everyone gasped. Apparently they thought I looked like the wife of 'the wild man of Borneo'. And I did. But it literally loosened up all that formality; for once, we pupils had a good time."

"A time *you* made for them."

"Well I tried. I soon became a law unto myself, and the whole school thought Americans were wild, untameable creatures. But I was careful to be likeable, always likeable."

Consuelo stopped and looked directly at me. "If you wanted to have a mind of your own, then why won't you allow me the same privilege?"

I stood beside Consuelo until Harold was well ahead. "I presume you are speaking of Winthrop Rutherfurd."

"I am."

"What makes you think you have so much in common?"

"He says I make him laugh, that I see things other people do not see."

"He is right, you do. But *he* does not!"

"He sees *me*, and that is all I care about."

I took her hand. "Consuelo, you are so beautiful. Talented, so well educated, and so really charming. The world is out there waiting for you. Don't stop when you haven't even begun."

"Why? I have more education than most girls of my age."

"But what about your dreams of studying modern languages at

Oxford University?"

"I am no longer interested. I have found my place in life. I have found Winty."

"Every girl feels that way about her romance with the first young man in her life."

"Did you feel that way about father?"

"There were, fortunately, several others before I met him."

"Oh? But you knew he was the one?"

"I *hoped* he was."

"Have you ever met anyone else — since — to change your mind?"

I let go of my daughter's hand and looked away. "I presume you are speaking of Oliver Hazard Perry Belmont?" I received half a nod. "But don't all *three* of you children like him, too?"

"Yes." She straightened her beautiful, long neck. "But that is not what I asked, Maman."

"Consuelo. This is difficult. What can I say? We have much in common. I admire him. He's like you. He, too, makes me laugh, and he sees what other people don't see."

"So *now* you know how Winty and I feel about each other!" She looked into my eyes for approval.

I could not give it. I could not. I felt it must be time to find a stall and buy Harold his toy. He already had gone ahead and was beckoning me to come see what he had found. As we joined him, we both agreed he had chosen a beautiful little sailboat.

But he pointed to the others. "And I don't want one just my size. I want one bigger. This one!"

I had a feeling this might be the *search* of my son for the rest of his life .... Rather like his mother.

I bought it. Immediately, he was off to the nearest water. Consuelo and I hurried to keep up. Harold chose a focal point to launch it, the boat responded, and he proudly held onto the tether. It continued to sail as if it were a duck which had finally found water. Harold was enthralled. And very amazed when he began to notice that the owners of smaller boats pulled theirs out of the way!

Consuelo and I sighed in relief and found a shady place to sit. On two of the marvelous chairs of the Tuileries. Always metal and always graceful. They looked as though they belonged there as much as the trees, shrubs and flowers.[12]

Consuelo was not about to let this opportunity pass. She knew I was trapped into supervising her brother and hoping he did not fall into the water. If so, she knew I would stand aside and allow her to rescue him, just as she had done so many times in the ponds of Central Park. So, again, we were a pair.

She did her own launching. "Father says you and I are now going to do a tour of Europe."

"And spend the summer in England. I will rent a house, and we'll send for little Willie. Consuelo, how about asking Mrs. Jay and the girls — for you?"

"I'd rather see them all, back home. May I return to New York with father?"

"He is not going till later."

"Why not?"

"Your father now has equal interests on both sides of the Atlantic. Horses, automobiles — and people."

"Doesn't he still run our railroads?"

"Yes, but he has handed over much of that to Chauncey Depew."

"But `railroads' is where we still get our money, isn't it?"

"No danger of not getting that!"

"Where do we put that money besides into houses, our *Valiant*, clothes, food —"

"— and `family' amusements."

"And church."

"And charities."

"Which ones, Maman?"

"Well, universities, hospitals, clinics, institutes, libraries, political candidates — even cathedrals."

"Winty says father is the only Vanderbilt who gets any real joy out of his money."

"By giving it away?"

"No no. Winty says by loving to raise his prize horses, racing his automobiles in the Grand Prix, and especially entering his *Valiant* in the America's Cup Races." She pointed. "Like Harold over there — it's the most exciting thing he can do!"

"Your father *is* more open and honest about it than his brother."

"Do you think Uncle Corneel and Aunt Alice will ever enjoy *their* money?"

"*She* will — by continuing to build bigger houses than your mother does."

"How about Uncle Fred and Aunt Lulu?"

"Rough Point is a real Newport showplace, don't forget. But they also plan a new mansion in upstate New York."

"What about Uncle George and Aunt-whoever-it-will-be when *he* finally marries?"

"I have a feeling their first house will be the biggest of all — a real castle. Richard Morris Hunt is designing that one right now. It is to be built in the forest near Asheville, North Carolina, no less."

"Did Grandfather Vanderbilt realize he had one son who loved trees and not railroads?"

"And books. Books, books, books. But no matter. He was the youngest son, so that meant he was expected to care for his mother until she died."

"Why don't Aunt Margaret and Aunt Emily do that for Grand-mother Vanderbilt?"

"W. H. Vanderbilt felt it was ultimately a man's responsibility."

"Is that why he left Uncle George one of the twin mansions?"

"Exactly."

"Then will Harold be *required* to take care of you when you get old?"

"No. I will take care of myself."

"Supposing you can't?"

"I will still do it."

"Maman, when that times comes, I will see to it that you have everything you want."

"Oh?" I was deeply impressed. "Thank you."

"Winty and I will protect you, always."

I had to sit up very straight on my chair. "Consuelo, I do not want that young man as a son-in-law."

"Then it's true what father says?"

"What does he say?"

"That ever since India you are only impressed with royalty."

"Does he also say I am impressed with getting you the right husband?"

"No."

"Well I am. And I want it to be a man with a solid family background and with a sound financial future."

"Even if I am only sixteen?"

"*But* old enough to want to marry Winthrop Rutherfurd tomor-row!"

"Yes. But perhaps I can have a two-year engagement."

"Just as long as you are engaged to a man worthy of you."

"Worthy. That sounds like royalty again." Consuelo patterned the ground with the edge of her shoe. "Did you first become impressed with crowned heads when you were living in the center of it all?"

"Quite the opposite. From the balcony of our apartment, I did used to see Napoleon III, sitting there on his white horse, reviewing his troops. Sometimes I would even catch a glimpse of the little Imperial Prince dashing by in his carriage. I admit I loved the pomp and color of it all. But one time I was told Queen Victoria was visiting and would soon be riding by and that I would be overcome with awe! I waited to be overcome. I wanted the experience. But when I finally saw her, she looked to me like a fat old lady wearing an ugly bonnet and bowing to people because she felt she had to."

Consuelo giggled. "Good."

"Why are you saying 'good'?"

"You weren't impressed."

"What does that have to do with it?"

"That is *one* member of royalty that I won't have to marry!"

Consuelo had an enigmatic sense of humor, and she could stop me in my tracks. I laughed but immediately decided it was time to check on Harold. I arose from my chair, taking my handbag with me.

Recognizing this signaled I didn't wish to return, Consuelo did the same thing. "I will go find him, Maman."

"I think this may be a project we will have to do together. It is lunchtime."

"Food *is* the only thing which will drag him away from that water."

I approached and leaned over Harold. "Come, my dear, it is time to eat. Pull in your boat. Here is my handkerchief, you can wipe it off."

"Sailboats don't dry off with handkerchiefs. They go into dry dock!"

"Very well. Hold it upside down by that middle ridge there."

"By this keel, Mother."

"Oh, very well. But let's go find a sidewalk cafe and sit in the sun so you *can!*"

"Wait. May we sit next to the street?"

"Certainly. But why?"

"I always like to see the horses and the carriages, but maybe an automobile will drive by!"

"One of your father's?"

"No. He said he would be out at his stables all day."

Consuelo sang out, "Then perhaps someone famous will come by on a bicycle!"

Harold's eyes grew troubled. "Like a king or queen?"

"Or on a pair of skates!"

"Then maybe a prince?"

I reminded, "Royalty rides in carriages."

"I know. And I hate that."

"Why?"

"Every person around us stands up and bows and claps their hands and crowds in front of me. I can't see!"

Consuelo alerted. "You can't see?"

"No."

"Not even a prince?"

"Not even a prince!"

"Then don't complain."

"Why not?"

"Just count yourself fortunate ...."

I blinked. Again I felt it was time to move on! I immediately led the way to go and look for a cafe.

14

TRIO WITHOUT MELODY

THE ARGUMENTS BETWEEN WILLIE K. AND myself continued. Letters were written home about it, apparently. Before we knew it, word got to Cornelius. He decided to cross the Atlantic and see if he could effect a reconciliation.

"Thank heaven Alice is not coming with him," I said to my husband.

"Or it would be a four-way fight."

"A three-way battle will be quite enough!"

"Alva, do you want me to see Corneel alone?"

"He will want to hear both sides, won't he?"

"Do you think the three of us can talk without your getting to the point of shouting?"

"I will try."

"My elder brother is not a sophisticated man. You may shock him beyond recovery."

"Alice has probably already cushioned the blow by telling him everything."

"Does she read the gossip columns?"

"She does not subscribe to *Town Topics*, but no doubt she has a trusted servant who does."

"And she believes that Colonel Mann?"

"She believes his spies."

"Disgruntled social climbers again?"

"Oh no. He also pays for gossip from anyone — from servants to musicians, don't forget. And that is only the published word. Alice must be aware he has a whole file of `not-to-be-mentioneds', Willie K."

"Which his *victims* pay for."

"You should know!"

And that ended this exchange until we could welcome Cornelius and choose a time agreeable to all three of us. It would have to be a time, of course, when Cornelius hoped all cards could be laid on the table.

It was decided all this would take place at a nearby restaurant, which we actually both chose to be conservative enough for his tastes. Willie K. arranged for his accommodations at our hotel, but when Cornelius arrived, he let us know he could stay only overnight because he had other Paris business to attend to.

As we met that evening in our hotel lobby, I gazed at him several moments before I extended my hand to greet him. I must say my brother-in-law had the tall, distinguished Commodore Vanderbilt frame. My husband did not. His build was more that of his father and mother. The W. H. Vanderbilts always looked important enough to me, but they made up in hierarchy for what they lacked in height.

So did my husband. We were proud people. And we at least *stood* tall. Actually we were well-suited physically, and I always thought the two of us made a handsome couple.

Willie K. was a man of stature, no matter what. He managed his railroad lines, even in absentee position, very well. He was a natural leader in all his social clubs and was often elected to do executive duty. As was Oliver. The two of them frequently stood shoulder to shoulder in crucial decisions regarding many of those organizations.

Not so with Cornelius. He cared little for the struts and stresses of society. He was building The Breakers in Newport and intending to enlarge his Fifth Avenue mansion only because Alice insisted on being *The* Mrs. Vanderbilt.

I had taken the title away from her, and she would not rest until she got it back.

Corneel knew this. When he, Willie K. and I walked in the evening air to the restaurant, were seated, ordered our dinner, and began with a round of white wine, he chose this as his first topic for discussion.

"Alva, I have always been concerned that Alice and I may be part of the problem — the present one between Willie K. and you."

"Yes, Corneel. Good of you to say so. Alice and I are indeed rivals. But you and Willie K. are not."

"That is correct," affirmed W. K. "If Corneel and I felt about each other the way you and Alice do, the Vanderbilt railroad empire

155

would long since have collapsed from internal strife."

Corneel was aware this was attack Number One on me. He countered. "But apart from that, my dear brother, I constantly remind myself it was your wife's building of the Metropolitan, your house at 660, and then yours and Alva's great party — all of eleven years ago — which put the Vanderbilt family on the social map."

I glanced my gratitude directly into Corneel's eyes.

W. K. was the first one to raise his voice. "I have always acknowledged Alva's part in our acceptance. The crux of our present problem is that she has never stopped!"

Corneel raised his brows. "But she has continued those banquets and parties and musicales at Marble House. That building is the accomplishment of the century. Richard Morris Hunt refers to it again and again as his best work. That is precisely why Alice and I chose him as architect for The Breakers."

"And no doubt told him to go us one better!" I laughed.

"If I don't run out of money in the approaching depression, it *will* be bigger. But I doubt, better."

"Again I thank you, Corneel. And I accept whatever the results. It should be very grand."

"So do I, my dear." He turned to his brother. "I just hope Alice doesn't expect me to be as good a host as you are, Willie K."

At that moment, the waiter brought all three of us our appetizer, and we began eating.

"You are kind, but I am on my yacht a great deal these days. And you've heard, no doubt, I'd like to go back to racing. My *Valiant* is built for it, you know."

"Instead of racing horses?"

"I have never stopped breeding and racing. It's a business. Just ask Oliver Belmont."

"You are competing against each other?"

W. K. took a deep breath and plunged ahead. "Only for the love of my wife, apparently."

I put down my fork. So did Corneel. Our eyes met.

With both of us at a disadvantage, my husband dashed on. "I don't suppose you have missed the social columns concerning their appearance together at everything from sporting events to being seen again in the same box at the opera."

"I never read that part of the paper. Alice does. And I told her Alva and Oliver were together because you were out of town so often."

W. K. nodded. "True. Many times I am grateful to Oliver, but I remind you we three have just been on a cruise together."

Corneel attempted to make a light joke. "A crucial cruise?"

My husband only half smiled. "You might call it that, since things are different now."

"Between you and Oliver?"

"Between Alva and me."

Corneel took a sip of water which he had ordered and began to neglect his wine, just as I would have predicted. But he asked with unwatered concern, "Is there any way in which I can help?"

"The problem is the same. Alva cannot stop raising the status of the Vanderbilts, particularly the W. K. branch. Now she, like hundreds of other American mothers, wants Consuelo to marry well. Preferably a European and probably some man with a title."

I felt it was time to be very direct. "Willie K., tell him what he is soon facing *himself*." My husband was silent, so I continued. "Corneel, your daughter, Gertrude, is also approaching the marriageable age. Both Consuelo and Gertrude, I am sure, have discussed this between themselves. They know they will soon be barraged by a group of swains. Each one will consider himself to be the perfect mate for our daughters and particularly for their financial standing. Corneel, you and Alice will have to make the same choices we will!"[13]

"But I have no doubt Consuelo and Gertrude will each have a great deal to say about this."

Willie K. cut in. "Consuelo already has. She is in love with Winthrop Rutherfurd."

"Isn't Winty rather old for her?"

So I cut in. "Old? It is just that he has never grown up. At twenty-nine, he is young for his age. At sixteen, Consuelo is old for hers. So Willie K. is convinced they are the same age!"

"Alva!"

I picked up my fork and resumed eating, with deliberation. And I began enjoying every bite.

Corneel tried to give a brotherly point of view. "Willie K., I have observed Winthrop myself. He is seldom in his law office. He is usually out riding with the Roosevelts."

"I thought that Winty's mother and your Alice were close friends."

"They are, especially since Margaret Rutherfurd has taken over Caroline Astor's position as social watchdog."

I smiled with quiet delight. Here, beside me, was the great

Cornelius Vanderbilt, the church elder and philanthropist, who gave most of his money to foreign missions. To the heathen, no less. Yet he could see New York society for what it was. Perhaps that was why he preferred to study the life of primitive peoples. There was yet hope for improvement there. *It* could be manipulated. Apparently, he had long since given up on his wife's "civilized" friends!

But his younger brother was not to be diverted. He had never stopped eating and was now even gesturing with his knife. "Corneel, listen to me. I do not want Alva to make one of these deals for a European title, in exchange for Vanderbilt stocks and bonds and cold cash."

"I understand, W. K. And as I sit here, Alice may be thinking of doing the same thing for Gertrude."

"Alice can do what she wants to, but I do not want Consuelo to be sold to the highest bidder!"

I removed my napkin from my lap and snapped it. "Don't you have any more confidence in our judgment than that? Do you think you and I are *not going* to carefully scrutinize every young man who asks for our daughter's hand?"

"As far as I am concerned, she can marry Winty tomorrow!"

"You are not going to even consider those other possibilities?"

"No!"

"Well *I* am!"

"Are you going to parade her across Europe and accept the best offer?"

I had finally raised my voice. But it did not match my husband's. "If you wish to put it that way. But I would like to think of it as making an intelligent search." I slapped the table. "A *very* carefully considered selection."

Willie K. glared. Corneel cleared his throat and put his hand on his brother's shoulder. "This can be no surprise, certainly. That is the way Alva has always done *everything*."

"I know, Corneel. And I respect her taste." He even smiled at me. "But *Consuelo* now has something to say about this. And she is willing to devote her life to being Mrs. Winthrop Rutherfurd. And I am not going to stand in her way!"

"W. K., perhaps she should wait and look over the other possibilities, herself. Winty might not be the best choice."

"He is for her."

"I realize this is a difficult problem, but do you, by any chance, want to solve it by simply getting her off your hands?"

"No!"

"Then let Alva continue the search."

"But what you don't realize, Corneel, is that this is going to cause a divorce!"

"Why do you think I have come all the way across the Atlantic?"

"All right, but it's too late."

"Oh? Then let's talk about where you are going to get this divorce."

"In the State of New York."

Corneel turned to me. "Alva, I have no doubt you are fully aware that this can only be obtained on grounds of —."

Not caring to hear the word again, I cut in. "Yes, Corneel. I have no choice."

"But do you have the *grounds*?"

I did not answer. I felt this should now become a discussion between the two gentlemen involved. I arose. "If you will excuse me."

W. K. stood up. "No, we will not. Sit down, Alva. The waiter will soon bring the main course. If it is evidence Corneel wants, I will give it to him. But only in your presence."

My husband knew I was congenitally polite to waiters. And to the chefs who prepared the food. I understood all their problems. And he knew I would sit down.

I did. So did he. And for several minutes, the three of us waited in silence.

Willie K. was ready to begin. I knew it was not easy for him. Particularly speaking to a brother who was married to a woman who felt it was nature's wish that she own her husband for the rest of his life. To a woman to whom he would never even *consider* being unfaithful. For the rest of that "possessed" life! So what does anyone say, in that case?

The waiter did come with our entree, beautifully prepared. As we gazed at it, it gave each of us the impression that food would give us strength to disclose what we must.

Willie K. decided forthrightness was the correct approach. "Corneel, do you remember some of the articles that used to be written about me? How they said how modest I looked? How quietly I spoke? How unwealthy I appeared? That I was not the ʻthe howling swell' everyone expected?"

"Yes, I remember."

"And how absolutely devoted everyone felt Alva and I were to each other?"

My husband seemed surprised to receive a definite nod from us both.

He drew in his breath. "Well, I have changed. I now find I have a new image. And this also seems to bring with it liking more than one woman at a time. In fact, many. And I surprisingly find they like *me*. I have apparently become what the columnists call `a woman-izer'!"

Corneel could not look at his brother. "Alice has told me. But that is a term I would never apply."

"Of course not. You would only call me wayward."

"Perhaps. Well — yes."

"I am not. I know exactly what I am doing. It takes a pattern. Many times it even begins as a lark. I can easily offer the winnings from a horse race to a pretty face, but a relationship seems to begin. I become involved. But I am consistent about it. Eventually I give the woman more money to confine her attentions only to me."

Corneel half glanced in my direction. I was wooden and would not commit myself either way. So he finally asked the question most natural to him. "But what about Consuelo, little Willie and Harold?"

"They don't know, of course."

"I do not understand, W. K. Don't they demand enough of your time?" Corneel leveled a gaze at his brother. "*Mine* certainly do. Neily, Gertrude, Gladys, Alfred, and Reggie run me ragged!"

"Perhaps I have a wife who is too efficient. She sees that their needs are cared for."

"But *both* parents must do that."

"Corneel. I don't think I neglect my children!"

"But, Willie K., they need you more and more as they grow older."

"And I will be there to attend to their wants. But *not* Alva and I together, that is the difference. She wishes to go her own way."

"Perhaps you have forced her to."

My husband shrugged. "It is time for me to go *mine*."

"There is no more love between you?"

"It depends on what kind of love you are talking about."

Was my brother-in-law going to understand what my husband had just stated? In the past, whenever I had watched Alice and Corneel at parties, I actually wondered if they ever indulged in physical relations except to create a child? I tried hard to assume that they did, but "the picture" was never clear to me.

Corneel struck back with one word, "Love!"

"We sleep in the same bed — for the sake of the children — if that is what you mean. But we are *not* really sleeping together."

"William, that is a mistake!" Corneel turned to me. "Is this true, Alva?"

"Yes."

"Why?"

"For protection!"

"Protection!"

"I do not wish to take the risk."

"What risk?"

"Of getting a venereal disease." Corneel sucked in his breath and almost choked on his food. Willie K. offered him his glass of water, and I tried to calm him.

Willie K. went directly on. "There is no danger of that, Corneel. I am not only discreet, I am careful."

"Who really knows? You *are* asking her to take a risk."

"I do not see it that way. And I have told her so."

"But how can she be sure?"

"How can she be sure of anything? How can she be sure of Oliver?"

It was now my turn to be included into the conversation. "Oliver and I are *not* sleeping together!"

"At least, Alva, that statement in court will get you custody of the children and a good settlement. And that's what you want, isn't it?!"

Corneel gasped. "Willie K., you are more blunt than Alva!"

"The Vanderbilts have always demanded their price."

"Alva is *not* a Vanderbilt."

"But she has *become* one."

I stood up. "If I *have*, Mr. W. K. Vanderbilt, once I divorce you on grounds of adultery, every other Vanderbilt in town will cut me dead, and I shall once again become a Smith. If that is what you want, have no fear!"

Fortunately, at that moment dessert and coffee were offered to us. I sat down. Musicians had suddenly appeared to make it a night that included dancing: "A complete evening for the customer."

We all three ate our dessert and drank our coffee in silence. But not because we were listening to the music.

Willie K. then asked to be excused to go outside, walk over to the Seine, stroll along and enjoy a cigar.

Corneel said, "Very well. I will stay with Alva and see her back to the hotel."

"That won't be necessary. I will do it."

"No, I will be happy to do it."

My husband nodded in deference, went to the cashier and paid the check, then got his cape and top hat. He returned to us, bowed, and was gone.

I knew that telling my husband he would see me back to the hotel was easier for Corneel to do than to explain to his brother, once more, that he didn't smoke! But I was still grateful.

Soon after, Corneel asked me to dance. I said, "I would be delighted."

As he held me in his strong arms at a proper distance, I smiled up at him. He smiled back, also, with the proper distance. I knew he would not dream of continuing the discussion without his brother's being present. It would appear to be taking sides, and he had really tried not to.

I did not mind. It was nice just to be guided about the floor. For such a strictly devout man, he was a very adequate dancer. I hoped perhaps it was because he had a partner who could dance better than his wife. But *not* so — Alice was really a good dancer.

So we made an evening out of it. At midnight, we danced the last dance, sang "Good Night, Ladies", and applauded the musicians.

As we strolled back to the hotel, we talked about the wonders of Paris. He seemed amazed that my background was so rooted there. At the door of our suite, I thanked him and bade him goodnight. Corneel bowed, kissed my hand, and promptly walked down the hall. I realized it was more than a goodnight. He was only departing tomorrow, but it was goodbye for several years, and I knew it. The Vanderbilts *would* cut themselves off from me. And me from them. Even if Cornelius ever uttered a word of sympathy in my behalf, Alice would not let him express it, and particularly *not* to his shockingly defiant sister-in-law.

I closed the door, checked on Consuelo and Harold, and went to our bedroom. I removed my clothes, put on my nightdress, brushed my hair, laid down, and began to think. But I must have fallen asleep.

I do not know what time Willie K. returned and came into the room. I knew he would undress, put on his nightgown, perhaps down some cognac, and finally lie down beside me.

But I would not have to worry. I could sleep soundly. I knew he would not touch me ....

162

15

THE SINGLE APPROACH

SOON AFTER THE VISIT OF CORNELIUS, WILLIE K. did return to the United States. After the Panic of 1893, J. P. Morgan, the banker the Vanderbilts still depended on, had organized the Southern Railroad Company to connect not only needed Atlantic coast points but also the Ohio River to the Gulf of Mexico. W. K. had to witness this piece of management for himself. And ride on it!

His departure left me in charge of Consuelo, Harold, their governess, Miss Harper, and my maid, Jeanne. This next year and a half of my life was the most complicated and stressful I have ever endured.

However, Paris in the spring was certainly the most desirable location a lady tourist could arrange for herself. And despite my estrangement from my husband, I determined that the remaining five of us should continue to explore and enjoy the wonders of this city.

So we four, and Jeanne, when she was free, walked beneath the flowering chestnuts of the Champs Elysees. In our "carriage and pair" we drove through the Bois de Boulogne. We visited museums and churches, listened to lectures at the Sorbonne and attended the classical matinees at the Theatre Francais. These matinees proved to be Consuelo's greatest pleasure. Still required at home to speak French, she had become even more proficient in the language. Her calling me Maman was now very natural. The Theatre Francais' tradition of perfect diction was too great for me not to utilize. I arranged lessons in elocution for Consuelo with one of their veteran actresses. Our daughter not only learned excellent diction, she developed a voice that would carry.

Years later, when Consuelo took the stump for the various causes she championed, that voice rang out loud and clear. Its message even reached the British House of Lords and all Parliament.

Visiting the fashion houses, on the Rue de la Paix, I happily made special purchases for Consuelo. A white tulle dress, created by the prestigious designer, Worth, was chosen for her first Paris ball. It was held at the Duc de Gramont's in the Avenue des Champs Elysees, specifically planned for the Duchess's eldest daughter. Consuelo's gown had a tightly laced bodice, her hair was piled high in a cascade of curls, and a narrow ribbon was tied around her beautifully long and slender neck.

The ball was white as contrasted with the pink balls, where young married women were included and where, inevitably, more flirtations occurred. Though very soon our daughter had a galaxy of partners, there was no opportunity at a white ball for conversation. A girl was invited to dance, danced, and was promptly escorted back to her mother. We chaperones lined the walls, were possessive, and obviously discussed the merits of our charges.

A particular young man, named Jacques Balsan, danced with Consuelo. He told his mother the following day, "I met at the ball last night the girl I would like to marry."[14]

Letters arrived from Winthrop Rutherfurd, but Consuelo reported no stated proposal. She simply answered the letters and hoped the relationship would sustain until she could see him again. Thereupon, I decided diversion would be a possible cure — not only for Consuelo but for me. I needed some contact with Oliver. Letters were not a substitute, just as they were not for Consuelo. I understood.

But, during the social events of May and June, our daughter received five proposals. All directed to me but none from young men "sufficiently exalted". However, I only turned them down after thorough investigation and discussion with her.

The next young gentleman to consider was Prince Francis Joseph, the youngest of the four handsome German Battenberg Princes. We met him at a party given by Countess Melanie de Pourtales in her house close to the Madeleine. This residence was a gathering place for the beau monde of Paris, and this particular party seemed to have all the statesmen, diplomats, and elegant women our hostess could gather. Consuelo was somewhat overwhelmed. The Contessa drew me aside and pointed out that Prince Francis Joseph was happily dancing with my daughter and weren't they a handsome couple? If I had once contemplated British titles, now I was being offered German royalty. I was told Consuelo's dancing partner could be elected king, to supplant his unpopular brother, if properly financed.

The strong smell of Vanderbilt money was apparently permeating the room, enough to overwhelm even me. I moved to the balcony for at least fresh monetary air, and in so doing, made a decision. Our daughter was not to be imprisoned in a provincial capital, ironbound by strict German etiquette, married to a prejudiced-view princeling who might or might not become king. *Or even assume the title of Czar of Bulgaria in the manner of his brother.*

I had a feeling none of Consuelo's friends would be welcome to visit her, let alone pleasure visits from her family, unless they brought money!

Consulting with my daughter, I found her views were even more advanced than mine. We concluded the conquest was not a wise one, and the two of us promptly terminated it.

We therefore left Paris to spend the summer in England, first settling in London's fashionable Brown's Hotel. Though the location gave us access to British social life, it was a dingy contrast to our Hotel Continental with its lovely view over the Tuileries Gardens to my beloved Seine.

But, fortunately, we were outside often. Our carriages and horses had preceded us, complete with French coachmen and no less imposing English footmen.

News from home in April had told us of rising unemployment and about Kelly's "industrial army" marching on Washington. In May we had heard about "Coxey's Army" marching from Ohio to Washington, D.C., to "take control of the government." This was discussed on our first outing to one of my oldest friends, Lady Paget. She was a member of the Prince of Wales' set, which included Lady Randolph Churchill, Mrs. Cavendish-Bentinck, and Consuelo, Duchess of Manchester — our Consuelo's Godmother and, again, the dear friend after whom we named her.

Lady Paget, whom I had known only as plain Minnie Stevens in New York, was quick to discount the unarmed armies marching on our Capitol, but she was quicker to realize she was chosen as our Consuelo's entrance into London society.

Taking this responsibility seriously, she looked our daughter over and decided that maybe decolletage must give way to a firm display of neck and arms. Consuelo began calling it "my skin-tight sophistication!"

Furthermore, Lady Paget gave a dinner party, at her 35 Belgrave Square house, and she seated Consuelo next to the Ninth Duke of Marlborough. Though six years her senior, he seemed young to her; however, she *was* impressed with his good looks and intelligence. But in contrast with Winty, she could only describe him to me as if she were sketching an acid-on-silver portrait.

"Maman, did you notice his aristocratic face was noticeably small but accented with a *large* nose? And that two of his possible three eyes were indubitably noble? And that he was fastidious with at least one of his hands — his knighted one?"

Chastised, all I could say was, "A very sharp observation, my dear."

She continued her satiric exaggeration. "Do you think he *might* also have been trying to impress me? Or more like ferret me out? Is it a nasty case of Vanderbilt money again?"

"But do you *like* him?"

"No. How about you, Mrs. Vanderbilt?"

I kept my temper. "We had no chance to talk, but I was very aware of the long tradition behind him and the responsibility he has taken for Blenheim Palace."

"Oh. Is it *his*?"

"Indeed, Consuelo."

"Then, of course, you want to see it."

"I can wait."

"But barely." She saw me nod. "Yes, I think my mother would be an excellent visitor. She will know more about its architecture and interior than the Duke himself."

"But I will *not* show him up, my dear."

"Then I shall! I will tell him, `I want to go back home to an American named Winthrop Rutherfurd. And as soon as possible'!"

"Consuelo, we have not even had a chance to enjoy the house I leased at Marlow. It's right on the Thames."

"All thirty-four rooms of it?"

"Yes. And we can motorlaunch and picnic all we want to."

"Really?"

"I have already asked Mrs. Jay and her two girls to join us."

Consuelo groaned. "Those two dear young things? For the past three months, Maman, you have wanted me to grow up!"

"But not that fast."

"Then when can we go home to New York where I declare growth at my own speed?"

"Home? No. Little Willie is arriving with his tutor."

"Personally, I find Mr. Noble more honorable than diverting. And what about my *own* lessons?"

"They can resume in September."

"At Idlehour, I hope. The fall colors are so beautiful, and I love the crunch of all those leaves."

"Nonsense, Consuelo. You love the location because you will be closer to your fox-hunting horseman!"

"Riding has also become *my* talent."

"Except that when *girls* pursue their prey, they must do it side-saddle!"

"That is precisely the approach you are making me take — I can only side-glance at my lover."

"Your lover? He has not even proposed."

"He will. But how can I get back to him, with all these people you have invited to Marlow?"

"Yes. Even your Aunt Armide."

"*She* is coming?" Consuelo watched me nod firmly. "Aunt Armide never seems like your sister. *She* gets older, *you* never do."

"Oh? Thank you, my dear daughter."

"Aunt Mary Virginia is even jealous of you. I have always wondered — you three must have been quite a trio-looking-for-triumph when you hit New York."

"We were. Except for my sister Julia Florence. She was just a baby."

"But only *you* married a rich man." She cleared her throat, as she always did when talking about something close to her. "Maman, you did not fool me by always being in the same bed with Papa."

"No? You mean at the Hotel Continental?"

"No. Before that. Remember, I know how much you two quarrel. Because I am the one, when you are not speaking, who has to carry your messages back and forth."

"I see. Then you *also* know it all seems to be ending?"

"Yes. But why? Don't you love father anymore?"

"We have drifted apart."

"Oh no. You have never drifted in your life. You lash about and change the current, maybe. But, Maman, you do *not* drift."

"Thank you again, Consuelo .... I can only say I feel I have no other choice."

"I know the two of you will be apart now, but I think Papa still admires you."

"And I shall always be proud of him. He has done wonders for the entire Vanderbilt family. And he will continue to do so."

"What do you think is next?"

"Oh, he will probably race in the America's Cup."

"And win?"

"Of course."

"Will he let Harold 'crew' for him?"

"I will suggest it."

"I want to see that! Will *you* be there?"

"Naturally."

"Even if the two of you are no longer married?" Apparently Consuelo could not say the word divorce. Her voice grew quiet. "Do you think Papa will ever marry again?"

I swallowed hard. "Is this your way of asking if there is someone else in the picture?"

She shrugged. "Well?"

"There are several. Perhaps he will choose one."

"Then I hope he chooses one with children, Maman, I want more brothers and sisters."

"Two brothers are not enough?"

"Yes, but I want younger ones."

"I see. Very well. Then tell your father to marry a young widow or a young divorcee."

"Do you think he will listen?"

"Why not? He adores you."

"Then perhaps Winty and I, the four of us — ". Consuelo broke off, embarrassed.

I filled in. "— can possibly have a double wedding?"

"Maman. I am sorry!"

"Oh, don't stop such dreaming, my dear. Maybe we can add *Oliver* and me. Perhaps make it a ceremony for six!"

16

THE WEDDING WHICH NEVER SEEMED
TO APPROACH

OBVIOUSLY, I NEEDED TO TALK TO OLIVER RIGHT now — to tell him of Consuelo's reaction —which I still could not believe. But this was not possible.

During this summer, I tried to make the house at Marlow pleasant for everyone, even though we had heard in May about the beginning of the Pullman strike in Chicago and its continuing into July when President Cleveland ordered U.S. troops into that city. Two men were killed and several injured when U. S. deputy marshals fired upon railroad strikers at Kensington. The American Railway Union, under Eugene Debs, boycotted the servicing of Pullman cars as a sympathy gesture for Pullman strikers. The general strike which followed paralyzed 50,000 miles of western railroads, but I was still sympathetic. I knew Eugene Debs would come to trial, and I was pleased that he chose defense attorney Clarence Darrow to defend him. I did not know where the sympathies of my husband lay, but I was increasingly on the side of the railway workers. I was aware the Vanderbilts were famous for developing and maintaining their railroads, but it was always difficult to ask about individual salaries — the picture was always changing.

I knew my William Kissam Vanderbilt was sensitive about the strike, but he would have preferred to discuss the February incorporation of the Jockey Club. Its purpose was stated loud and clear, in all the British newspapers as well as the New York. "To encourage the development of the Thoroughbred horse" and "establish racing on such a footing that it may command the interest as well as the confidence and favorable opinion of the public." Favorable opinion, indeed. How could any family in New York avoid attempting to become a member? Membership was tantamount to being declared head of the family!

Oliver would be involved in all this, and I longed to discuss it with him. We two always had our irreverent comments, and I only wished I could share them with him. But this would also not be possible, even if we returned home and took up residency, *without* Willie K., at 660 Fifth Avenue. Oliver could not make a proper call at that house, as he had done countless times before, and not endanger my divorce proceedings. And certainly he could never be seen with me in public.

It would take residency in another state, Rhode Island, to allow the two of us to ever have a conversation — a decent conversation, no matter how private. W. K. Vanderbilt was right. I wanted custody of our three children. And that was that.

Our 1894 summer in England was climaxed, on schedule, by my booking passage for all of us on the *Lucania*, to arrive in New York on September 28. This included Armide, Mrs. Jay and her girls, and at the last minute, our charming and respected U.S. Postmaster General Thomas L. James. With our *own* six members, this made quite an entourage, but I was still successful in keeping my name off the printed list of passengers.

When we arrived, I declined to be interviewed. So the *New York Times* reported on my clothes and appearance, instead. The account read, "She looked strikingly handsome. There was high color in her cheeks, and her ocean trip had tanned her. She wore a black satin dress, the waist being heavily trimmed with jet and draped in front with a cream-colored foulard. She wore a collar and epaulets of green velvet, a black hat with feathers, and white kid gloves." I felt that if Oliver read this description he probably cut it out. I hoped he even carried it in his pocket.

I had already made a decision. I had written to my New York servants to be at Marble House by September 17, in order to get our home ready. It had not been open all season. After saying goodbye to the other members of my party, I did not intend to even stay overnight at our house at 660. Let Fifth Avenue look for us in vain. The six of us went straight to Grand Central Station. I sent a telegram to the same servants telling them we would all arrive in Newport, by train, at 10:00 on the morning of September 29. I knew we would all be met at the station by our coachmen and footmen, driving the biggest conveyance and finest two horses lodged in our stables and carriage house. With the exception of a tallyho. I would save that for a great picnic in the country for our children and their friends. No Newport summer was complete without a rousing tallyho-all-day picnic in that countryside. Also one for us adults …. But I was not sure I could pull it off without Oliver. Even though this would be his first season in residency at his Belcourt, I knew he would have the best horses and the most elegant tallyho in town. You did not *pretend* at this recreation without the expertise of Oliver Hazard Perry Belmont! And, in truth, I was not sorry.

Everything went off as predicted, and both little Willie and Harold were thrilled to be back at Marble House and reestablished in their old rooms. But not Consuelo. She longed to be at Idlehour near Winty on his riding weekends — hoping, before the year was up, that he would become her true Lochinvar. Her eyes accused me daily of wanting to be near Oliver, while at the same time preventing her from having the same opportunity for such dalliance. And she was right.

I knew Consuelo would eventually get to Long Island, even if she had to walk! All of which reminded me of a grande dame in Mobile, who once observed to my mother, "Love will go where it is sent, my dear, even if it is up a black cat's ass." Not knowing that her daughter, Alva, overheard, my mother chuckled quietly and nodded her head. And I have never forgotten this remarkable lady's ability to transfer to my mother a few moments of quiet, if outrageous, Southern truth.

But right now, I appreciated Newport more than I ever had previously. Within a day I sent a note to Oliver and received a reply. Yes, he would call on me, but only late at night after the children were all in bed. As much as he loved all three, he felt this was wise, at least for the first time.

And Oliver did as he said. To say that I was glad to see him would be a physical understatement. The two of us had been apart so long that, more than absorb, we absolutely drank up each other. Our chatter broke into logical catching-up of the intervening events and illogical observations of present and predicted happenings. I had planned all this to take place in the intimacy of our library, and I was not disappointed. The log in the fireplace agreeably crackled its warmth to offset the chill of one of the first nights of October.

I realized many of the summer residents had returned to their big-city homes; therefore, my prospects of a tallyho were slim. But somehow I wanted to capture a whole Newport season into a few fall days. As I gushed some of this to Oliver, he was all for reopening Gray Craig Park, his country place in Middletown, just three miles out of Newport. But I calmed down and knew I should wait until next season. Perhaps at that point the search would be over and Consuelo's proper suitor found. This young gentleman could then be invited to Marble House. I wanted him to enjoy not only the picnics but also the events at the Casino, the private parties at the mansions along Bellevue Avenue, and day-cruises plus lunch or dinner aboard the yachts anchored in the harbor.

"And, Alva, how about a trip to Boston or Philadelphia or New York on either my or your private railroad car?"

"Or to Atlanta for the Exposition next year?"

"Marvelous. Your letter sounded doubtful, and I take it you had no final success in finding an interesting mate for Consuelo."

"Not yet. Though there was one young man I did not write about. The surprise came just at the last. He was Paul Deschanel, a cultured Frenchman who used to read poetry to me. And that wasn't all. I should have known it was not simply a case of similar literary tastes. He wanted to be considered the ideal husband for Consuelo. He announced he someday intended to become President of the French Republic. A real possibility. He was already a member of the Chamber of Deputies, and would soon be its President."

"And you turned him down?"

I offered Oliver more of my coffee, cakes, and liqueur to soften the truth. "Yes, I did. There was something about him I felt was emotionally — well, irregular."

"And, just as you had been right about all the other suitors, you were correct about this one?"

"It's too early, I don't know yet."[15]

Oliver was still nudging for more details. "Any more proposals from anxious young Englishmen?"

"Yes, my dear. All uninteresting and obviously slanted toward Consuelo's dowry."

"So you came home. Ah, ah. But you are going back!"

"I must, since my search is incomplete .... But you are aware I first have some legal matters to attend to."

"Such as a divorce. And no ordinary one. This one will rock all of New York."

"Yes, I am afraid so."

"No time to be afraid, dear. Just go after what you want."

"But I want none of this to be embarrassing to you, Oliver."

"That is inevitable. If you wish custody of the children, the first thing the deciding judge will ask is whether you and I have ever slept together."

"And I will say no."

"And that is the truth."

"Though I am consistently a correct woman, Oliver, it is a terrible price to pay!"

He took my hand, mused for a moment, and finally let his dark eyes meet mine. "It is indeed. But you will find, my dear Alva, that the judge will not consider it so. He will only be interested in the legal definition of 'adultery'. *And* who committed it."

"What does he know about adultery? Any judge will define it as the giving of the body without marital license."

"Ah yes."

"But I have quite a different concept."

"Good. What is yours?"

"True adultery is — or was — the giving of your body, time after time, year after year, to a husband you once gave your heart to, but no longer *could!*"

Oliver took me in his arms and kissed me in response. "Yes, my darling. No one really *knows* who hasn't been through this …."

Oliver continued to try to assure me he agreed, but I was still upset. Finally, I laid my head on his shoulder and released the tears which had collected from all the time we were apart, but especially from the months I had no one to talk to who understood the way this man did.

Though all of us tried to make the most of the few days we had, Marble House and Oliver's Belcourt soon had to be closed for the winter. Each one of us was obliged to return to New York. Little Willie had to get back to his school. And Harold and Consuelo to their regular tutoring, special lessons, and social activities with their friends. Life must go on even though I would be suing for divorce, and we all would be living in a house without father and husband. Of course, Willie K. could see his children whenever he wished, but time had to be arranged for the convenience of everyone.

Still restricted from seeing Oliver, under any circumstances, it was a matter of communicating only by letter. We wrote almost daily. We had to, there were so many developments which must be noted and discussed. Nothing could be covered up with social chitchat.

Summons for divorce was served to William Kissam Vanderbilt

on January 3, 1895.

On January 11, he visited Newport, along with his cruising friend, Mr. Winfield S. Hoyt. At Marble House he arranged for furniture to be sent back to New York. Then he sold part of his wharf to our friends Robert and Ogden Goelet. On returning to his club at which he was staying, W. K. had his lawyer report all this to me. I approved.

Oliver then informed me in his next letter that on January 16, Willie K. bought two horses, including one named Coitsville. This horse had lost, at the last national horse show, to Oliver's horse Buckingham. How symbolic was this? We both wondered....

The New York Times then reported that, on the same day, W. K. sailed for Europe on the *Teutonic*. Alone. "Mr. Vanderbilt locked himself in his room as soon as he reached the ship, and refused to answer a question as to a settlement which it is rumored he recently made with his wife."

They were right. It was in regard to the houses. His lawyer offered me our mansion at 660, but I refused, feeling it would be too much of a financial burden to maintain. He then offered me Marble House. I accepted. But what about Idlehour? It was to go to W. K., but the children and I would be allowed the use of it as long as we wished. Fair enough. And what about *Valiant* — it was almost a house to us all? The yacht would become the sole property of W. K. In answer to my request, Harold would be allowed to "crew", but not for the upcoming America's Cup. He would be only 11. But *someday*. Yes. And his father *did* win the America's Cup Race of 1895, with his third yacht, *Defender*. Against UK Challenger *Valkyrie III* owned by the Earl of Dunraven. We were all very proud.

By February 5, Edmond Kelly had been chosen as our divorce referee and was hearing the case. On February 21, the case was actually heard in court.

Though the children were taking this very well, I was always concerned about them. I even allowed Consuelo to spend several weekends at Idlehour, but chaperoned by me, of course. I did not instruct the servants to intercept any communication with Winthrop, so I assumed several were made. But the two were together only at riding events or the usual seasonal social banquets and benefits, and then only briefly.

Consuelo felt that having her social debut that spring might prove embarrassing. The Vanderbilts, true to prediction, were ignoring us. They would, of course, not attend. But our good friend,

Belcourt's 13th century stained glass windows in its baronial hall.

Belcourt's oval dining room. Recessed ceiling lights by Thomas Alva Edison.

Original appearance of Belcourt
Castle's baronial fireplace.

Belcourt's ornate upper hall.

Rare photo of O.H.P. Belmont's country home Gray Craig.

Mr. and Mrs. Perry Belmont at Belcourt.

Painting of Oliver Hazard Perry Belmont by Benny Collin.

Painting of Alva Vanderbilt Belmont by Benny Collin.

1899 Belmont electric automobile rally. Ava Willing Astor (Mrs. John J. IV) and Harry Lehr.

August Belmont Stakes Trophy.

Alva, 1909, in mourning dress after 1908 death of O.H.P. Belmont.

Alva and Anna Howard Shaw at 1909 Marble House Suffragist Meeting.

Alva's office at 505 Fifth Avenue, National American Woman Suffrage Association, 1909.

Julia Ward Howe in wheelchair pushed by Alva,
at 1909 Meeting at Marble House.

Alva leading 1912 New York suffragist parade.

Rare photo of Alva, with signature, c. 1912.

Alva in veil and usual carefully chosen attire, c. 1914.

Alva, in veil, in front of Political Equality Association banner, 1914, Newport headquarters.

Alva at podium and Consuelo in corner of speaker's box, Marble House
Conference, 1914.

Original Chinese Teahouse, with participants in 1914 Marble House "Conference of Great Women."

Authentic interior of original Chinese Teahouse.

Suffragists listening to Chicago Judge Mary Bartleme.

Consuelo as guest of honor at Alva's 1914 "Conference of Great Women."

Alice Vanderbilt (Mrs. Cornelius) and daughter Countess László Széchényi.

Summer family picnic at Vanderbilt Mausoleum, New Dorp, Staten Island, N.Y.

Rehearsal for "Melinda and Her Sisters." Written, and produced at the Waldorf Astoria, 1916, by Alva (center, writing on pad). Music and lyrics by Elsa Maxwell (far right). Cast: Marie Dressler (forward, far left), Marie Doro (second from right); with other members Josephine Hull, Addison Mizener, Frances Alda, Maud Kahn, and Kitty Bache (possibly in group).

Alva during the final effort to obtain the vote, c. 1919.

Alva in final days of financing drive to get
the vote, c. 1919.

Alva, 1919, continues raising funds for the vote.

Alva's castle, Beacon Towers, Sands Point, L.I., site of National Woman's Party 1920 Conference.

Alva at 1922 opening of National Woman's Party headquarters, Washington, D.C.

Alva, as head of N.W.P., aboard
S.S. Aquitania, August, 1924.

Alva on one of her annual
returns to the U.S., c. 1924.

Alva during the 1925 U.S. visit,
sailing on the *S.S. Olympic*.

Alva with Alice Paul at N.W.P. headquarters, c. 1926.

Woodlawn Cemetery, N.Y., burial chapel for Alva and Oliver Hazard Perry Belmont.

Detail over entrance to Belmont burial chapel.

Interior of Belmont chapel, showing crypts and Maitland painted glass windows.
Architects: Hunt and Hunt.

John W. Mackay, Jr., felt he had a solution for this. He would give a dinner at the Hotel Waldorf, honoring Consuelo.

Carried off in the First Empire style, the affair was quite a success. Besides Consuelo and myself, those who attended included Mr. and Mrs. Ogden Mills and Mr. and Mrs. James A. Burden. Though the Burdens had married into the Vanderbilt family, they felt it was now most desirable that they come. And we were delighted. *The New York Times*, however, played down the event, to spare the other Vanderbilts unlikely embarrassment, by saying, "The dinner was in keeping with current fashion — a small dinner party with simple menus."

On March 5, 1895, the *Times* further reported, "Alva Vanderbilt won a decree of absolute divorce from W. K. Vanderbilt. Justice Barrett of the New York Supreme Court would have signed it earlier, but he was ill. When Edmond Kelly heard the case in court on February 21, he ruled that Mr. Vanderbilt was guilty of adultery and that Mrs. Vanderbilt was a capable mother, and had not committed adultery. The court concurred. The settlement gives Mrs. Vanderbilt custody of the three children: Consuelo (born March 2, 1877); W. K., Jr. (born October 6, 1878); and, Harold Stirling (born July 6, 1884). Mr. Vanderbilt may visit the children `at all proper times'. Mr. Vanderbilt is not allowed to remarry unless he marries outside New York State. Mrs. Vanderbilt probably gets the Fifth Avenue mansion, Marble House, and the Islip House, and three to ten million. In the decree, in the County Clerk's office, the name of Mrs. Vanderbilt's co-respondent does not appear. Mrs. Vanderbilt's lawyers were Joseph H. Choate, William H. Duer, and Colonel William Jay. Neither they nor W. K. Vanderbilt (in Europe), nor Mrs. Vanderbilt (at the Fifth Avenue mansion) would comment on the divorce. The court sealed the records, as is done in all divorce cases. When Mr. and Mrs. Vanderbilt were married 20 years ago, the match was generally looked upon with satisfaction on both sides. Mrs. Vanderbilt was Miss Alva Smith of Mobile, Alabama, and comes of one of the oldest families in the South. She came to New York with her mother and two sisters early in the seventies. They were at once received in the best circles, as their social connections were of the highest. Things seemed well until the November, 1893, *Valiant* cruise, which ended suddenly in March, 1894. Shortly afterwards, the Vanderbilts separated."

In the the *Times's* report, the co-respondent whose name did not appear was Miss Nellie Neustretter, a native of Eureka, Nevada. It seemed she had wandered to Paris after marrying and abandoning a cigar drummer in San Francisco. Always a gentleman, at least in society, Willie K. never questioned "his former wife's allegations". For this, I was very grateful to him. So was Oliver.

On March 8, the *Times* further reported, "Mrs. Alva E. Vanderbilt (the *first* time I was not referred to as Mrs. W. K. Vanderbilt) bought a house at 24 East 72nd and Madison in New York, for $250,000."

I did, indeed. We needed a place to live. It was a comedown from our Fifth Avenue mansion, but the children actually liked the intimacy of the house, plus not having so many stairs to climb to their bedrooms. With Willie K.'s being in Europe so often, the mansion at 660 would frequently stand vacant, but I did not regret my decision. I could never have afforded the necessary staff to run it. Not now.

Even though I was divorced and ensconced in a different house, I could not suddenly be entertaining Oliver. I felt it would not look right to the children. I decided to let *them* request to see him. And very soon they did. I realized they missed their father. But so did Oliver miss Willie K. — theyhad been close friends for too many years. But now, Oliver was marvelous about visiting Consuelo and Harold at home, and little Willie at school, plus taking all of them out driving in one or the other of his collection of carriages he had brought with him from Belcourt to the Belmont New York Stables. Consuelo liked the cabriolet, little Willie the curricle, and Harold preferred the spider phaeton. I stayed home. I did not want Oliver to be embarrassed in public by having reporters follow *any* of the three of us.

The time was too short. He was right, I was returning to Europe to continue the search for an eligible young man for Consuelo — in fact, the day after her eighteenth birthday. However, on her actual birthday, I had still planned a complete celebration.

The morning had been taken up with her receiving a staggering succession of floral offerings. Plus one perfect American Beauty rose, alone on its foliage. From, no doubt, the same man she was now *calling* her Rosenkavelier. I said nothing, nor had I prevented him from joining the afternoon bicycle ride I had planned for us and some of her friends along Riverside Drive. This was the latest thing in recreational events, and my eighteen-year-old was delighted. So was Winty, apparently. He took full advantage. I was shocked. I saw Oliver that night, reluctantly to tell him goodbye, of course, but now I had to also tell him the whole story.

"Consuelo and Winty pulled ahead. The rest of us were huffing and puffing behind. I could see him talking to her ardently. I think he proposed marriage. At least, Oliver, in their own eyes, they became engaged!"

"Then he must have agreed to follow her to Europe. And confront you, Alva."

"If so, I will consider him only as one more suitor."

"With a bad reputation. Why don't you tell Consuelo what you have found out?"

"I want her to dislike Winty on his own merits. Not on the ones I offer her. She will feel *my* objectives are very contrived, to say the least."

"They aren't. I checked on them myself."

"Really? Thank you, Oliver. I thought by exposing her to a lot of young men at all those European balls and debuts, she would learn to pick and choose naturally."

"But like her mother, she seems to have become a one-man woman."

"One at a *time*, that is! However, Oliver, I have not given up."

"I think you will have better luck this time. The young men have all been presented to Consuelo, and have had time to think it over."

"Also to find out how much she is worth."

"Exactly, Alva. They should be able to come to a definite decision: Their financial needs versus their ability to be a good husband."

"And all I need to do is referee?"

"Isn't that what you've *been* doing? And a very good job of it, I must say. Now zero in on the kill."

"The kill? Oliver, supposing Consuelo and Winty plan to elope when she returns home again?"

"Then I shall certainly have to tell her all about him!"

"But — elope? That may be another thing he told her on the bicycle ride today!"

"Did Consuelo's face glow?" He got an immediate nod from me. "Then you are undoubtedly right." Folding his arms in his typical manner, Oliver went on. "Does Winty, also, realize you are only one of five hundred mothers whose daughters are marrying foreign titles?"

"I suppose so, but Consuelo feels I am the most manipulative of all those mothers."

"Then I take it you are going to confiscate Winty's letters *and* hers and refuse to let him see her?"

"He is one suitor who will not take no for an answer."

Oliver took my hand and warned, "She will become very moody and hard to deal with."

"I will keep her busy with invitations to dinner, benefits, and balls."

"It will do no good, believe me."

"Except that it will allow me to again look over the field and finally choose a suitor for her. Tell me, Oliver, would you do the same for Natica?"

"Oh *that* young lady. Yes, yes. But my daughter is also going to choose the wrong man. I can feel it coming on."

"Why? You don't think her mother will exert the same influence I have?"

"More. Much more. And she will make sure that Natica does *not* marry someone who even remotely resembles her father!"

"Sara Whiting Belmont Rives is a fool. Natica's father is the most marvelous man in the whole world!"

"Bless you, my dear. But would you care to consider him as a suitor. For *you*?"

"I would consider no other."

"Ahhhhh. A girl who doesn't have to play the field to make up her mind."

"I love to play the field, but my mind has been made up for a long time."

Oliver took me in his arms. "Then I haven't a chance."

"No. You really haven't, Mr. Belmont."

"Then shall we set the date?"

"Yes! After the international-Consuelo-alliance has been completed. Finished. Over and done."

"And how long do you think that will take?"

"I will hurry it — in every way I can. Oliver, that look again. You want a deadline? After the first of the year?"

"That is ten whole months away. I can't endure. I shall never make it!"

"Oliver, dear. That is less than a year since my divorce."

"Bully for you. But not for me. I want my woman. I don't care *what* social etiquette says."

And from the way he kissed me, I knew that he meant it.

I realized I would have to hurry. And as Consuelo and I boarded the ship to sail for France the next day, I leaned over the railing and waved not only my hand but my whole arm at Oliver. I had already promised to write every day. I threw discreet kisses to further assure him. But as I watched the small, dark figure in the magnificent cape down below me, I felt the tears come. I loved this man. And it was not fair that Consuelo and I were sailing to Europe to find a suitor when I already had one at home and had to leave him!

Sensing this, Consuelo turned to me. "Maman, are you sure you really want to leave?"

"No, I am not."

Pleased that I at least admitted it, she grabbed my arm. "Then let's get off!"

"No, no. We can't."

"Mother!" She was calling me that for the first time. "Oliver may not be here when you get back."

"Oh, yes. And he will be the first one to meet the ship and greet us."

"As two *engaged* ladies, no doubt."

"I do hope so, Consuelo."

"But don't you realize we never need to leave the shores to do it? Maman, we are both engaged right now!"

I gasped. "You are?"

Consuelo caught herself, then finally nodded.

"That settles it. We go!"

At that moment, the ship began to pull away from the dock.

My daughter faced me squarely. "Mother, I am serious about this, does it occur to you that *you* may be the one who is actually taking a chance?"

I could not answer.

As I watched the figure of my Oliver move farther and farther away from me, I had to feel she was *not* right. I had to hope we would still be in love. And I had to believe it would be — forever ....

17

THE FINAL FIND

W HEN WE RETURNED TO PARIS, I INDEED TRIED
to interest Consuelo in visits to churches and museums and attendance at lectures and concerts. But
she was like an automaton. Even when I took her to
the best salons to try on clothes, I felt I was unfortunately the one
who had to go ahead and choose which dresses she might prefer —
if she was *ever* to assemble a wardrobe.

And I had to do even more. As Oliver predicted, I allowed no
communication with Winthrop Rutherford even when he followed
us to Paris and attempted to see me, to ask for her hand in marriage,
I was told. None.

Consuelo got even with me. She refused to enjoy her social debut
in Paris. As a result, I soon felt it was high time to move on to
London.

There the Duke and Duchess of Sunderland gave a grand ball at
Stafford House. Consuelo seemed to come alive when the young
Ninth Duke of Marlborough wrote his name on her card several
times to claim dances with her. She had not seen him since the
dinner at Lady Paget's the previous year.

The Duke did more than dance with my daughter, he invited us
for a weekend at Blenheim Palace. Having talked about it earlier, I
was still surprised but very pleased. We went out to Oxford by train
and were met there by his steward, carriage, and horses. We then
began the drive to the Palace.

It seemed the Duke was in residence alone. His two unmarried
sisters sometimes stayed with him, but not his mother, Lady
Blandford. She had divorced his father after many years of unhappiness, and the Eighth Duke had married an American. That lady
was Mrs. Lillian Hammersley. She was wealthy enough to install

central heating and electric lights throughout his Blenheim Palace.

That should have told me something about other Dukes of Marlborough right then and there. But it didn't. I had to learn it years later on my own.

On this visit, as we approached through the magnificent grounds, our carriage entered a park through a stone arch. A porter in livery, complete with wand and tassel, stood at attention. There before us was the great house. Below and to the right was an ornamental lake spanned by a monumental bridge. We turned into a fine avenue of elms and passed through another arch leading into a court. Along with what appeared to be offices and a porter's lodge, I recognized hothouses.

I had heard that, formerly, these plant sanctuaries were a gallery which housed a collection of the sensuous works of Titian. The ladies of the household were never allowed to view these paintings. In fact, the gallery was kept locked. So, when the whole place was eventually destroyed by fire, the ladies very much regretted the loss of the Titians, but felt secretly and fully revenged.

Passing through still another stone arch, we drove into the central court. To the north, in the open area, Consuelo and I could see the monument to the First Duke, who so brilliantly won the Battle of Blenheim. We were aware trees were planted around this very tall monument, in the order in which the British regiments stood at the opening of the Battle of Blenheim. Otherwise, we realized there was no connection with it, much to the confusion of visitors, we presumed.[16]

From the monument-column, the High Park sloped gently down in glades of varied greens to the lake. There were great oaks, some being over a thousand years old. One oak was given the credit for hiding Alfred of Wessex from the Vikings, for the park had been part of the Royal Forest of Woodstock. There was also the well of Fair Rosamond, named after a king's love. Nearby was a High Lodge, where the Earl of Rochester, a wicked High Ranger to Charles the Second, had taken his pleasure. This High Lodge was a small house, with what must be a lovely view over the park and surrounding country. We were told it was now used only for picnic luncheons when the gentlemen of the Palace hunted pheasants and rabbits in the park.

We turned around and walked to the main entrance of the palace and up the steps. The doors opened onto an immense hall with a domed ceiling. Craning our necks, we tried to see the Great Duke, dressed in a Roman toga, driving a chariot. Consuelo immediately leaned over to me and inquired, "Is he hurrying through those clouds to join Julius Caesar, or Alexander the Great, *or* Napoleon?"

Hoping no one had heard, I smiled stiffly, but was really pleased and relieved that my daughter at least had her caustic sense of humor back.

Consuelo seemed delighted to become a true tourist. Though there were attendants around, the red baize druggets were a welcome boundary to tell her and others where they must walk. I hated those boundaries. Weren't we the Duke's special guests? Why didn't we receive a special and unguarded tour?

But Consuelo continued to be quite happy to wander on, room by room, into the great Saloon. I followed at a distance, so she would be unable to make further curt remarks. But I was unsuccessful. On the walls of the great Saloon, we saw the French murals painted there by Laguerre, amusing renditions of the First Duke and his household. All of them were "falling out of the picture" and joining the imaginary persons at the long and stately dining table.

"Maman, do you think they are friendly, curious, or only hungry?"

Again I hoped the attendants nearby did not overhear. I suggested we move on to the drawing rooms stretching in vistas on either side of the Saloon. And on to the far west side of the palace where the Long Library seemed to stretch forever. I observed the many bookshelves, but was surprised to find that many of them were empty. At that point I did not know that the Eighth Duke had sold the fabulous 18,000 volume Sunderland Library *and* the white, carved bookcases, in order to pay the costs he felt necessary to equip his laboratories for his chemical and electrical experiments.

But this did not get past Consuelo. She raised a brow and remarked, "Don't these people read? I wonder if there will be any books in our guest rooms? If we intend to read ourselves to sleep, we may have to go to the local village library to obtain even a single volume!"

I blushed, but she was right. However, I was able to direct her attention down the room to the massive pipe organ I was told had been installed by the Eighth Duke. I immediately observed this organ's size was in wrong proportion to the room, but I realized it would probably never be corrected, and I had better not point this out, or I might set off Consuelo on some *other* observation uttered in her usual broad enigmatic style!

182

At this moment, the young Ninth Duke and his sisters, Lady Lillian and Lady Norah Spencer-Churchill, joined us. A tea table had been set in front of one of the mantelpieces in the Saloon. Young gentlemen friends of the Duke joined us, as well, and we all had tea. Even with these many people, we were still a small number of souls lost in the huge, ranging rooms of this Palace.

After dinner in the family quarters in the east and opposite end of Blenheim, we again traversed the long hall to listen to an organist from Birmingham play that still over-sized organ in the Long Library. I thought him to be quite competent, but Consuelo evidenced the usual restlessness. She had inherited it; all the Vanderbilts were known for their fidgets. So we were happy to finally be able to go to our guest rooms upstairs. Blenheim was truly magnificent, but, we found, quite exhausting.

The following day was Sunday, so I asked if I might see the chapel and be allowed to worship there. The Duke immediately agreed, but announced that he would be showing Consuelo the terraces and the fountains of the Palace instead. I wondered why.

As I moved into the great chapel, alone, I gazed for many moments before realizing why the Duke was happy to leave me alone here. The inscriptions on the tombs told me that the entire first line of heirs of the Marlborough family had tragically died. This meant that the Marlborough line had to shift to the Churchills, the Spencers, and the Sunderlands. The sarcophagus of each member of the family was overwhelming to me. I said my best Episcopal prayers of sympathy in front of each one. I then sat in one of the pews and conducted my own private Sunday service. Realizing that the family had apparently all worshiped earlier, I did not expect a special service to be conducted for me.

Even this did not dispel my sorrow for the family, and I finally rose and returned outside to take my own diverting tour of the terraces and their fountains.

I was pleased when lunch was announced, and all of us gathered at the outdoor dining area attached to the family quarters. This luncheon was served to only the three of us. Once again, I heard the Duke pronounce that he would be spending the afternoon taking Consuelo on a tour of, first, the formal gardens, then the working farm, the rolling land, the lake from its various angles, and, finally, the surrounding village of Bladon, with its lovely old church and gray stone cottages, which we both had noticed on the journey in.

I only hoped the allegiance of the villagers would *not* prompt

Consuelo to make a speech about what her favorite political econo-mists, Gladstone and John Bright, were now saying about the "rights of man." She would no doubt observe, "Are the villagers receiving the same rights?"

Obviously, I was not asked to go along, so the Duke would have to take his chances. I hoped that he might discount all her remarks, in favor of the prospect of marrying an American heiress. If not, the possibility of at least trying to change the *mind* of one?

I amused myself the entire afternoon by retracing my steps through the Palace. I could identify all architectural tradition, but I was very upset that Sir John Vanbrugh had decided to design the great hall without a grand staircase. To me this was a terrible mistake. What Duchess of Marlborough would not wish to descend a grand staircase in the best of all her finery? What Duke would not care to accompany her? Vanbrugh had decided to sacrifice all this for the true impression of overwhelming space in the great hall. And the ability to gaze at the ceiling murals without the interrup-tion of a staircase. I still felt he was wrong, and I decided never to forgive him. If my daughter ever became Duchess of this Palace, I intended for her to have the most exquisite of wardrobes, and I certainly wished that she would have the ultimate in a chance to show it off.

After several hours, when Consuelo returned, riding beside the Duke, she descended to take me aside and tell me that he was really amused by her. He thought her witty. Whatever she had said to him as a political extremist, he had apparently only taken with a grain of salt and discounted in favor of more earthly gains.

I was hoping they might even be somewhat in love. If so, I could only feel relieved that at last my search was over!

Still cognizant of the many American girls who were exchanging their money for a European title, at this moment, I hoped the Duke's attentions to my daughter were nonetheless more special. He might be thinking of her as the new mistress of this great house and its entire estate—Consuelo only, as the Ninth Duchess of Marlborough.

What more could I ask? Was I not overwhelmed, though critical, of this great creation of Sir John Vanbrugh? Wasn't I the most appreciative-of-architects? At least for an American woman? And didn't I understand gardens and fountains and landscaping — from attending all the World's Fairs and Expositions, if nothing more? And wasn't I possibly the most knowledgeable American person regarding period furnishings who had ever walked into this

Palace? Furthermore, wasn't I thoroughly impressed with them? So what was more natural than for me to want my daughter to be *equally* impressed and appreciative?

To this end, I quietly took the Duke aside and invited him to visit the Vanderbilt mansion in Newport, our Marble House. And as soon as convenient; perhaps this August?

The Ninth Duke of Marlborough said he would think it over and give me his official answer.

As Consuelo and I ascended the side staircase, off of the great hall, she immediately asked me what I had been saying to the Duke. I had learned my lesson, I waited until we got into our guest rooms before I replied. "I asked His Grace if he would do us the favor of a visit to Newport."

Consuelo looked at me. "But I don't *want* the Duke to come to Marble House!"

"How else are we going to give him the same chance he is now giving us?"

"I don't care if he has a chance!"

"It is only proper."

"I think the owner just wants to show off her mansion and how much *she* knows about European architecture and French decoration."

"That is probably true. But I think Richard Morris Hunt and I taught *America* a few things."

"The Duke will not be impressed — believe me, Mother."

I looked at her. Consuelo was calling me Mother again — she must be serious. "Why do you say that?"

"He is very haughty. He will never think that we have enough tradition in our family to equal even *half* of his."

"And the Duke will be right. But the U. S. is a much younger country."

"That won't make any difference to him. Look at his father. What did *he* do? He married an American woman for her money. *Not* for her sense of architecture or decor."

"A Hammersley is not a Vanderbilt."

Consuelo raised her brows at me. "You are still calling yourself a Vanderbilt, Mother?"

"I was a Vanderbilt when I built Marble House."

"You are really a Smith."

"But I had a *lot* to live up to, my daughter."

"And you did it very well. But that is all over now. You and father are divorced."

"Nothing has changed. Marble House will welcome the Duke, just as it does everyone else."

"But father is not standing at the front entrance."

"He can entertain the Duke at 660, if he wishes."

"More likely aboard our *Valiant*. It seems the Duke is fascinated with American yachts."

"In that case, your father will entertain him royally!"

Consuelo sat on the edge of the bed and stared at the wall. "Mother, as far as you and father are concerned, I still do not think it is fair for everyone to be saying you divorced him on the grounds of adultery."

"I did."

"Oh, no. It was really over a disagreement about me. He wanted his Consuelo to marry Winty Rutherfurd. And you wanted me to marry a European title!"

"It doesn't look as though you are going to marry *anyone* — until you can learn to return a social favor."

"Obligation, mother. Obligation. And I would stop the whole relationship with the Duke right here and now. No more attentions from him. Not another moment of being indebted."

"Do you think he would understand?"

"Yes!"

"Really? He would think it was a great rebuke. And he would be right."

"I will tell him I am betrothed to someone else."

"You are *not* betrothed until that young man has asked your father for your hand in marriage."

"I am sure Winty has!"

"And since your father and I are divorced, he must also ask *me*."

"But you never let him do it!"

"That is correct. I wished to come to London and see what opportunities were here."

"I don't care about any opportunities, except the one to become Mrs. Winthrop Rutherfurd."

I sighed and studied her for several moments. "I sometimes wonder if you have really asked yourself what that would be like."

"I have asked myself that a thousand times."

"Not the *real* question, Consuelo. Would he be true to you? I say no. He is too much older. He has been linked with too many other women. He will go back to them, particularly back to the ones who were very special to him."

"I don't believe it."

"I feel those women may be more sophisticated, but none will be more intelligent. You are better educated and better informed than any woman he has ever known. And that is what makes me so afraid. This will not mean very much to Winty. He will look for the typical American wife. The dear doll who will not interfere with his life but will always be available to charm, amuse, comfort, and sleep with him."

"I will do all that."

"No, Consuelo. Think what doing that will mean. He will be attentive at first. Then he will begin to drift away and to make excuses. He will go off for his riding weekends and not take you with him. Remember, he is not much of a lawyer, so his presence won't be required on a regular basis in New York City. He will probably prefer to put you up in a country place — some house his family has left behind on Long Island. And there you will sit, while he goes about his life in town and his life on and off his favorite horses."

"No." Consuelo stood up and began moving aimlessly about the room. "We *are* in love."

"Perhaps for now."

"What makes you think the *Duke* would treat me any better?"

"Well, he can't *mistreat* you. Consuelo Vanderbilt will be the Duchess of Marlborough. You will have a *position* in this world."

"But always subordinate to his?"

"Married women in Europe have a much different status than married women in the United States."

"Perhaps as far as tradition is concerned, Maman. But I am sure that many of them are much worse off."

"In what way?"

"They are neglected and abused. Quietly. With tradition and respectability behind both kinds of treatment."

"Consuelo, no. I am staking these next few months — just as I have staked the last few — that a European marriage to the right person is the best thing for you, the best thing for *any* American girl!"

"Mother. A bad husband is a bad husband."

"*Look* what you are perhaps being offered. You don't want to be the mistress of this Blenheim Palace?"

"No."

"You don't wish to be the Ninth Duchess of Marlborough, to follow the tradition of all of those former duchesses?"

"Not Lady Blandford. Look how she was treated."

"The Eighth Duke simply chose the maintenance and improvement of the Palace over her."

"How do you know this Ninth Duke won't do the same thing?"

"I don't. But we have to give him the chance not to."

"At *my* expense."

"Perhaps. But you can always get a divorce, my dear."

"Do you think so? If he is receiving money from the Vanderbilts each year, he is not apt to give his American heiress a divorce!"

"But you are damning him without ever giving him an opportunity to be honorable!"

The door opened. The argument between us had to terminate at this point. One of the servants was carrying a note on a silver tray. He offered it to me. He then bowed, returned to the hall, and closed the door after him. I slowly opened the envelope. The note inside was an acceptance "to visit the W. K. Vanderbilt home in Newport, Rhode Island." Signed by His Grace, Charles Richard John Spencer-Churchill, Duke of Marlborough.

18

GOODBYE TO MY MAGNIFICENT
RICHARD MORRIS HUNT

W HEN CONSUELO, HAROLD, MY SERVANTS, and I arrived in New York, on July 5, 1895, aboard the *Lucania*, we went directly to the Murray Hill Hotel. And on to Newport.

For the next three weeks, we did exactly what I said we would do. Prepare for the visit of the Duke of Marlborough. I with great enthusiasm, Consuelo with none. Her attitude was a daily damper, and there were times when I wished Winthrop Rutherfurd would announce himself at the front door of Marble House. Then all three of us could have a royal battle, terminate his attentions forever, and get on with our daily lives! But Winty always preferred to hover "in the wings". It was maddening. Particularly insofar as Consuelo's father was aboard his *Valiant*, anchored in Newport Harbor. Was Winthrop staying with him? Were all three scheming together against me?

On top of all this, I was frequently at the bedside of Richard Morris Hunt. He and Catherine as usual were summering at their Hilltop Cottage in Newport. But the most important thing in the world right now was the fact that my beloved Mr. Hunt was ill. It was his second severe attack of gout in a year. Though pain was always present, he still tried to conduct his business. But he was now doing it from his bedside.

Mrs. Ogden Goelet was demanding of his time in the construction of their Newport mansion, Ochre Court. And Alice frequently made him miserable in changing her mind on the building she and Cornelius were doing of The Breakers. George Washington Vanderbilt was making his own demands — on the emerging towers of his Biltmore "Castle" in Asheville, North Carolina. In addition to this, Mr. Hunt was doing the Naval Observatory in Washington, D.C., and had projects going at Cleveland, West Point, and the Fogg Museum at Cambridge. Though he had his usual capable assistants, he still employed a small staff, in his continued belief in maintaining an atelier.

Because of her concern for her husband, Catherine summoned a doctor from Philadelphia; but, on examination, he felt R. M. H. would recover and had many creative years ahead of him. I heard about this and was delighted.

I again went to visit the Hunts. Receiving me as usual, lying on the sofa in the Morning Room of Hilltop Cottage, Mr. Hunt accepted my gift of flowers and his favorite summer fig preserves I had asked one of my French chefs to prepare for him.

"Alva." He doffed his hand to me. "With all you have to do, you come to see me. I have said it many times. I am saying it again. You are a wonder!"

"In spite of all of those arguments you and I had when we built 660 Fifth and then Marble House?"

"My dear, there are arguments and arguments. The ones with you were different. I admit we were often eye to eye and nose to nose over materials, or window placement, or the quality of gold leaf on the interiors. Remember? Especially whether the entrance hall was grand enough, or if the marble staircase took exactly the right curve? Alva, these were all structural questions. You *knew* what you were talking about. You never let go as some of my lady clients did, and waved your arms and described some whim you had seen used on somebody else's house. Never. Your requests were always carefully thought out. It was the W. K. Vanderbilt house we were dealing with. Nothing else."

I appreciated this so deeply I could only nod my thanks.

Catherine came to his side. "As his wife, I agree, Alva. And why? Because I was the one who always had to listen to how he felt at the end of a day. At what was said at the office, or on the job. And by whom. What was wise and what was nonsense. Richard never once reported anything Alva Vanderbilt had said as nonsense."

"Thank you, Catherine." I felt the tears coming. "But I would do anything in the world to help the two of you now. Mop your floors, change your beds, get your meals, read to you. Richard, I would remove your pain, this very instant, and let it be mine."

"I know, my darling."

"You have tried so many times to do this — for me." Again, I was speaking of those four years from 1888 to 1892 when we were planning and then doing the construction of Marble House. I could never seem to understand why Willie K. was so untrue to me. I had fulfilled my part of the marriage contract. Why hadn't he?

Catherine could see I was crying. She walked around behind me and leaned my head back against her breast. "Even though your pains *were* heartaches, Alva, Richard would have done the same thing for *you*, if he could. You know that." She kissed the top of my hair.

Resting against her was like resting against my mother. After those early obstreperous years of mine, a different relationship began with my mother. And she always held me so that I could see straight ahead. I think she knew it was necessary for me. Catherine instinctively did the same thing.

I could thus still gaze into Richard's eyes. I could see they seemed so tired. So weary of pain. So weary of just being weary.

"The doctor said you will get well. He even pronounced that you will build many more beautiful houses and great public structures."

"He's young. Why discourage him with the truth?"

"You won't? What about, for one, the Naval Observatory?"

"Not as great as the Yerkes Observatory for the University of Chicago."

"Perhaps not, Richard, but the *building* will be."

"Think so?" He gave me a twinkle of appreciation. "But this old body of mine is tired. Catherine and I attended the wedding of Adele Sloane and William Burden. It rained. When I came back, my clothes were wet. Even traveling from Massachusetts to New York was enough. I got this *second* awful attack."

"Perhaps nature was trying to tell you to slow down."

"How could I? On top of everything else, Mrs. Astor and her son were getting nervous about *their* house. It was nearing final completion, and things had to be checked. Then, in March, we wanted to get to Washington to see Kitty and Livingston's new son — after all, that grandson of ours was born in August of last year!"

Catherine was amused and went on to remind him. "And don't forget the next thing — Sargent wanted to paint your portrait. At Biltmore, no less."

"Ah yes. And he couldn't understand why I kept falling asleep."

Catherine turned to me, "So Richard said, 'Then paint me with my eyes closed!'"

I laughed and remarked, "I'm jealous, Catherine. I've always wanted him to at least have a photo, standing beneath his medallion at Marble House."

Richard raised a finger. "Alva. Not unless the medallion of Hardouin-Mansart and the bust of Louis XIV are in full view!"

All three of us laughed. But I could see even that act was painful for Richard.

I tried to keep the small talk at a minimum. "I will engage a photographer. So we *must* get you well."

"And I must remember that Alva Vanderbilt is a very determined lady."

"You don't believe Catherine and I can do it?"

"No. I'm like that rag — the one everybody is singing now." And he spoke the words of Ben Harney's "You've Been a Good Old Wagon, but You've Done Broke Down."

"A very amusing song, but, Richard, it isn't true of *you*."

As though being tired of explaining, he surprised me by changing the subject. "Tell me — I honestly don't know. Who won the Belmont Stakes this year?"

"Belmar. He also won the Preakness."

"Really? And how is Oliver? I understand the Belmonts are also saving the country these days."

"Oh? You must mean that $62 million in gold. Yes, Oliver's brother and J. P. Morgan, together sold it to the U. S. Treasury. Our dear government has gold reserves again." I studied him. "Richard, you are not answering my question."

"Which one?"

"Don't you believe you will get well?"

"Alva, listen. It seems I get well only to get sick again."

I was now really alarmed. "But Richard Morris Hunt, listen to me. The world cannot get along without you!"

"It will do very well. Catherine has given me three sons. Our Dick and Joe can carry on — and someday even Herb."

I sang out. "And Kitty and Esther!"

"Ah, yes, Alva. Always the champion of women, whether they're our daughters or not. I dare say someday you will make this country hear about it."

"I have no plans."

"As yet."

Catherine patted my shoulders. "Richard feels the same way about women as you do. He has told many people, Alva, how impressed he is with your broad grasp of architecture and especially your intellect."

"My intellect!"

Richard reached for my hand. "Indeed. Exactly what I have said."

I held that magnificent hand of his, the hand which had drawn so many lines that took structural form. That hand I had bent over and watched countless times as we studied his drawings for the houses he had done, both for W.K. and me and for Oliver.

I became intentionally formal. I could not help it. "Mr. Hunt lies here before me and tells me about his three sons. But he has more. The products of his atelier. His architectural sons include Henry Van Brunt, Frank Furness, Charles B. Gambrill, George B. Post, and William R. Ware, no less!"

"I am proud of *all* my boys, Alva. You are right, my dear. Again."

Returning to Richard's side, Catherine smiled at me. "It is so kind of you to say so."

Richard tugged at my hand. "And you are a third daughter, my dear. And if you were a man, certainly one of my architectural sons!"

"Oh thank you!"

"As I have told you many times, you should be a member of the American Institute of Architects."

"And, as I have said many times, I have had no formal training."

"Oh come, you spent as many hours in my studio as those architects you named did."

Catherine cut in. "That is an argument neither of you will ever win." I felt this was my cue. I stood and held her close. Then I moved to Richard. I bent over and I kissed him. I longed to hold him close, but I could only hold his hand. And finally I had to even kiss it in farewell. All three of us said nothing as I departed — slowly.

By the next day, I hoped beyond hope that his Philadelphia doctor was right. I kept in close touch. Days of recovery proved him right. Then one day Richard began to fail rapidly. Catherine telegraphed Dick. He hurried up from New York. He came in time to have a few last hours with his father.

Richard Morris Hunt died about noon on July 31, 1895.

We were told the news. I was stunned. Consuelo tried to comfort me. I gave her my appreciation. But where was there comfort for *such* a blow? For such a loss? Even from a daughter who suddenly felt sympathy for me.

Catherine wrote a note, informing me that the funeral would be held at Newport's Trinity Church, and asking, "Alva dear, would you be so gracious as to do our family a favor? Would you come previous to the service and arrange the floral pieces around Richard's bier?"

I wrote back that I would be honored.

My grief had to now transform itself into strength in order to perform this last thing I could do for this beloved man.

On the day of the funeral, as I arrived at the church, flowers were still being brought in, both by footmen who were attached to particular families and by the employees of local florist shops. I left each card as it was, tied to every piece, but I read it carefully.

I was determined all flowers would be arranged in a harmonious display of color — only color — and not by the importance of the family who sent them. Surprisingly, no one argued with me. As I worked, I blessed Catherine's heart. She must have given specific instructions that the decision was to be completely mine.

The casket was open. When I picked up the first spray of flowers and approached Richard's body, I wondered if I would drop every blossom and begin to weep, again. Finally, I had to gaze down at this man. True, he was now free from pain. But he seemed to lie there in a kind of false peace. I had always known Richard when he was discussing details, making decisions, and hurrying from one assignment to the next. This very still body was one I had never seen. It was an unnatural pose.

Somehow this fact seemed very unfair to me. I knew it would seem even more unfair to him. I was only able to continue with my job by feeling that Richard Morris Hunt was actually annoyed and impatient, and was, therefore, somewhere else and as active as ever. It was truly as if I were arranging flowers around some kind of a mask or around a bust of him or some artistic, carved full figure he had sent to his own funeral, to be laid perfunctorily in the casket, because he was much too busy to attend.

This interpretation further sustained me. When I completed the laying of the last spray in this tier upon tier of love for this man, I stood back. I now knew the color emphasis had been the right one. The eye could travel in a soft sweep of appreciation, and not in a checkerboard hierarchy of notation. I even wished he could have interrupted that schedule and have been right there with me to enjoy it.

As I continued to gaze, I still somehow expected some florist or some important vestryman to tap my shoulder and say, "You are all wrong, Mrs. Vanderbilt. We will have to postpone the funeral and rearrange the whole thing!" Perhaps only then, Richard Morris Hunt would come back to say, "Leave her alone. She always knows what she wants."

But no one objected, and Richard did not need to come. Catherine later wrote me a note, saying that she could not have approved more.

Right now, the guests were arriving, and I took my place among them. I was comforted by the presence of Consuelo and Harold, and we sat together. Willy had come in a few moments earlier, with his father. They sat nearby. I noticed and nodded my gratitude for their presence, as well. I did not know if they had come up to Newport by train, or if *Valiant* was still in port, but, at that moment, I did not care. I honored the appreciation of all of us for this dear architect. Every one of us realized how important he had been in the entire family life of the W. K. Vanderbilts.

Consuelo looked over at me. She had not seen me when I dressed and left the house. She was now appraising what I was wearing. It was not black; it was a dark green with chartreuse trimmings. Only my hat and its feathers, my gloves, and my shoes were black. Consuelo seemed surprised, but she approved. Even Harold looked over and smiled. I assumed Willie K. and Willie liked it also, but I felt I should not glance over and ascertain this. Certainly now now.

We were all then soothed by a special musical program which was prepared of Hunt's favorites — from the world of symphony, chorale works, hymns, opera, and current ballads. Needless to say, in his usual excellent taste. Church hymns had their place but not one of dominance here. I was proud of his family for doing that. And I even expected to hear Richard's favorite rag, but it was not included. I was rather sorry.

His obituary was impressive in its factual computation. If the rector had simply abbreviated his architectural accomplishments, it would still have rung out with great familiarity in the ears of those present, for the pews were filled with not only his neighbors, but with professional colleagues and associates from his various societies and organizations.

Pallbearers included Martin Brimmer, Henry G. Marquand, the great Charles F. McKim, Joseph H. Choate, Sidney Webster, Maurice Fornachon, and his student, George B. Post. An incredible tribute from the men of his very own world!

Burial took place in the Island Cemetery at Newport. I noted it was not far from the Belmont Chapel and Memorial. And near the Ledyard, Russell, and Marquand monuments. Mr. Hunt had designed all of these. Catherine must have felt he would be at home here.

Many days later, I could not give up my feeling that he was still alive and somewhere else. I decided I must finally face the fact that my magnificent Richard had truly died. So I made a trip to the cemetery. Alone. His marker had already been put in place. It was an austere piece, two slabs of highly polished dark granite. I read the dates — October 31, 1827 — July 31, 1895. Then the words, "Laborare est Orare."

I somehow felt Richard believed cemetery-marker-design would progress to this simplicity, and he wished to be in the vanguard, even in death. He also wished to be only a *part* of a large plot, in which the other members of the family could someday join him.[17]

I stood looking at Richard's grave until my heart grew heavy and I wished to sit down. There was a low concrete wall which bordered the large plot, but I preferred to sit on the edge of Richard's marker. The center rectangular section was raised, and it was as though he had purposely left me a comfortable area on which to sit and had even given me a proper place to lean back.

I put my hand on the gray marble. Yes, it was cold. And I still resented its being there. It was not fair to imprison a man so needed in the world. His vision was not a moral one; he did not care to elevate anyone. Nor did he wish to reform them. He only wished to bring them coherence and order. Richard felt any individual could more fully realize his own self in an atmosphere of beauty. He wished to reduce the crassness and roughness too often apparent in the America of that day. He established no school of architecture. There was no special style identified with him. He could see the worth of all styles, and he used them. He followed his *own* artistic vision. As I sat there, a long time, I had to realize eventually the body of Richard Morris Hunt was truly dead. But what he *believed* could never be contained in this cold and formal structure. It was all out there in the world — alive — to be lived in, worked in, and experienced.

Even if some day, despite all the future recognition Richard Morris Hunt would receive, some grasping persons saw fit to tear down his structures, their existence would endure beyond the wrecking ball. Our three family homes at Oakdale, New York, and Newport all had a life of their own. The W. K. Vanderbilt family simply participated. It was true — Richard created beauty, so that each of *us* could grow and create. Even though the relationship of Willie K. and myself had led to a permanent separation, the houses themselves were never at fault. They had kept all of us together as long as possible. Without them, we could not have sustained recognition for the Vanderbilt family, nor kept any solid orientation for our own personal lives.

A division of property would mean that I could call only Marble House my own. But what a house! Hadn't Richard always felt it was his best? Even now, wasn't it protecting me in this period of personal transition? And wasn't it now giving our daughter a chance to be nationally and internationally recognized?

Richard's favorite house had only *begun* to live.

I stood up and backed away from the great gray marker. I could come there again, but right now I must go, and live in, and sustain what Richard had created for me. Each time I returned, until the day of my own death, I could lay a bouquet of flowers on the tomb of Richard Morris Hunt. It could become a ceremony for me.

And it did.

But I knew this man was increasingly somewhere else — out there — letting me live a fuller and fuller life by surrounding me with the beauty of his own belief.

19

THE REAL GAMBLE

MY COMMEMORATION OF RICHARD MORRIS Hunt led directly to action. The visit of the Ninth Duke of Marlborough was the goal of every day of preparation. I planned a fête in his honor. Consuelo had still had no formal American debut, and probably never would, at this point. So the fête must be a special one not only to introduce the Duke to Newport society but to also announce that the absent W. K. Vanderbilt and I had a daughter eligible to enter the social ranks, to be engaged, and even to marry a European title.

I began to plan invitations, a guest list, a menu, flowers, entertainment, and favors, particularly some $5,000 worth, which I had already purchased in Paris. I realized favors were really keepsakes.

Afraid that she might run away, I asked Consuelo not to leave the house unaccompanied. But there was a second reason: I was receiving hate-letters that my daughter's marriage settlement would take too much money out of the country. It eventually would drain U. S. resources because too many American girls were doing it!

I depended on glimpses of Oliver to keep up my courage. Riding down Bellevue on his coach, I again could see his skill in guiding the proud Rockingham and Hurlingham. Oliver's carriages were copies, designed in France, the very ones I had always loved in the pictures of Carle Vernet and the drawings of Guys. Whenever Oliver turned into my driveway, I was proud to realize I would one day be a partner, on the seat beside him.

But all this courage came to an end after one of the summer's evening parties. Winthrop Rutherfurd had been present and had danced long enough with Consuelo to apparently assure her the two of them were still engaged. When we returned to Marble House, I requested she come to my bedroom. She did and immediately asserted she had a right to choose her own husband. At this late stage, after searching for *two years*, and finally making preparations for the visit of the best of these selections, I went into a rage.

I said too much. The next day I was extremely upset about it. Mrs. William Jay was staying with us. Dear Lucy was not only my best friend but the wife of my attorney. Unfortunately, she *also* went to Consuelo. And said too much. I was shocked.

I needed to see Oliver. As he arrived that night, we hurried into the library to talk. Before he would listen to a word, he had to fling his cape off for me — a necessary ceremony with Oliver. Though I loved it, I let him know I also needed all the sympathetic affection he could give me.

"Of course, Alva, my dear, but what now?"

"Consuelo danced with Winthrop at the party last night. They feel they are still engaged!"

"Party? And I was not invited?"

"Oliver, it was not your kind of party."

"Then I will have to give one that *is*. For the Duke. *After* your fête, of course."

"Good. I am burning for him to see how an American gentleman can live in his own individual style."

"With horses! Did I tell you my two brothers are scandalized? Only darling little Mo was amused."

"Your mother died much too early — she and I could have become great friends."

"She always admired you. So, Alva, when can you and I get married?"

"One wedding at a time."

"But the Duke has *not* yet proposed."

"And Consuelo, naturally, is pleased …. Oliver she has learned nothing."

"All right, my dear. Did you tell her there is a rumor Winthrop Rutherfurd can have no children?"

"Yes."

"And that people whisper there is madness in the family?"

"Yes. But she doesn't believe either one."

"Does she know he had an affair with a married woman?"

"She is still convinced he is in love with only *her*."

"Alva, I saw Willie K. at a club the other day. He says Winty has never approached *him* about Consuelo."

"And Winty has never approached *me*."

"I can see why you are furious."

"I was in such a rage that I told her I would not hesitate to shoot any man I thought would ruin her life!"

"Shoot him?"

"I said it. I did!"

Amused, Oliver pointed his finger at me. "And of course you are *such* a skilled marksman."

"I am willing to buy a gun and learn."

"We'll see. What else was said?"

"Consuelo asked if I shot Winthrop and went to prison for it, would *she* be responsible?"

"And promptly went to her room and didn't climb out the window?"

"Apparently not; she appeared at breakfast. But yesterday Lucy Jay told her I had a heart attack, and the doctor had to be called. Oliver, it wasn't true."

"You had a perfect right."

"But Consuelo believed it. She then asked Lucy to let Winthrop know she could not marry him."

"Your daughter is that much concerned with your well-being? Ah hah. Then you must be concerned with *hers*."

I stared. "Oliver. I am!"

"Alva, since you were an obstreperous young lady, as you were growing up, you must give Consuelo the same chance."

"Chance?"

"Give Winty and Consuelo a third chance to elope. I, myself, gave them the first chance at my Gray Craig Park party. They didn't do it. The party you described gave them a second chance. They didn't do it. I am giving a party at Belcourt on August 30 for the Duke. Winty will again be invited."

"Oliver! And you *still* want me to become Mrs. O. H. P. Belmont?"

"All right, then, Alva. Word will be sent out that I am ill. But I will schedule a *second* one for September 2."

There was nothing to do but laugh. I did until I had to sit down. Oliver sat right beside me.

"My darling, don't you see? If they do not elope *this* time, Consuelo hasn't a leg to stand on. And neither has Winty. It simply means — you know what."

"That Winty feels if he whisks her away, he will lose all claim to Vanderbilt money?"

"Yes."

I stared at him for several moments ….

"I have believed this for a very long time."

"So, if the Duke proposes, Consuelo should accept!"

"Oliver, I love you."

"I know it." He kissed me and made it obvious for both of us.

I suddenly drew back. "But wait! On August 29, the Wilsons are having a big evening affair. The Duke, Consuelo, and I have been invited. And I am sure Winty will be there. He and young Wilson are friends."

"Good, let's make my party the *fourth* chance. Then you can be absolutely sure!"

"I may survive the Wilson's party, but not yours."

"Oh yes you will. Alva, you have as much sporting blood in you as any of us Belmont have."

"You think so? That is a great compliment."

During the next few days, Oliver and I both did a great deal of thinking, but the decision was still the same.

The Duke arrived on August 23, 1895. *The New York Times* reported "The 24-year-old Duke of Marlborough arrived in New York for his first visit to the United States. He is about 5'7". Slender, and 'a likely chap for a Duke as Dukes go'."

Arriving in Newport shortly after, the Duke made a difference in Consuelo's attitude. Miss Harper, her governess, impressed on my daughter that she would find opportunities for usefulness, social service, and high idealism in Great Britain.

I gave an informal drop-in for the Duke on Sunday. And Oliver registered him the next day for the Tennis Club at the Casino.

At the Wilson's party, Richard Wilson Jr. and his sister, Grace, welcomed the guests including Winty, as expected. As the evening went on, I controlled myself and did not interrupt Winty's and Consuelo's eating and dancing together, so long as she did the same thing with the Duke. But by the end of the evening, my concern was great. I watched. Consuelo did allow Winty to put her wrap around her shoulders, but she accompanied the Duke and me home in my carriage, without complaint.

She appeared the next morning at our breakfast buffet. Then was told by the Duke that he preferred driving around in a carriage by himself, rather than playing tennis. We raised our brows. A rumor we had heard was apparently true. The Duke was still looking over the young ladies of Newport. But for money, I suspected, not good looks.

On schedule, my fête was given on August 28, 1895. The newspapers later said "it was the most beautiful ever seen in Newport."

That night with mother-daughter pride, I felt Consuelo and I were as selectively dressed as possible. She was wearing her grandmother's lace-trimmed, white satin gown. This was the very one worn by my mother when she was Phoebe Desha, the belle of Mobile. Consuelo was impressed.

As for me, the *New York Times* reported I was wearing a gown "of pale green satin, trimmed with white satin and Spanish lace", accented with "a pearl necklace." Consuelo again wore her hair in a glorious cascade of curls. Mine, now even more "artistically" auburn, was piled on top my head, with a French twist at the back, and the whole coiffure dotted with pearl ornaments.

We stood together, welcoming guests into our entrance-arboretum of palm trees, ferns, hyacinth, hollyhocks and lotus flowers. Hovering around all this, on wires, were flocks of artificial hummingbirds, butterflies, and bees. Impressed, the Duke now seemed happy to stand at our side.

Dick Wilson led Consuelo in the first cotillion. Mullally's Casino Orchestra began the dancing, then alternated, throughout the night, with a Hungarian *tzigane* band.

My footmen, in their wigs and maroon coats, served the midnight supper on the terrace courtyard, overlooking the broad lawn and the ocean. The entire thirty-five tables were illuminated with white silk Chinese lanterns. And the tables would be again, three hours later, when a second supper was to be served.

Our favors were greatly appreciated: Old French etchings, fans, mirrors, watch cases and sashes of ribbons of the Louis XIV period. Plus lanterns and even miniature bagpipes which really squeaked. Each favor was marked with a Marble House Medallion. The Duke observed it all.

But what my guests were really expecting was a drum roll, a blare of trumpets and an announcement. They received none. There was no engagement to announce. Apparently the Duke was again "spreading out" all festivities as long as possible, as Oliver reminded me while drinking in the whole evening with his usual Belmont fervor!

I, from that night on, tried to keep Consuelo and the Duke busy with dinners and even a cruise on the John Jacob Astor yacht. As we rode down Bellevue Avenue in my "sociable" carriage, Consuelo was clad in elaborate batistes we bought in Paris, and the Duke sat opposite in flannels and a sailor hat.

Sometimes Oliver would drive us all to the Polo Field. As we watched the matches, my Oliver would take great pride in reminding the Duke that Harry Whitney and Devereux Milburn had recently won back the Westchester Cup from England.

Furthermore, the Duke was to learn that four years ago Oliver had persuaded Richard Morris Hunt to design him a house, to be called Belcourt — for horses and carriages downstairs and his own elaborate quarters upstairs. From the street you could drive through one arched entrance, then curve through the stables, and drive out a matching arch. This enabled Oliver to show off his horses from a second story open loggia, thus delighting his frequent guests. Plus surrounding them, in other rooms, with his magnificent collection of books and his medieval armor worn by equestrian knights of another time. Something not only to impress *them* but to amaze a Duke!

Amid splendor and on schedule, Oliver's ball *did* take place on the night of September 2, 1895. Oliver was not trying to outdo me. He simply always entertained this way at Belcourt. Fascinated with the new possibilities of electric lighting, he had created wonderful luminous effects amid his tropical plants. His huge, magnificent baronial hall and its twenty-six tables were quite at home alongside the statues of four of his favorite horses!

Oliver was also scheduled to serve a midnight supper, and then another at 2:30. It *would* be a long and uncertain night for me.

As the guests arrived, I was honored and delighted to see his brother, Perry, and his brother and sister-in-law, Mr. and Mrs. August Belmont, Jr. Even Alice and Cornelius were present, and their daughter, Gladys, younger than Gertrude but a longtime friend of Consuelo. But, of course, Winthrop Rutherfurd also appeared. I then had to control myself.

I began to wonder if the Duke was not noticing Winty's attentions toward Consuelo. Was he not jealous? The Duke danced with all the beautiful young ladies quite imperviously. Including Gladys. I wondered if Alice and Cornelius had come to the ball to look him over. Perhaps their interest had a point.

Apparently I had *two* things to worry about. A possible elopement. And a possible upstaging of my daughter by a rival Vanderbilt family. It was proving to be quite an evening!

Oliver danced with me as often as he could. We loved dancing together, but tonight we often had to pause in corners to talk.

"Alva. You are doing beautifully. Your eyes snap at Winty, but they also snap at Gladys."

"Eyes that snap are more visible when they're brown."

"So which are you more worried about?"

"Winty. If they elope, there's nothing I can do about Gladys. She may be automatically *in*."

"True. But I think that your giving Consuelo more latitude may make her cautious and feel that she is involved in the decision."

"You're giving my daughter a lot of credit."

"You raised her to think for herself."

"Oliver, you are the only person in the entire world who gives me credit for that!"

"Thank you, my darling. So you have to let it work."

"And you predict what?"

"Nothing. Have supper with me at 2:30. We can watch and wait together."

"I may become unconscious, or simply stiffen and, God forbid, throw up."

"No. Not on *my* food."

"No, my dear, not on *your* food. Oliver, this is a magnificent party. And I love the orchestra's playing up there in the loft. Perfect place, gives more room on the dance floor."

"So let's use it."

We whirled from our corner, and the other couples made way. Oliver could dance as well as he could remove a cape —and with as much circular motion!

At 2:30 we had supper together on schedule. The Duke and Consuelo were at another table, with Winty close by. I kept observing to see if they both left their tables at about the same time. I wondered if Consuelo had asked Winty if he had received her message that she could not marry him? Obviously he could see I was hale and hearty and not dying from a heart attack. Would he tell her never to trust such news again?

Suddenly Winty put down his napkin and went over to Consuelo and asked her to go out on the dining room balcony with him. I presumed it was not just to attempt to look over Bailey's Beach. Consuelo declined.

I could not believe it, but wondered if the two of them were doing it for my benefit. As soon as I relaxed, they would steal out of Belcourt and dash away in Winty's waiting carriage.

I did stiffen as I kept waiting.

"Alva. If you are not going to eat, you might as well tell me what is wrong with my late menu."

"Nothing. It is superb."

"Ah, I am learning to manage my chefs as well as you do."

"And to help me manage my daughter."

"I have, yes. And you are doing well. Now sit here and quietly suffer, my dear."

I watched Winty try again. Consuelo consented to give him the next to last dance. After several moments, they broke away from the dance floor and went down the stairs together. Down the stairs! The Duke did not follow. He simply asked Gladys to dance. She accepted.

Was I going to lose both battles? I started to get up, to race after Consuelo. Oliver did not attempt to stop me. He just sat and stared.

I had to spar with myself. The decision was mine. Finally I decided no and sat down. The dance was over, and the Duke took Gladys back to her table. Alice and Cornelius nodded their approval. Their approval of what? That he brought her back? Or that his attentions toward her were increasing? I wished Consuelo would become aware!

Suddenly she came up the stairs. By herself. I held my breath and waited for Winty to follow. He did not. She looked distraught but had come in time to see the Duke seat Gladys, then return to his own chair.

Consuelo made a direct line to her table. The Duke arose to seat her, but she drew him onto the dance floor instead.

I could not believe it.

They danced to the end of the evening. And I swore I saw her firmly glance at least once at Gladys.

Oliver took my hands in his. "Alva, you can sleep tonight. I just took a look over the courtyard. Winty has gone home by himself."

"Sent away by Consuelo?"

"Oh no. It must have been his own decision."

"Oliver! Do you know what this means? That if Winty *cannot* have access to Vanderbilt money, he *is* willing to give up Consuelo?"

"Yes. Right now. This night, at least. And forever, we can hope."

"But does Consuelo realize it?"

"She suspects. We can only wait, my dear, and see if she truly believes it!"

20

AT LAST

A S MY REWARD FOR BEHAVING MYSELF AT HIS fète, Oliver said when we returned to New York, he would be giving a grand coaching party for Consuelo and the Duke.

And he would *not* be inviting Winthrop Rutherfurd.

On October 3, 1895, the great day occurred. During the party's long trip to Lake Mohard, and then on to Tuxedo, we laid over to fix a horseshoe at Courier Square in Poughkeepsie. Consuelo was very amused to see a small crowd of men and women gather round to see this heiress and her new friend, "the young British gentleman".

One of the ladies in the group of onlookers volunteered, "He's the Ninth Duke of Marlborough, you know. And the Sunderlands are in with that clan, so the British call him Sunny."

One of her wide-eyed listeners countered, "I saw in the *New York Times* that they call him 'Your Grace'."

"Grace?", she corrected "No no, Grace must be the Duke's sister!"

Hearing this, Consuelo was in a state of cover-up giggles. I handed her my Chinese fan. After that, she tittered coyly as if she were an Oriental. So it was my turn to giggle.

Our feelings toward each other had mellowed. We could now see our way through to the wedding. We had already exposed the Duke to the Atlanta Exposition in September, a welcome respite to the public, because of all the strikes going on. And an Exposition which sorely missed Richard Morris Hunt. His work would have been the greatest of the architectural innovations. Even the Duke knew enough of his reputation by now to admit it.

I had been determined not to call His Grace Sunny until he declared himself. But this he did, previously, on a quiet evening at

Marble House. In the Gothic room, he asked Consuelo to become the Ninth Duchess of Marlborough. Apparently the exterior lighting from my collection of Emile Gavet leaded windows and my matching polychrome ceiling added to the occasion.

Consuelo came upstairs to my bedroom to tell me. I kissed her. She actually seemed relieved and chatted about our plans. As she left the room, she turned and could not resist one last example of Consuelo-humor. "I'm glad he chose the Gothic room. So propitious to sacrifice."

I sighed and had to lie back on my pillow, and be quiet. Then I turned over and went to sleep. It seems to me it was the second sound sleep I had enjoyed since Oliver's party. In fact, the second in two years.

Unfortunately, the Duke dragged his feet about having the engagement announced. He was waiting to go aboard *Valiant* and "have his talk with William Kissam Vanderbilt." Finally he did. Accompanied by his English solicitor, George Lewis, the Duke accomplished a remarkable settlement. Willie K. must have been amazed to hear about the engagement and totally astounded at this young man's ability to bargain.

Shares of Beech Creek Railway stock were granted to the Duke, totaling $2,500,000 on which the interest alone would reach around $100,000 per year. Plus 1.6 million in cash. In addition to that, he would receive straight out another $100,000. Annually. In concerned protection of his daughter, W. K. pronounced the same amount must go to Consuelo each year for a use of her own choosing. Apparently the Duke agreed. After securing her position, on the opposite side of the Atlantic "as his wife", he may have felt her share would automatically go to him.

Finally, to my great amazement, I read in the *New York Times* that the Duke *and* Creighton Webb, only a *relative* of the Vanderbilt family, had announced his engagement to Consuelo at an informal dinner at the New York Waldorf!

Needless to say, I felt it was high time I give my *own*. Unfortunately Alice Vanderbilt and I chose the same night. She was presenting the debut of Gladys. I was announcing Consuelo's and the Duke's engagement. Which one would win?

Because my twenty-four guests were the most important people in Newport, I knew Alice would have to wait to begin her debut ball, until they all arrived. I did not feel obligated to hurry this engagement dinner. But Alice was seething as we entered. Oliver tried to smooth over by asking Alice for the first dance. She accepted, and he whirled her around on the marble floors of that immense great hall at The Breakers. From then on, the evening *did* belong to Alice and Gladys. But Alice still never forgave me.

I knew no Vanderbilts would attend the wedding. Even any gifts from them should be returned. In New York, they had all done a very thorough job of snubbing me ever since the divorce. All except my mother-in-law, Maria. And I did feel she would attend the wedding, no matter what.

W. K. Vanderbilt would, of course, accompany his daughter down the aisle. And she would naturally accept *his* gift. But, out of deference to Oliver, W. K. would not be invited to the luncheon after the wedding. I knew both men would feel it was best.

As for my gift to Consuelo, I would give her, with pride, all the pearls her father had ever given me. Including one necklace owned by the Russian Empress, Catherine, and another by Napoleon III's Empress Eugenie. She accepted.

The Duke chose his own wedding date. November 6, 1895. I would have preferred the 5th, but he protested that was Guy Fawkes Day. "Don't commemorate the day an attempt was made to blow up Parliament!" Very well, Your Grace.

He also refused to attend rehearsals. "Those are for ladies."

I therefore asked Consuelo, "Does he realize how beautiful your bridesmaids are?"

She promptly reviewed the faces of Elsa Bronson, Evelyn Burden, Katherine Duer, May Goelet, Julia Jay, Edith Morton, Daisy Post, and Marie Winthrop. "Are you saying the Duke looks only at pretty American faces?"

"I am, Consuelo. And let's hope he doesn't do it for the rest of his life."

"But he didn't even like Niagara Falls!"

"No doubt. But you won't be 'dressing American.' Your wedding dress is French."

"Designed by Worth and much anticipated by you."

"The Brussels lace on the white satin of that dress is much easier to obtain in Paris."

"Don't forget, Mother, I am receiving a flood of letters from suitors who want to save me from marrying the Duke!"

For days we both maintained a good silence on this subject, and I was glad when the day, November 6, finally came. I had already purchased the house on 72nd Street in New York, so all should go smoothly.

Dressed in my blue satin gown, topped by my Russian sables, I had to get to Fifth Avenue's St. Thomas Church *early*, no matter what I was wearing, for me to check on the candelabra, the garlands draped from the dome, the New York Philharmonic, and even the little baskets to be given to the guests during the long wait while the bride and groom signed all the official papers. Also to check on the ushers and the policemen outside. They were holding back the onlookers, some of whom had arrived equipped with opera glasses!

An organ recital, featuring Beethoven's "Fugue in C", would begin the procedures, as the guests took their seats. Director Walter Damrosch would then take over with his sixty-piece symphony.

I finally was able to take my seat. My sons Willie and Harold had already been ushered to seats beside me. As I watched the cluster of clergymen gathering for the eventual tying of the nuptial knot, I began to check my watch.

Something was wrong. Things were now behind schedule.

I knew exactly what was happening. Willie K. was to drive by the house while Consuelo was dressing, to have a private visit with his daughter. He had no doubt done so. But what else was happening? Was I to go into panic about a last-minute elopement arranged by Willie K.? Were the two of them going to make a dash for his *Valiant*, where Winthrop Rutherfurd would be waiting, and sail away?!

As I sat there in my pew, I knew how the conversation must be going at the house. Our maid, Jeanne, would be finishing dressing the bride, but the bride must be addressing W.K.!

"Father, I called your *Valiant*. Did you get the message? Is it waiting?"

"Consuelo, you asked me to go to Winthrop's house first. I did. No one knows where he is."

"He's not on *Valiant*?"

"No! Did you think he *would* be?"

"We can hurry down the back stairs and go see!"

"Consuelo, you seem to forget that you told me you sent Winthrop word you could not marry him."

"Father! *You* want me to marry the Duke, too?"

"What else is there to do, my darling?"

"But Winty will come, I know he will!"

"Not with all those police out there on both sides of the street all the way to St. Thomas."

"They are there to protect me from all the threats. So what are you trying to tell me?"

"Look, has Winty ever thrown a rock against your window here at this house — or called to you or whistled?"

"No."

"I thought so."

"You thought so?"

"Then that's his answer, Consuelo. He knows if he elopes with you, he will cause such a disaster, at this point, that he will be cut off from access to Vanderbilt money for life."

"Cut off? For life?"

"Life. He is not coming, my darling. Believe me!"

Sitting in my pew at St. Thomas, I knew Consuelo would burst into tears. Then Jeanne would scream about her getting tears on the wedding gown. The butler would show up with Willie K's boutonniere, but there would be frustration over the fact the bride's bouquet had never arrived from Blenheim Palace. Probably not even at this final moment!

Jeanne would put the court train, embroidered with those seed pearls and silver, around Consuelo's shoulders, exclaiming, "Magnifique. Superbe!" Then she would run to get a cold washcloth to soothe Consuelo's eyes. "The veil, now the veil."

"I will put it on at the church."

"No, no. You will be riding in the carriage. Everyone will see you have been crying."

And on would go the veil. Then Consuelo would be handed a substitute bouquet. "Such a grand nouvelle marièe!"

Willie K. would present his daughter her wedding handkerchief, and off they would go.

So,that by the time they arrived at the church, and the orchestra had played on and on for an extra twenty minutes, *everyone* would be monstrously relieved to see them. Let alone the mother of the bride! The wedding could then finally take place.

This was true. But it hurt me to see Consuelo's eyes, red and still wet even through the veil. If I had guessed right, how heavy her realization about Winty must be. Knowing this a few minutes before a bride walks down the aisle was not my idea of fairness. I felt, dear God, if I could only help her!

Willie K. was doing his best as he led her down the aisle. I looked into his eyes and knew we were in agreement.

I also knew something else.

The wedding could go on now. But afterward, I could only hope the luncheon would be everything Oliver and I wanted it to be. That Lord Pauncefote, the British Ambassador, would attend, and there would be a missive from Her Majesty Queen Victoria. Finally, that Consuelo and the Duke would leave for our Idlehour, to begin their honeymoon, a honeymoon which would then extend overseas, as a gift from Willie K. and me. I could stand at the window and watch them go. With tears of my own.

Even though all this *did* gracefully happen, I knew I could be aware, for the rest of my life, that the world would feel I had out and out forced Consuelo into marriage with the Ninth Duke of Marlborough.

Only a few people would believe that was not quite the case. Not quite true.

21

A NEW LIFE FOR ME

ON JANUARY 11, 1896, OLIVER AND I WERE married.

The ceremony took place at my house at 24 East 72nd Street. Because no Episcopal minister would unite a divorced couple such as we two, William L. Strong, the Republican banker who had been elected mayor of New York City, on his pledge to clean up the city, was happy to perform a civil ceremony! Young Willie and Harold were the only two Vanderbilts present. And because the Belmonts did not think I should ever take alimony from a Vanderbilt, *none* of them was present.

After the ceremony, we entered one of my maroon carriages, drove to Grand Central Terminal, and boarded a train for Newport. Oliver's Belcourt chateau was to be my new home. As a welcoming present, Oliver had taken his sitting room and converted it into a gorgeous bedroom for me. Oliver's own was very nearby. And he had built and equipped a sumptious bathroom for me off my new bedroom. Considering that Oliver had installed the first shower in Newport in his own bathroom, my fixtures were equally innovative. What a touching and considerate gift from my new husband. And it could not have come at a better time. I needed that personal statement!

Oliver also turned over all his Newport property to me. He said he felt I would manage and perpetuate it far better than anyone in his own family! For the next five years, Oliver kept my life a swirl of continual interest as I watched him continue to participate in his multiple clubs and organizations. Very typical of his many charity activities, he donated Gray Craig Park's bird and beast collection to Roger Williams Park in Providence.[18]

Ever mindful of his nautical background, Oliver sponsored

commemoratives for his granduncle, Commodore Oliver Hazard Perry, especially for his victory at Lake Erie. Again for his grandfather, Commodore Matthew Perry, and his continually apparent feat in sailing to Japan and opening that country to world trade. Belcourt contained and honored treasures from both events.

In 1898, during the Spanish American War, Oliver even offered to equip a torpedo boat for the U. S. Navy. *If* he would be allowed to command it. The Navy's reply was, "Oh no, that would be privateering"! We had a good laugh. Needless to say, this highlighted the realization that I had a whole new family to learn about. And I was never bored learning.

We also began plans to someday build our chateau at 477 Madison Avenue in New York. Yes, I was dreaming about building again. I could *never* stop.

Politics increasingly became a whole new aspect of our life. Working as his impressive father had done for the Democratic Party, Oliver gave speeches in New York, opposing trusts and monopolies — and for or against Tammany Hall, depending on what they were up to! In 1899, as leader of the William Jennings Bryan Democrats, Oliver published a newspaper, *The Verdict*. It became a voice of protest.

All this centered in the Hell's Kitchen 13th District in New York, an area between 23rd and 40th streets, and 7th Avenue to the Hudson River. Oliver represented this District in Congress, from 1901 to 1903. As a Congressman, he was present for two sessions within one term. When we were in Washington, we stayed at our favorite hotel, the Willard.

During this period of Oliver's life, I always kept in the background. I had been criticized so heavily for my divorce and for the Vanderbilt's taking money out of the country, I felt the less said the better. But I was fascinated watching Oliver in action, and I backed him every step of the way. We two *wanted* to make a difference in the life of our country.

Since 1896, we had made trips back and forth to Europe to see Consuelo, now very much the mistress of Blenheim Palace and the mother of two handsome and active sons — John Albert Edward William, Marquess of Blandford, and Lord Ivor Spencer-Churchill. Oliver and I loved being grandparents, which, of course, included being grandparents to that new Tenth Duke of Marlborough. The Marlboroughs had snubbed Oliver at the christening of each son. I was furious, especially after all his contributions to the maintenance of Blenheim Palace. But it obviously didn't matter to Blandford and Ivor — they adored Oliver.

Consuelo and the Duke had been busy entertaining everyone from Winston Churchill and Ethel Barrymore, to the future King George V and Queen Mary. On those long hunting weekends, known for their continued political discussions, they all explored the issues which would unfortunately lead up someday to World War I. Our Consuelo expressed her own opinions. She was making her mark and being recognized for it.

So, in 1899, Oliver and I decided it was about time to "round off the century" by having a motor car rally and race at our Belcourt Castle. The vacant grounds around Belcourt would be perfect for it. The area at the end of Bellevue Avenue could be the center; it was all situated conveniently close to us. The race would be held on September 7, 1899, and invitations would be sent out to car owners plus those who simply fancied the new electric "Bubbles", as they were called. I, myself, was the first owner in Newport of a "Bubble" — a victoria. It all seemed very appropriate.

We planned the route in great anticipation. Though we knew all cars would be heavily decorated with flowers, we desired a real rally, even with checkpoints. And most of all with pedestrians — yes, pedestrians. They would be merely dressed-up dummies, but the point was that every time a driver missed a pedestrian, he would earn points.

I had a specific reason for doing this. Reginald "Reggie" Vanderbilt, that son of Alice, was barreling down Bellevue Avenue at terrible speeds. His car was known to have knocked over several pedestrians, and two were even reported killed. Whether this was true or not, Alice *always* managed to get Reggie off in court. And at that time Cornelius was unfortunately too ill to be consulted. I knew my own son, young Willie, now a handsome twenty-one, did the same thing as Reggie, but he never hit anyone. Perhaps it was because he and Willie K. were planning what, in 1904, became the Vanderbilt Cup Races on Long Island. He and his father had their own considerable collection of foreign automobiles, used frequently. Perhaps he had more practice — in any case, judgment. So, by placing pedestrian dummies at strategic points along the route, I felt I was making my protest about Reggie and, at the same time, supporting the newborn concern about automobile safety. We would see what the afternoon would bring.

My own son, Willie, when he arrived, got the point immediately and laughed uproariously. I could hope that he would convey the message. In his own particular way.

As Oliver appeared in his goggles, the afternoon began with champagne and got underway. Let the horseless carriages loose!

Sightseers began to gather along Amy's Pond and Coggeshall Avenue. The line of cars was drawn up at Wheatland Avenue. I arrived, "dressed in blue in my victoria", as the papers said, and joined the line. Weaving through the red and white flags, our autos all coughed and sputtered, and the "tests" began.

Winthrop Rutherfurd, now safely only a guest and accompanied by Miss Fifi Potter, was having difficulty getting started. The next mishap occurred to my friend, Tessie Oelrich's carriage. The rear axle broke, and a wheel fell to the ground. To the Tessie who later owned Rosecliff mansion, this was quite a blow. But the judges — Dyer, Cushing and Tailer — wanted the car to be left where it was so that it could become an additional hazard-test. Tessie agreed. She loved all the excitement around her, and so did I. Anyway, when the awards were later given out, she got "first prize for decoration". And Mr. Stuyvesant LeRoy for "best driving".

At 5:00 with sixteen of us left, we still drove with skill as we paraded on Bellevue. Until we got to Old Beach Road and we began hitting hills. All of us scattered to try to take them at our own power until we finally could regroup at Allen's Pavilion. We were like scurrying mice, and most of us laughed ourselves sick.

There were times when we even tangled, as the reports said, "with all types of conveyances known to God and man", but driven by the onlookers themselves. It would inevitably become a jolly mess for all of us.

Buffets of food and drink had been served to our guests all day long, but now it was time to go to our great party carefully planned at Gray Craig Park. Some guests safely traveled there in horsedrawn vehicles. Others of us made it in our cars.

As for the lavish decorations of each vehicle, I will only describe three — to give evidence the *rest* were equally marvelous. And that included those of Tessie Oelrich, Mr. John Jacob Astor, the Marquis de San Vito, Mr. George von L. Meyer, Mr. Joseph E. Widener, Mr. H. Roger Winthrop, Mrs. E. Rollins Morse, Mrs. Burke-Roche, Mrs. William E. Carter, Mrs. J. R. Drexel, Mr. Henry R. Taylor, Mr. Clarence W. Dolan, Mr. Harry Lehr, Mr. Winthrop Rutherfurd, and

Miss Scott. All this as reported by the *Newport-News*.

My son Willie's runabout was decorated with cleotatis on the body and wheels. The canopy was an airy structure, trimmed with the same flowers, plus red roses with pink ribbons hanging from the rim of the canopy. His new wife, the beautiful Virginia Fair, the sister of Tessie Oelrich, rode beside him.

After a reported sampling of French music hall stars, Willie had made his choice. We were delighted. Furthermore, Virginia shared his interest in automobile racing. Willie and his father were said to own a Bugatti, a Stevens-Duryeâ, a Rolls Royce, a Hispano-Suiza, a De Dion Bouton, a Duesenberg, a Mercedes-Benz, a Bentley, and an Isotta-Fraschini. So of course they would *have* to initiate an event called the Vanderbilt Cup Races — what else was there to do? Usually Oliver delighted in inquiring about each car individually, but today Willie went into detailed hysterics with "his old buddy, Oliver", about the unexpected antics of each of their prized vehicles.

Finally my son sobered a little and turned to me. "Mother, dear, I think your marvelous pedestrian charade was lost on Reggie. He didn't show up!"

"Cornelius is still not well, as you know. Alice probably wants him to be near his father."

"Well, Reggie's absence was certainly safer for everybody at the rally."

"Willie, the word may never get back to Alice. But, apparently a lot of the other guests got the point and seemed to enjoy it."

"Another *first* for you, mother. 'Don't hit a pedestrian if you see him first!'"

Oliver and I had an appreciative laugh at the double meaning.

"Mother, I was impressed with the way you had your 'Bubble' decorated. I saw how you covered it with blue cloth, and then covered the cloth with flowers. Even had a round canopy with blue ribbons. But the genius part was that large blue butterfly placed on those shafts in front of the auto. It made the whole thing look as if it were drawn by the butterfly."

"It was, Willie, it was!"

"Ah, hah. Then was Oliver's drawn by those four great seagulls?"

"Yes. But don't forget that eagle with those long yellow streamers."

"How can I?"

"Good. Then we will let the newspaper describe the arch — a

double arch, no less. Yellow daisies on the body. Blue hydrangeas on the pillars. With yellow flowers and cat-o'-nine-tails above."

"But I felt the crowning triumph, Mother, was the spread of small electric lights through it all."

"Oliver is passionate about electricity. It lights our life."

"Mamie Fish was so proud to ride with him, but she can't wait until she sees his whole auto aglow at the party."

"We'll all be aglow!"

The *Newport-News* reported the party very accurately — they seemed to enjoy it themselves: "At Gray Craig Park, in Middletown, dinner was served at a large table, in the center of which was a miniature lake, surrounded with grass and palms, representing in an artistic manner a dainty bit of landscape, in which numerous electric lights among the foliage and on the borders of the lake, gave an additional charm. There were ninety guests in all.

"The illuminations at the Park were by Landers & Son. The entrance from Paradise Road was lighted its entire length of 1500 feet with reflecting lanterns on either side, and through this canopy of light the automobiles wound their way into the Park. A dancing floor, twenty-five by fifty feet in size, covered with a red tent, was put up for the dinner and dancing. This was placed between two large apple trees, loaded with red fruit, the trees filling the two ends of the tent. The table was built around the three center poles, from which three immense arches were made with oak leaves and flowers. At each side pole, reflecting lanterns with amber glass made a beautiful effect. Turkish rugs covered the tent floor and the lawn in front, and after dinner the floor was cleared. The Hungarian orchestra furnished music during the dinner and the dancing.

"At a late hour, the party members returned to their homes, using the electrical displays which had been arranged as a part of the decorations of the automobiles and which, if they could have been used at the start, would have added materially to the picturesqueness of the spectacle.

"As the carriages started from the Park, their illuminations were all turned on, some of which had been wired while the guests were dining. All went well until the limits of Newport were reached on the return, and then trouble began. O. H. P. Belmont and another car became stuck on Beach Hill. Vehicles were soon stranded all over town. The trial course on the soft ground at Belcourt was a very severe strain upon the stored power." The report ended with, "The repair wagon was soon very much in demand — it was still in condition to run."

Yes, indeed it was. But it couldn't handle all of us. So we abandoned automobiles all over town, to be retrieved the next day and lovingly returned to welcome shelter. Each was safe and sound.

This abandoning only heightened the merriment and brought many of us home in horsedrawn cabs, singing at the top of our lungs in a false belief that the Hungarian orchestra was still around to back us up.

Accounts, about this *first* automobile rally-race to be given in Newport, went on for years. Stories were joined, augmented, and repeated for decades. The "first" of any event of this kind is always the best, somehow. The original excitement never quite repeats itself. Oliver and I were glad that we had done it. And proud that we apparently had done it so well.

22

THE HEARTBREAK

URING THE YEARS UNTIL 1908, OLIVER AND I improved and enjoyed Belcourt to the fullest. We even entertained the Duke of Windsor and Kaiser Wilhelm. At different times, of course!

We provided a third-floor suite for Harold and his tutor, and Oliver and I shared those happy young-manhood years with my son. Oliver was a marvelous second father, and Harold adored him.

I became known for swimming at Bailey's Beach with a green umbrella over my head to protect the always sensitive skin of an originally auburn-haired lady. But I went to Bailey's Beach for a second reason. I walked along the shore because I wanted to discover and invite home to lunch the most interesting writers, artists and musicians who were visiting Newport. They were difficult to meet, but when they learned I was searching for them, they complied with their own walk on the shore. They brought their world of interest to me, and I took them home to Oliver. My buffet table, that stretched the length of the first- floor's new banquet hall, was set every day with turkeys, hams, lobsters, imported delicacies and fine wines. A great stimulus to conversation.

Our discussions could lead anywhere. Edith Wharton was a frequent guest and would spark a lively and caustic appraisal of present day society. Oliver would take care of politics. And the others would explore the arts. It was as if we were the intellectual center of the world during those days. Perhaps we were.

Alice never seemed to care to join these afternoons, though she certainly would have been welcome. She lost Cornelius on September 12, 1899. In June of 1896, Corneel had had a stroke, reportedly after an argument with their son Neily over his wanting to marry Grace Wilson. Intrigue was immediately whispered. Whose friend

219

was she? In any case, I felt Alice had enough on her hands, and my heart went out to her — and I told her so — for the next three years, as she took Cornelius on an endless round of European spas and physicians. Even to Dr. Charcot, the French hypnotist, who finally gave Corneel some relief from his nervous disorder. But it was too late. My barbs at the time of our motorcar rally were *not* at all well timed. I only realized this — again too late.

His illness was a blow to the entire family. Some of them crititicized Alice for continuing her social schedule to the extent that Corneel escaped to their farm for relief. But I did not, I was no longer competition to her. I had long since handed her the title of being *The* Mrs. Vanderbilt. However, I wished to learn a lesson from Alice. Was she trying to give me a heartfelt warning? "Don't let this happen to Oliver. Slow down, Alva dear, slow down." I listened, talked with her, and felt grateful.

But the Belmonts continued in their role as "movers and shakers." Oliver's brother, August Jr., was planning the financing of the Cape Cod Canal, in addition to the New York subway system. His brother, Perry, served four terms from the Long Island District in the U.S. House of Representatives and was the U.S. Minister to Spain from 1888 to 1889.

Though Belmont Park, the commemorative park to his father, continued to further Oliver's interest in horses, my husband always had a lighter side, and I was glad. On July 27, 1907, a pet chimpanzee, named Consul, was very much a guest at Belcourt— at a breakfast to introduce Consul himself to society. Oliver had long had a valet named Azar, a six-foot-six Egyptian.[19] There was a circular stairway near Oliver's bedroom, leading upstairs to Azar's quarters. He always wore a turban, but for *this* breakfast Azar donned a turban with a tail. It seemed to spark the whole affair, and everyone from Mamie Fish to party-arranger Harry Lehr insisted on remaining in a state of formal hysterics, always in due honor to Consul. Every guest, after leaving, told everyone about it who was not there. The story of Oliver's chimpanzee-breakfast grew into an actual folk tale, and, even after all these years, someone will still happily remind me of it.

The less light side of our life was Consuelo's growing problems with the Duke. She had become good friends with an American beauty, Gladys Deacon, a darling of most of the courts of Europe and the French impressionists as well. She brought a fascinating chronicle of the times to Consuelo, veritably too involved to leave

Blenheim Palace. Gladys Deacon also brought fascination to the Duke, and he began to "fancy" her. As a matter of fact, he continued for the next thirty-four years, to some degree or another!

By the time Blandford and Ivor were in school, Consuelo felt it was high time for "a deed of separation" from the Duke, and obtained it in 1906. To my amazement, Willie K. tried to effect a reconciliation, but it was not possible nor desirable.

From that time on, our daughter went to live in London at Sunderland House, a previous gift from her father. Maintaining her sense of humor, she ordered placed, at opposite ends of the great hall, a bas-relief of the original Duke of Marlborough and a bas-relief of the "the original" Commodore Vanderbilt. Consuelo then went to work and made Sunderland House the center of some of the greatest social advances in London's history. She started with helping the wives and families of all types of prisoners and, over the next fifteen years, continued into the field of education for women, eugenics, a hospital run by women, temperence, birth control, political pressure groups, measures against the white slave trade, hospitals and protection for vagrant children, wartime hospitals, and a master list of war-trained women with special skills. Oliver and I applauded her every move, and did so personally whenever we could.

The last straw had come for us all when, because of England's economic condition, there was real poverty around the little town of Bladon, so dependent on Blenheim Palace. Consuelo knew it and immediately decreed that anyone, who wished to do daily work on the roads or grounds, would be paid. And she meant out of her own Vanderbilt pocket, and did so. Usually absent at one of his various posts in London, the Duke returned. "Consuelo, I absolutely forbid you — I have heard all about it."

"But, Sunny, these people need a job to put food in their mouths."

"And you are doing it."

"Out of my own funds."

"I don't care where the money is coming from. Consuelo, what you are doing is socialism, do you hear, socialism. And I will not have the name of Marlborough connected with it. You are to inform the people of Bladon that you have to stop this nonsense immediately!"

Consuelo still tried to carry on quietly until this crisis was over. Years later, when Consuelo made an arranged return to Blenheim, the lane and terraces were filled with people, grateful to her for this economic help but also for the many other kindnesses she had done for them. And not just gestures but always the filling of a real need. Their gratitude was deep, and they wished to honor her.

Oliver's and my attentions were taken away from Consuelo abruptly and tragically on February 21, 1908. Oliver's daughter, Natica Rives Burden, was found dead of asphyxiation, by a maid, at the house of her mother-in-law (Mrs. James Ambercrombie Burden) at 908 Fifth Avenue, New York.

The precise *New York Times* report went on to say, "Natica, who had had the grippe (flu) for several days, went to bed Thursday about 10:00. At 11:00, she told the maid she was not sleepy and would read. The maid fixed a drop gas light on the table beside her bed, with a tube attached to the wall gas bracket, four feet above the bed. A few moments later, her husband, Williams Proudfoot Burden, came in and spoke with her, and then went to bed in another room. Sometime later, Natica turned off the gas lamp at the table, and went to sleep. She had recently had headaches and insomnia."

The report continued, "Apparently later Natica turned off the table lamp. The gas stopcock at the wall was still on, and the loose tubing on the lamp's socket allowed gas to leak into the room. As time wore on, the pressure in the hose forced it open some more. She had left the window (on the third floor of the 72nd Street side of the house) about six inches open. Unfortunately, this forced the gas away from the window and toward her bed. Her dog, with its head by the open window, survived."

Still continuing: "When the maid came in at 10:00, she immediately called for help, and doctors came. They estimated Natica had been dead three to four hours."

As a kind gesture, it went on, "Natica was one of a group of young Newport women called The Gigglers, due to their wit and humor. They all wore long hair down their back. During Natica's debut in 1902 she was called a `veritable beauty', and she was noted for her wit and also a certain `piquant beauty'."

When Oliver finished reading all this, I felt he would collapse, but instead he began to pace, and finally went into a rage.

"Why didn't they call her *father*? Did you notice — her father was never informed? And he *still* isn't? *Any* fool can read this in the newspaper. Why don't they contact `next of kin'?"

"They should, darling. The names Rives and Burden are all they know."

"Rives! Am I supposed to go to the funeral and thank him for raising my own daughter?"

"It was her *mother's* choice. Oliver you only tried to make things easier by standing back."

"How many years is a father expected to stand back? I've carefully noticed Natica every time I could. On the playground, at restaurants, at the Tennis Casino, at any and all parties we both attended!"

"You may think your eyes never met, but I observed her many times watching you with great pride. You fascinated her."

"Why didn't she say so? By now she was twenty-six years old!"

"Gossip would have started immediately, and then there would have been trouble at home."

"Alva, do you think Natica loved me?"

"I certainly do. She had a whole secret part of her heart all set aside for you. In fact, it was a magical note-book, and she mentally wrote down every antic, every joke, every outrageously marvelous thing you did."

"But I feel I failed her."

"Never. I know what you mean. I have tried to make up for Consuelo's unhappiness with the Duke — I can *never* really call him Sunny — by choosing and giving her gifts, lots of gifts."

"Everything from an Italian cradle to a motorcar to a gold standing-mirror, dear. I remember every one. And I hope to hell she took them with her when she left the bloke."

"Whatever she did, I have a feeling they will end up at Blenheim someday for Blandford when he takes over."

However, I felt like sending the Duke a bill for all the O. H. P. Belmont money which has gone into major repairs for his Palace.

"At least we kept a roof over her head and new good books in that bare library. Alva, Consuelo had a fine reign as Duchess. She improved the whole palace immensely!"

"I hope women will remember she still is the Duchess. That title will carry her through all her social work and everything she has to do in Parliament, to make what she desires for those women a reality."

"But, Alva, we both know it doesn't take the place of love. Natica was married to that Williams, a man she not only didn't love, but couldn't even *sleep* with."

"How do you know, Oliver?"

"Because that's why she sat up at night, reading — always reading. I heard talk of it."

"Perhaps my Consuelo did the same thing."

"But she's alive!"

"I know, darling." I put my arms around him. He could not yet be comforted, and I knew it would take a long time. I turned to fix him something hot to drink. He followed me as if he were a very haunted child. He wanted me close by. And I wanted to be there for him. Always.

During the next few months, Oliver busied himself with serving on all the organization boards of which he was a part. He began to eat more, to assuage his grief. Soon we were housed at his villa, Brookholt, near Hempstead, Long Island.

I knew that his heart was not as strong as it once was, but the doctor felt liver trouble was his problem. However, on June 4, 1908, he was operated on for appendicitis.

Suffering from septic poisoning and peritonitis, the doctors still felt he was improving. Harold, Willie and I were at his bedside. Consuelo sent an urgent message of love and said that she wished she could join us.

Oliver fought to the end to live, but the complications were too great for his body. My Oliver Hazard Perry Belmont died at 6:30 A.M. on June 10, 1908.

Even during the last ten days of his life, he wanted me to take him motoring and to the Belmont races. I did. Impending death was not going to prevent O. H. P. Belmont from living to the last.

His funeral took place at the Church of the Incarnation in Garden City, Long Island. It was an Episcopal service.

In 1896, it was often said, "Do you know Alva is the first one to divorce a Vanderbilt and marry a Jew?"

The statement seemed to stop there. Oliver's family had never given him any orthodox upbringing. They recognized they had a "free spirit" on their hands in his case, and they left him free to choose. To the end, he chose no religion, not even mine. His feeling was, "Look, Alva, if I want to criticize any form of religion, I feel I am free to do so. If I were a member, I might be careful. And I don't want to *ever* be careful!"

The Episcopal service was in deference to me. Afterward, his body was taken from Garden City to Long Island City, on a special train, along with all of us as members of the funeral party. But he was finally laid to rest in Woodlawn Cemetery in the Bronx. It was the most beautiful place I could find, and I later built a memorial chapel for him and moved his body there. My own is someday to lie beside his.

Tributes came in from all over the world to honor Oliver. Over 100 wreaths of lilies and roses. Even two especially beautiful wreaths from both members and employees of the Brook Club. This was typical — Oliver was loved as much by the Club's workers, as by the members themselves.[20]

His coffin was velvet-draped in the purple he loved and heaped with purple orchids. My own tribute.

But Oliver was gone.

I felt my life was over.

23

CAN I BEGIN AGAIN?

AGAIN, OLIVER LEFT ALL HIS WORLDLY GOODS and property to me. During the next few years, I tried to handle it wisely and use it to advance a new cause which came into my life. I felt Oliver would approve. And that, somehow, it would make him live again.

But the first thing I felt I should do was to continue to improve Belcourt. I could not return to all its memories, and I wished to sell it. I hired John Russell Pope as my architect. Together, for three years, we repositioned the grand staircase, added guest rooms, and converted the parallel passageways for coaches and horses into a hall, music room, English library, a larger kitchen, and a fine reception area to add to my existing banquet hall. The indirect ceiling lighting in our oval dining room had already been done by a friend of Oliver's, a young man named Thomas Alva Edison.

In 1916 I sold Belcourt to Perry Belmont, but had to take it back in 1932. During the many years following, the house changed hands within the family, and was sold to various outside purchasers.[21]

I also finished Oliver's and my dream mansion at 477 Madison Avenue in New York. I only wished the two of us could have lived there together to the end of our lives.

The Women's Movement in England had been introduced to me by Consuelo. I now transferred my interest in it to the U. S., and became involved through the inspiration of Anna Howard Shaw and Ida Husted Harper. I wanted, in turn, to inspire others.

On August 24, in the summer of 1909, I reopened Marble House and gave a public party to further the Cause. After twelve years, Marble House responded to the warmth of voices of people — 500 attended, and the affair was a great success. Charging $5.00 per ticket, we were able to give a substantial amount to the National Suffrage Association.

New York then became the center of my efforts. But the leaders of the Suffrage Movement were appalled that so rich and influential a woman should wish to work tirelessly in their ranks. I, in turn, felt their "grass roots" approach was not an effective one and pointed out to them, "It is a slow-suffering way to go. I want action and feel the best way to get it is to work with the most powerful people in the city. I know these people well and find, if I explain the problem, it is not difficult to get what I want. Any goals, without these contacts, mean we are working fruitlessly."

They agreed. So I moved the National American Woman Suffrage Association from its center in Warren, Ohio to New York City. I rented effective office space, furnished it, and founded their own press bureau. They were calling me The Bengal Tiger!

Not content to simply sit in this office, I made speeches, walked on the shirtwaist workers' picket lines, wrote articles, passed out leaflets, carried banners, organized soup kitchens, opened eleven settlement houses for suffragists, and opened up my Madison Avenue home for meetings and lectures.

On May 4, 1912, I led the shopgirl section of a suffrage parade up Fifth Avenue to Carnegie Hall for a rally. This was our first coalition effort and we all marched dressed in white — gleaming white.

At Marble House in 1913, I built a unique Chinese Teahouse, on the Cliff Walk edge of that property. The sons of Richard Morris Hunt designed it for me. Together, we found our carefully researched and dramatic Chinese structure soon became an additional center for Suffragist rallies. There was no room for kitchen facilities beneath the perched structure, so I ran a small railway, in good Vanderbilt style, out from the main house to assist the servants in my entertaining. They not only enjoyed the experience, but my grandchildren thought the whole idea was very exciting.

The Teahouse, of course, had its social opening, actually on July 24, but what I wanted was a really public one. So I organized an event, called The Conference of Great Women, to be held July 8 and 9, 1914.

And guess who was to be the guest of honor? Consuelo, the Duchess of Marlborough. And why? Because of all the impressive work she had continued to do in London at Sunderland House. Besides all her work for the families of prisoners, she had found that giving women higher education meant they could obtain better jobs. She even managed hotels for working women, hotels that were now nearly self-supporting.

Publicity was sent out. And again, over the two days, about 500 people attended, many from the press. They were charged $2.00 for general admission, or $5.00 if they wished to also tour Marble House. The money was once more used for the Cause.

The specific approach was to invite women from across the country, and to give them ample time to report on what was going on in their own areas.

Alice Paul was the most prominent woman reporting the United States scene. It was always her hope and mine never to let the Movement get bogged down in the local scene. We felt we should all have our eyes on the bigger picture — the national scene — which *must* someday culminate in *Votes For Women*. By that time, I had become a manager and financier for the Movement, and this remarkable Alice Paul and I worked together daily. After 1920 we continued on *all* projects, national and international. I admired her greatly!

For my two-day 1914 Conference, speaker Dr. Cora Smith King warned that the Movement gave the Democrats heavy opposition because of their Solid South connections and their flirtation with Tammany Hall.

Mrs. Katharine H. Hepburn, Miss Elsie Hill, Mrs. Mina E. Van Winkel, Mrs. Stuyvesant Fish, Tessie Oelrich and Miss Lucy Burns were among the many enthusiasts.

Even two Vanderbilts — Mrs. French Vanderbilt and Reggie's first wife, Cathleen Gebhard Neilson Vanderbilt, were present.

Katherine B. Davis, Commissioner of Correction in New York City, and formerly an assistant judge, gave a very graphic picture of not only women's working conditions but the conditions under which they *live*. No one knew this subject better than she.

The Congressional Union for Woman Suffrage was further served by Mrs. Helen Ring Robinson, Colorado State Senator. She described the important part which the appointed Colorado women had in quelling the recent labor war there, thus serving their state government in a very effective way.

Mary M. Bartelme, Assistant Judge of Chicago Juvenile Court, made her position plain on the treatment of prisoners. "Where men have blundered in force and brute logic, women have used logic and added love and sympathy. That is why men have failed in their prison tactics." She went on to say, "To help the ex-convict is as

228

necessary as the helping of the prisoner. We have our Hope House, which is a stepping stone from the cell to a world which we are trying to cure of hostility. We have placement bureaus to help the ex-prisoner hope for and gain a new life." And she reminded her audience that men had finally been voted the eight-hour day, but that the working hours of women had only been reduced from twelve to ten.

Other speakers were Mrs. Maud Ballington Booth of the Volunteers of America; Mrs. Florence Kelley of New York, Secretary of the National Consumers League; Miss Kate M. Gordon of New Orleans, President of Southern States Woman Suffrage Conference; Miss Rose Schneiderman of New York of the National Women's Trade Union League; and Mrs. Harriot Stanton, President of the Women's Political Union.

But my proudest quotes were from my own Consuelo: "In the homes for prisoners' wives and children, the women are given employment to maintain their economic independence. The same for the prisoner when his sentence has expired." She described the horrors of the usual lodging for single women which made them prey to disease and infection. "I am the President of the National Association for Women's Lodging Houses, assisted by Mrs. Mary Higgs, and we have now put out propaganda throughout England and Scotland for municipal housing for women. Our own London model hostel must prove the example, and I hope it will spread into every country!"

The addresses were delivered from the podium on the terrace at Marble House, while our 600 guests sat on folding chairs and listened. Our ladies then sold tea and cakes at the Teahouse. I was pleased that everyone seemed to enjoy my new Chinese structure.

Covering Consuelo's visit, all newspaper accounts made statements similar to the *New York American's*, "Duchess Makes Hit with Suffragists." I was very proud of her. Consuelo told guests she learned so much she wished she could do it all over again.

"Tons and tons" of literature were sold, and our coffers even bulged a little.

Magnificent photographs were taken of both days of the gathering, and I kept them all in a treasured scrapbook, with duplicates for Consuelo and our grandchildren and great-grandchildren.

At that point, it was very logical that a second gathering had to be held at Marble House. This time a meeting of executives to plan definite strategy. This occurred on August 30 and 31, 1914. The delegates all wanted to give the impression we were ready to act. We were. It was the turning point!

We made plans to systematically boycott any candidate or party who was not working toward Votes for Women.

In 1916, Elsa Maxwell, the author and composer, and I wrote an operetta, "Melinda and Her Sisters", which was performed at the Waldorf Astoria, and included Marie Doro, Josephine Hull, Marie Dressler and Addison Mizener in the cast. Though a fund-raiser and not about the Cause, it was a great success. Even Governor and Mrs. Charles W. Whitney of New York came.

At this time, though realizing the seriousness of World War I, I felt my energies and financial backing should remain with the Women's Movement. After all, my two sons were in the Navy, and there were extended members of the Vanderbilt family in ground combat, air squadron, and hospital and ambulance services.

I was approached by a delegation of women from the South, opposed to action on a federal level. They felt they had their own way of "getting around men." Fully conscious of my own Southern background, I listened. Intrigued, I gave them $10,000 to pursue their own methods. When called to task for this, I explained, "I plead guilty to so strong a desire for the political emancipation of women that I am not at all particular as to how it shall be granted!"

Founder and President of the Political Equality Association, I had been an organizer of the Woman's Party Convention in San Francisco in September, 1915, and in Washington, D.C., in December, 1915. I then gravitated to the Congressional Union for Woman's Suffrage, a group founded in 1913 by Alice Paul and Lucy Burns. I worked militantly alongside them for a *federal suffrage amendment*. Serving on the executive board of the Union, I continued, after 1917, on that of its successor, the National Woman's Party. We marched, picketed the White House, pleaded with President Wilson, were jailed, forced-fed, attacked by police and jeered by the public. But we fought on. I financed the final push — the train trip of pro-suffragist lobbyists to Tennessee to convince their legislators we *must* have their crucial consensus to get over the top.

Though referendums had been passed in various states, we now needed everything certified in Washington. Then ratified. And declared a law. This was finally obtained August 26, 1920.

As soon as possible, we toasted our victory at the National Woman's Headquarters in Washington, D.C.!

Now simply known as Alva E. Belmont, I was accompanied

closely by my secretary, Doris Stevens — always with book in hand, ready to record all things past and present, which the press missed. First, she pointed out to them, at my request, that Louise Bethune of Buffalo, was appointed in 1888 as the first woman member of the American Institute of Architects. *Not* Alva E. Belmont. Again this was fitting and proper: Louise Bethune *was* the formally trained woman, and I was not.

Doris Stevens then insisted on reminding the newspapers that I, not "that rich woman" as I was frequently referred to, founded and was President of the Political Equality Association. That I served on the board of the Congressional Union for Woman Suffrage. But most of all, that she and I organized Christabel Pankhurst's 1914 U. S. lecture tour. We both had felt it was necessary to present this British Suffrage firebrand to the American public.

And right now, my same Doris Stevens was behind me all the way to celebrate this greatest victory yet, for American women! I knew her heart had hurt, almost as much as mine did, each time I marched, in a parade during those eleven years, past a Vanderbilt house I had known and been entertained in so many times. Especially the one at 660 Fifth Avenue. Only the month before our victory, William Kissam Vanderbilt had died of pneumonia complications after a previous heart attack. Willie, Harold, and Consuelo had all attended the services which were held at this 660 Fifth Avenue château. But, of course, I was not invited. However, I was aware of all the great tributes paid to the father of my three children, and I paid my own private respect to every one of these tributes, and to him.

During the 1912 parade I led up Fifth Avenue, our Suffragist ranks grew, as working women dressed in white came out of building after building. The crowds watching were increasingly impressed. And we held high our Susan B. Anthony final-words banner: "Failure Is Impossible".

As our individual strength gave out in the marching, other leaders filled in to take our place.

I always wanted to march *down* Fifth Avenue all the way to Washington Square, past the Church of the Ascension. There were so many moments when I felt Oliver was marching right alongside of me. I wanted to tell him the story of how I, years ago had sat through a service, wearing a new French chapeau on my young head. A boy near me kept pointing to and giggling at this hat. Finally at the end of the service, I located him outside in the little courtyard — and promptly beat him up.

Oliver would have loved the story, so much so that it would not have been necessary on that particular day of August 26, 1920 to point out the parallel between *Our Great March For Votes For Women* over the years and all the giggling and pointing we had endured from unsympathetic men to finally —finally — achieve our goal!

24

CONSUELO AND I

WHAT NEXT?

In 1917, I had built a Scottish castle at Sands Point on Long Island, just to prove I could. And it was an ongoing building project and tribute to feminist martyr Joan of Arc. I called it Beacon Towers.[22] Financially I made the castle a refuge for many women exhausted from the Suffragist Cause — just as at Oliver's Brookholt, in 1911, we had conducted agricultural experiments operated entirely by women, for both employment and funds. I was proud that these country homes could be used for more than just dwelling places.

In addition, in 1920, I held conferences at my Scottish castle for the National Woman's Party.

After the July, 1920 period when Consuelo attended the funeral of her father, she also came to my Beacon Towers castle, and we discussed the absolute necessity that she obtain a divorce from the Duke. Enough of this "deed of separation" he had held over her head for so long! He had leaned on Vanderbilt money long enough. Besides, he wanted, finally, to marry Gladys Deacon. But even though Gladys had a yearly grant from her family, Vanderbilt money still came first. There was only one person who could make the Duke give Consuelo a divorce, and that was Winston Churchill, who was not only his cousin but his best friend.

I personally confronted Winston. I also berated him for the lack of help and protection he had given the British Suffragettes. This berating was too much. Winston publicly stated, "Alva Belmont is the only woman in the entire world I am completely afraid of." The Duke was promptly directed by Winston to give Consuelo a divorce. He did so. Then the Duke married Gladys Deacon in June of 1921.

Consuelo had had many suitors during the days she had a weekend home, named Crowhurst, outside of London. But her true love was her 1894 dancing partner, Colonel Jacques Balsan, great French aviation hero of World War I and one of the sponsors of the famed Escadrille Lafayette, later integrated into the American Army. For exceptional service, he received the French Legion of Honor.

Jacques Balsan was a Catholic, but Consuelo remained a member of the Episcopal Church. On July 4, 1921, they were married in London at the Queen's Chapel in the Savoy Hotel complex. I was the second happiest woman involved in this union! But I chose not to dampen the ceremony by attending. The British press were still very hostile because I had pushed for the divorce.

Because of Consuelo's divorced status, she and Jacques were *not* allowed to sign the official church marriage registry, but it made no difference to them. They were completely happy.

Consuelo and Jacques began an active life. This included visits with sons Blandford and Ivor and their families. Plus the building of Lou Sueil, at Eze in the south of France. This was a stone mansion patterned after the Convent of Le Thoronet in Provence. As with Oliver's and my Belcourt, this mansion became the scene of entertaining the famous — everyone from Lord Curzon to Edith Wharton to Charlie Chaplin.

I, myself, was now called "a busy international figure". After being elected President of the National Woman's Party in 1921, I was in Europe frequently and, among other issues, worked for international citizenship for the women who desired it.

Remaining international with my concern about women, in 1926 I would be attending the convention of the International Woman Suffrage Alliance in Paris.

As late as 1930, at the Hague Conference on the Codification of International Law, I would urge the removal of legal disabilities against women.

But nationally, in 1921, I contributed $146,000 for the purchase of a Washington D.C. house to be used as headquarters for the National Woman's Party, which opened in 1922. In 1927 the U. S. Government wished this property as the site for the new Supreme Court Building. We complied. In 1928, with the money from this sale, the Sewall mansion was purchased nearby, and it in turn later became the new headquarters, and, in 1931, was named Alva E. Belmont House in my honor. I was pleased and remain eternally grateful.

I had kept a house in Paris for many years, both as a residence and earlier as a hide-out for British Suffragettes, such as Christabel Pankhurst, who were fleeing the British police. In 1923 I decided to retain the Paris house but to also join the Balsans on the Riviera.

Acquiring a villa at Eze-sur-Mer, which I called Villa Isoletta, I remodeled it, of course. But the great feature, for me, was that I was near Consuelo and Jacques, and the three of us could once again plan grand parties together in the old style of Newport. It was a great change to our guests after the trials and tragedies of World War I, and we were rewarded with much gratitude from those who received welcome relief, or charity and employment.

When Consuelo lived at Sunderland House, I had always admired her for giving her famous formal Friday night dinners. Guests could include anyone from H. G. Wells to George Bernard Shaw. When the political talk got heated, Consuelo found she could step in and use that moment to resolve some piece of legislation she had long sought. She normally would then be able to go to the proper authorities and ask for it. But time after time "the proper authorities" were present right at the dinner. They got the direct message, and prompty acted on it. That prevailing sense of humor of Consuelo's could still manifest itself in rather public ways!

But what happened next, about 1926, was not so funny. The Duke had long since worn thin the patience of the clergy of his little Episcopal church at Bladon. So His Grace decided to become a Catholic. But he could only remain a *lay* Catholic as long as he was divorced. Ever mindful of his own welfare, he approached Consuelo and suggested an *annulment* of their marriage. After thirty-one years, no less! "Wouldn't that also put you in better favor with the Catholic Church and the family of Jacques Balsan?", he asked.

He was right. It would. But what a schemer!

In addition, the Duke was sure the Rota would sustain the Marlborough status of their sons Blandford and Ivor. They would not be illegitimate. Again he was right. The Rota confirmed. For the expected but still very regular fee.

The Duke told Consuelo that all she had to do was come to me, as her mother, and ask me to testify before an English tribunal of Catholic priests, that Consuelo had been married *against* her will. Consuelo hesitated in asking me. But on learning that the proceedings would be entirely private, I naturally consented — for my daughter's happiness — to take the proper steps. It was about time! In addition, we both agreed to testify in the strongest words possible. And we did. The application was then sent to the Rota, and they immediately granted the annulment. On July 29, 1926, it was final.

All would have gone well had not the Duke, later in the year, gone to Rome to be received in audience by the Pope. And *not* as a divorced man. News, then, of the annulment got to the *New York Times*, and they published the story.

This unleashed an avalanche of Protestant wrath aimed at the Rota for annulling an Episcopal marriage. As a result, gone was our privacy and gone was our peace of mind!

Consuelo said, "Mother, you are taking this with your usual courage, and you are remaining undaunted."

What else was there to do? But is there any wonder I preferred to live in France for the rest of my life?

The religious controversy raged on for months. The Episcopal Church and St. Thomas were not about to have the biggest international marriage which had ever occurred so conveniently wiped out by the Catholics. They stated the Rota had been bribed. This was not true.

The Rota, in turn, struck back by saying this was not the business of the Episcopal Church but solely of the Catholic Church.

And so it went, on and on. I became the subject of cartoons, jibes, gossip, and long pointed fingers.

Consuelo came to me in tears. I assured her, "Look, my darling, there is always something to laugh about. You know what the Catholic Church is saying? That the Episcopal Church accepted a bribe from the Vanderbilt family in performing the wedding ceremony in the *first* place!"

"But, Mother, please listen to me. For the first time in my life, I now know what *you* have gone through in realizing you made a mistake in hoping the marriage of the Duke and myself would be a favorable one."

Really? Was *she* saying this? There were tears in my own eyes.

She continued, "I hoped the same thing for the annulment. You were doing it for me. Now I could marry Jacques in a *Catholic* ceremony and join his family circle in more than just a social way. But it all went bad — just like my marriage to Marlborough. Now the shoe is on the other foot. I owe you an apology. Much more, Mother, I owe it to you for the rest of my life!"

"As I have owed it to *you*."

"I know. Yes, I know. Mother, you have told me in so many ways.

But, in spite of all, I want you to understand that my being the Duchess of Marlborough has given me a life I could not have known otherwise."

"Consuelo, all that is true, but it was no substitute for love."

"I have it now with Jacques. Very deeply."

"I know."

"And it is *not* too late ...."

25

THE LAST TRIP AROUND THE GARDEN

I THINK MY DONKEY KNOWS THESE ARE THE LAST OF my memoirs. His pace is getting slower. So is mine. But he should be knighted for the rounds and rounds he has made. Not me. After all, I was having an adventurous time recalling. He could only guess and surmise. And keep putting one foot in front of the other.[23]

I suppose, after all, that is what every one of us does. Except when you are paralyzed. And then your mind has to do it for you.

Foresight has always been one of my strong points. In 1913, at Woodlawn Cemetery, the new resting place I had built was a beautiful miniature chapel of St. Hubert. It was a copy of the chapel at Château Amboise in France, which housed the remains of Leonardo da Vinci. All the other surrounding family mausoleums had the name of their particular families emblazoned across it. Not Oliver's and mine. Just a quiet and well-designed chapel. No label. After his body was moved there, this remained the final resting place of Oliver Hazard Perry Belmont. And as planned, the projected one for Alva Erskine Smith Vanderbilt Belmont.

In point of time, I am, of course, at my château near Fontainebleau. Near the summer home of Consuelo and Jacques Balsan at Saint Georges-Motel. This was also where Consuelo laid the groundwork for an eventual sanatorium and a preventorium for children with tuberculosis or threatened by it. Consuelo had always understood physical problems. Her own hearing had remained impaired ever since she had a severe cold during the 1902 trip which she and the Duke made to Russia. Though she joked about her hearing-aid, it never really had been any laughing matter to either of us.

In the little village of Augerville-la-Riviere, in 1928, I was still determined to do something for its residents. There was an old stone church, which for me, lacked a statue of Joan of Arc. Joan represented Militant Womanhood. Being a Protestant, I could not donate the statue, but I persuaded my Catholic friend Bessie, Mrs. Harry Lehr, to do it. I selected a fine life-sized example of St. Joan, myself. The Archbishop of Orleans agreed to induct the Saint. Mrs. Lehr, as donor, was prominent in the ceremony. But having been married all those years to an announced and public homosexual, Bessie, in some sort of compensation, had become incessantly chatty. She could *not* keep still, and she desecrated the solemn silence. I, who could always be relied upon to dominate a situation, furiously and loudly observed, "Bessie, will you shut up!" Thankfully, Mrs. Lehr thereafter maintained the dignified deportment the occasion decreed.

St. Joan was devoutly ensconced in her niche, embellished with votive candles and flowers, and a Mass was celebrated in her honor. I was relieved.

The next unexpected outburst from a woman came from miles away. From Blenheim Palace itself. From Gladys Deacon, who, for twelve years, had been the new Ninth Duchess of Marlborough.

I had asked Consuelo to bring me up to date. She tried. Apparently as long as Gladys had been having that interminable affair with her Duke, along with affairs she had with many of her European admirers, she was happy. But once she married Marlborough, the Palace and the marriage began to bore her to death. She started giving parties. The Duke said that such entertaining cost too much and suggested she could do some landscaping instead. She tried doing a rock garden, but had to give it up — she was having her third miscarriage.

"Mother, I feel sorry for her, but Gladys has always created her own aura of discontent."

"Yes. Consuelo, and what about that wax implant she had put at the bridge of her nose, to make its shape absolutely perfect?"

"It began to melt inside her skin, and her whole face became blotched. She tried to cover it up with large tulle bows tied around her neck. Nothing worked. Meanwhile, she and Sunny continued their daily battles. He eventually left her, alone, at Blenheim and went to live in London."

"Did she want to get even?"

"She tried. Gladys hired a Mrs. Agnes Grylls, who knew all about purebred dogs. They began to breed a Marlborough line of spaniels. The entire main floor of the Palace was turned into a kennel. Dogs everywhere. I am told, by people who visited, "the stench was unbelievable."

"When Blandford becomes the Tenth Duke, I hope the two of you don't have the whole mess to clean up!"

We both had a long overdue nod and groan.

There was something else I wanted to know. "My dear, now that my house — I still called it 'my house' — is torn down, what building now bears the address of 660 Fifth Avenue?"

She did not want to answer. I waited.

"Unfortunately, just another office building. After father died, what could Willie and Harold do — when it immediately went to Anne and she sold it to a trust company?"

"Yes! That Anne Harriman Sands Rutherfurd *sold* the house!"

"After all, she *was* Mrs. William Kissam Vanderbilt."

"And I always was uncomfortable, hearing 'Mrs. W. K. Vanderbilt was doing this, and Mrs. W. K. Vanderbilt was doing that'."

"They were not talking about *you*, Mother."

"But most people thought they were. And I received a lot of comment. If Anne did something good, all right, but if she did *not*, I was blamed for it."

"That's all in the past."

"Not exactly. Because of *her*, did you know that if you had married Winthrop Rutherfurd, you two would not only have been man and wife, you would also have been step-brother and step-sister?"

"I have thought about it."

"Too close, my dear, too close." This did not divert me. Again I wanted to know about "my house". "I realize, before it was torn down, that Willie and Harold tried to have its status converted to an historic monument or an architectural museum, but that the best they could do was to rescue precious parts of it and have them placed in the basement of the Metropolitan Museum of Art — so much so that for awhile I thought I would have to —"

"— take up residence in the museum!"

"Yes! They tried, bless their hearts, they tried."

"But to me, the worst thing was when we heard that contractors were grabbing up precious parts of all your rooms and incorporating them into houses *they* were building!"

I nodded. Again this hurt. We said no more. Why couldn't the City of New York identify, preserve, and enjoy its architectural treasures?

To somehow change the subject, Consuelo said, "Mother, I am sure you are wanting to ask me one more question."

"What is that"?

"Whether Winthrop Rutherfurd ever tried to get in touch with me."

"Well, did he?"

"Wouldn't we both rather that question would go unanswered? However I think you would be interested to know that he married and had five children."

"I apologize. He was not sterile."

"No. Then his wife died, and he married Lucy Mercer. She became, as you know, the social secretary for Eleanor Roosevelt. And eventually the reported mistress of Franklin Delano Roosevelt."

"Enough said. I will ask no more."

We both sat and absorbed this piece of information. We were sitting in the garden. It was apparently easier to do it that way. And for another reason.

"Consuelo, I want to talk about my funeral."

"Mother, you're getting better."

"Yes, but I will die someday. And it may be soon. Take me back to my little house in Paris, where I can be near a hospital, if you need one. Or where I can just quietly die."

"Paris? Yes — if you wish."

"And you know what is the most important part and the most pleasant part of a funeral?"

"No. Is there one?"

"Yes. Giving the *family* a chance to visit. Usually afterward, and at length. Remember, you have two new sisters-in-law to get acquainted with. Willie's Rose. And Harold's Gertrude — he plans to marry her next year you know.[24] What a wonderful time that visit should be. For *all* of you."

"We will remember you said that, Mother. And we will all try."

"I am so proud of each of you. *Your* great accomplishments, Consuelo. Then the hard-won 1930 America's Cup, with his yacht *Enterprise*, for our Harold Stirling Vanderbilt. You realize everyone else calls him Mike, but you and I still call him Harold."

"I know, he kids me about it. But don't forget he also invented contract bridge, even though you always insist on playing the old way with him"

"Yes — still stubborn .... And Willie. First, all those ships he sailed, then the great Vanderbilt Automobile Cup Races, and now the second cruise, as the newspapers say,' for William Kissam Vanderbilt, Jr.'s new interest in maritime exploration.' I can just hear all the conversation that will take place!"[25]

"Your words will be in the minds of all of us, Mother."

"My Christian words? All right, but don't forget to remind them about the time the United States Episcopal Church willingly accepted my generous contribution to their Seaside Home for Children, *but* they made me resign my executive board position 'because I was a divorced woman'."

"I will, and I'll tell Harold and Willie every word of the blasting you gave them!"

"Please do. But wait, dear, you may also tell them that St. John the Divine, next, wanted a contribution. So I told them, 'I'm not worthy —I'm a divorced woman'!" Very amazed, she laughed. I continued, "But they all know I still love them and what their Church has meant to me through my life. They feel safe."

Again a silence.

"Consuelo, I suspect I will die in the wintertime."

"Why?"

"Because then the snow can etch the marvelous figures on the outside of Oliver's and my burial chapel. What an enhancement!"

[Alva Erskine Smith Vanderbilt Belmont died in her Paris home on January 26, 1933.]

"Mother. Only *you* would think of that."

"And I suppose they will want to hold two funerals for me. I am spread over two continents, you know."

[The first of two funerals was held for Alva, January 28, 1933, in Paris, at the American Cathedral Church of the Holy Trinity. This was an Episcopal Church.]

"You and Jacques can then take my body to the United States. Of course, Consuelo, after living so quietly in the French countryside, you will be shocked by New York police escorts."

"Sirens?"

"At least. Racing all the way up Fifth Avenue to St. Thomas Church."

[Alva's second funeral was held at St. Thomas church on February 11-12, 1933.]

"Of course, Consuelo, the newspaper won't get away with listing my funeral as being held on just *one* day."

"No?"

"No. If I know my women in the Movement, they will take

advantage and make a *two*-day memorial for me. More attention for the Cause, you know, and I am all for it. My body will lay in state for two days. With the National Woman's Party members standing honor guard. They will alternate, but I know that two members will at least be Florence Bayard Hilles and Mrs. Victor du Pont. However, my dear, say hello to them *all* for me."

"Yes, Mother."

"At the actual service, the official banner, *'Failure Is Impossible'* will be displayed."

"And the poem which you composed, 'Weep, Ah Weep No More' will not be spoken. I will see to it that it is *sung* as a hymn."

"I would like that."

"And you know good and well, Mother, that the service will be triumphantly symbolic. Suffrage societies, flying their banners, will come up the aisle — wave upon wave!"

"How grand! I shall love *all* of this. Most dead people never have the experience of enjoying their own funerals."

"Not too fast. I have no doubt there will be a later commemorative service held for you in Washington, D.C."

[There was. On July 8, 1933. A commemorative pageant at the Sylvan Theater.]

"Now, my daughter, back to the St. Thomas service. Those in attendance?"

"Ambassadors, I am sure. Judges and supreme court justices. And many of the intellectuals you know."

"And don't forget all my friends in the arts."

"But only the family will be there as they lay you opposite Oliver in your chapel."

"Good."

"Those listed may well be Harold Stirling Vanderbilt, William Kissam Vanderbilt, Jr., and Colonel and Mrs. Jacques Balsan."

"Perfect."

"The Marquis and Marchioness of Blandford."

"Fine."

"Vanderbilt grandchildren."

"How nice!"

"Representatives from the Belmont family."

"Both Oliver and I will be impressed!"

"And by selected persons in the Woman's Movement — particularly your staunch co-workers, Alice Paul and Doris Stevens."

"I bow my head in gratitude to them, and to everyone. *Everyone!*"

[Consuelo guessed correctly about all those attending.]

"But, my darling daughter, there is something more I must say to you."

"What is that?"

"Regarding the police escort I will be given all the way to St. Thomas — true, it *will* be led by sirens, but I won't mind. Not after all the snubbing, jeering, scoffing, and — yes even rock throwing, which I and my co-workers have had to endure while marching on Fifth Avenue. But now, that will all be over. Consuelo, *not* that our rights won't have to be won, in other ways, again and again in the future! But for the day of my funeral, I will appreciate those sirens. In fact I will enjoy them. Their sound will be a clarion for us all ...."

—

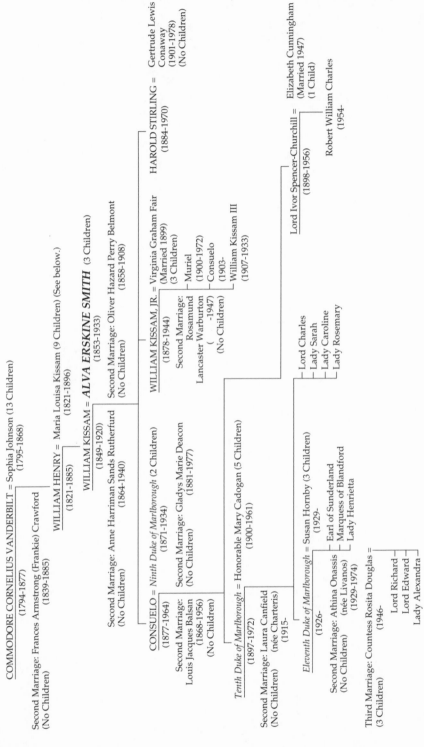

· Genealogy Chart of the Vanderbilt Family Members Covered in the Book ·

COMMODORE CORNELIUS VANDERBILT = Sophia Johnson (13 Children)
(1794-1877)   (1795-1868)

Second Marriage: Frances Armstrong (Frankie) Crawford
(1839-1885)
(No Children)

WILLIAM HENRY = Maria Louisa Kissam (9 Children) (See below.)
(1821-1885)   (1821-1896)

WILLIAM KISSAM = ALVA ERSKINE SMITH (3 Children)
(1849-1920)   (1853-1933)

Second Marriage: Oliver Hazard Perry Belmont
(1858-1908)
(No Children)

WILLIAM KISSAM, JR. = Virginia Graham Fair
(1878-1944)   (Married 1899)
                              (3 Children)

Second Marriage: Muriel
Rosamund   (1900-1972)
Lancaster Warburton   Consuelo
(-1947)   (1903-
(No Children)   William Kissam III
                          (1907-1933)

HAROLD STIRLING = Gertrude Lewis
(1884-1970)   Conaway
                       (1901-1978)
                       (No Children)

CONSUELO = Ninth Duke of Marlborough (2 Children)
(1877-1964)   (1871-1934)

Second Marriage: Second Marriage: Gladys Marie Deacon
Louis Jacques Balsan   (1881-1977)
(1868-1956)   (No Children)
(No Children)

Tenth Duke of Marlborough = Honorable Mary Cadogan (5 Children)
(1897-1972)   (1900-1961)

Second Marriage: Laura Canfield
(No Children)   (née Charteris)
                     (1915-

Lord Ivor Spencer-Churchill = Elizabeth Cunningham
(1898-1956)   (Married 1947)
                                    (1 Child)

                              Robert William Charles
                              (1954-

Lord Charles
Lady Sarah
Lady Caroline
Lady Rosemary

Eleventh Duke of Marlborough = Susan Hornby (3 Children)
(1926-   (1929-

Second Marriage: Athina Onassis   Earl of Sunderland
(née Livanos)   Marquess of Blandford
(1929-1974)   Lady Henrietta
(No Children)

Third Marriage: Countess Rosita Douglas =
(3 Children)   (1946-

                    Lord Richard
                    Lord Edward
                    Lady Alexandra

246

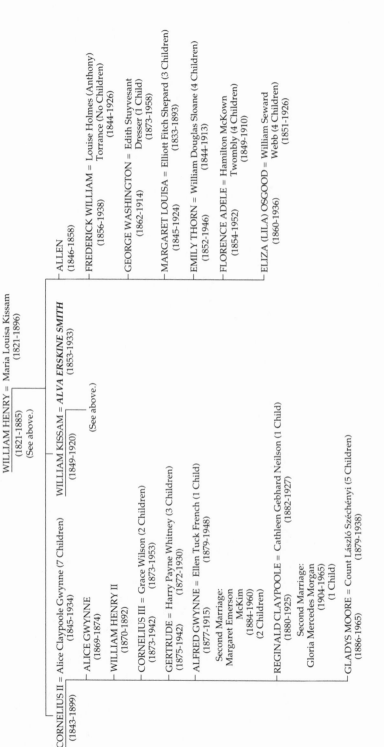

WILLIAM HENRY = Maria Louisa Kissam
(1821-1885)   (1821-1896)
(See above.)

CORNELIUS II = Alice Claypoole Gwynne (7 Children)
(1843-1899)   (1845-1934)

    ALICE GWYNNE
    (1869-1874)

    WILLIAM HENRY II
    (1870-1892)

    CORNELIUS III = Grace Wilson (2 Children)
    (1873-1942)   (1873-1953)

    GERTRUDE = Harry Payne Whitney (3 Children)
    (1875-1942)   (1872-1930)

    ALFRED GWYNNE = Ellen Tuck French (1 Child)
    (1877-1915)   (1879-1948)
    Second Marriage:
    Margaret Emerson
    McKim
    (1884-1960)
    (2 Children)

    REGINALD CLAYPOOLE = Cathleen Gebhard Neilson (1 Child)
    (1880-1925)   (1882-1927)
    Second Marriage:
    Gloria Mercedes Morgan
    (1904-1965)
    (1 Child)

    GLADYS MOORE = Count László Széchényi (5 Children)
    (1886-1965)   (1879-1938)

WILLIAM KISSAM = *ALVA ERSKINE SMITH*
(1849-1920)   (1853-1933)
(See above.)

ALLEN
(1846-1858)

FREDERICK WILLIAM = Louise Holmes (Anthony)
(1856-1938)   Torrance (No Children)
    (1844-1926)

GEORGE WASHINGTON = Edith Stuyvesant
(1862-1914)   Dresser (1 Child)
    (1873-1958)

MARGARET LOUISA = Elliott Fitch Shepard (3 Children)
(1845-1924)   (1833-1893)

EMILY THORN = William Douglas Sloane (4 Children)
(1852-1946)   (1844-1913)

FLORENCE ADELE = Hamilton McKown
(1854-1952)   Twombly (4 Children)
    (1849-1910)

ELIZA (LILA) OSGOOD = William Seward
(1860-1936)   Webb (4 Children)
    (1851-1926)

THE CHRONOLOGY
AND THE ACCOMPLISHMENTS OF
THE WILLIAM KISSAM VANDERBILT FAMILY

WILLIAM KISSAM VANDERBILT
1849-1920

Born December 12, 1849, at his parent's farm near Stapleton on Staten Island, N.Y. Fourth child and second surviving son of William Henry and Maria Kissam Vanderbilt. Brother of Cornelius II, Frederick, and George Washington Vanderbilt. Brother of Margaret, Emily, Florence, and Eliza Vanderbilt. Nicknamed Willie K.

1860. Moved with his family to 450 Fifth Ave., N.Y.C. Studied under private tutors. Later attended school in Geneva, Switzerland, where along with his other studies, he became fluent in French.

1868. Began work, at age 19, in office of grandfather's Hudson River Railroad, and worked his way up.

1875. On April 20, married Alva Erskine Smith, daughter of Murray Forbes and Phoebe Ann Desha Smith, originally from Mobile, Alabama. At Calvary Episcopal Church, 4th Ave. and 21st Street, N.Y.C.

1877. On March 2, welcomed birth of first child Consuelo.

1878. On October 26, welcomed birth of first son William Kissam, Jr.

1878 – 89. Began construction on home planned by Richard Morris Hunt at Oakdale, L.I. Called home Idlehour, a rambling 100-room mansion in the Queen Anne clapboard-and-shingle style. Continued by adding greenhouses, stables, and two gatehouses.

1878 – 82. Planned, again with Richard Morris Hunt assisted by his wife Alva, an impressive Renaissance chateau to be built at 660 Fifth Ave. on the northwest corner of 52nd St., and completed in 1882, with the project of furnishing continuing on into 1883.

1882 – 87. Was president of the New York, Chicago & St. Louis Railway. Begin traveling in his own private railroad car, a custom of the time.

1883. Was elected chairman of board of directors of the Lake Shore & Michigan Southern Railway. Became president of the Nickel Plate Railroad after it was jointed to the Vanderbilt system.

1883. On March 26, assisted his wife in giving the largest costume ball of the century, for 1200 guests, to celebrate the opening of their new chateau, and to establish the Vanderbilt greater family in New York society — seeking and receiving approval from the head of society, Mrs. Caroline Astor.

1883. Helped finance, as a lifetime supporter of the arts, the completion and opening, as promoted by his wife Alva, of the Metropolitan Opera House at 39th and Broadway, on Oct. 22; to counteract the lack of opera boxes for the new N.Y. families by the old Academy of Music on East 14th St. and Irving Place. Saw that his Vanderbilt family assumed 750 of the 10,500 shares authorized. Attended, with his wife, still instrumental in its completion, the opera house's royal opening with its production of Gounod's "Faust."

1884. On July 6, welcomed birth of his second son, Harold Stirling.

1885. On December 8, was shocked by death of his father, W.H. Vanderbilt. He, because of pressure on W.H. Vanderbilt by his wife Alva, inherited his well-deserved $65,000,000. Was grateful.

1886. On October 14, attended with his family, the christening of his first yacht *Alva*, the largest steam yacht in the U.S., with a crew of 53. Took many cruises, circling the Atlantic and Mediterranean.

1892. Was saddened by the sinking of *Alva*, in a collision during a storm, off the coast of Martha's Vineyard, south of Cape Cod.

1892. On August 19, formally opened, along with his wife Alva, Marble House, the most beautiful Newport, R.I. mansion of its time, and the work of Richard Morris Hunt, with Alva at Hunt's side in the four years of planning, construction, and furnishing. Gave it to Alva as her 39th birthday present but did not always join her for the many social events held in the next two years.

1893. In May, attended, along with his family, the christening of his new yacht *Valiant*, designed by St. Clair Byrne and built by Laird's Shipyards in Birkenhead, England; it was a 2,000-ton, full-rigged, sail-and-steam private ocean liner with a crew of 62.

1893. On November 23, began a cruise, along with family and guests, to India, by way of St. Michael's, the Azores, Gibralter, Alexandria, the Suez Canal, Aden and the Red Sea. Realized daughter Consuelo was falling in love with guest Winthrop Rutherfurd, not approved of by wife Alva. Left cruise in Southern France, along with Alva, Consuelo and Harold to head for Paris, argue it out, leave them in Europe and return to the U.S., allowing them to search for an alternative possible future husband for Consuelo.

1895. On March 5, was divorced by Alva when differences and reported infidelity could not be resolved. Was divorced on traditional N.Y. State grounds of adultery. Gave Alva Marble House in the settlement but continued to live at chateau at 660 Fifth Ave. and at Idlehour.

1895. Attended the christening of his third yacht *Defender*, designed to race in competition.

1895. Won the America's Cup with his yacht *Defender*: Length Overall, 123 feet. Waterline length, 89 feet. Draft, 19 feet. Tonnage, 150. Sail Area, 12,500 square feet. Skipper, H.C. Haff. Owner, New York Yacht Club Syndicate (William K. Vanderbilt). Designer, Nat Herreshoff. Builder, Herreshoff Mfg. Co. Built, Bristol, Rhode Island. Challenger: the Earl of Dunraven with his yacht *Valkyrie III*.

1895. On November 6, accompanied, reluctantly, his daughter Consuelo down the aisle for her marriage to Ninth Duke of Marlborough. Previously arranged the marriage settlement, but was astonished at the Duke's ability to bargain.

1896. Was in control of the Vanderbilt railroads and property, after the stroke which his brother Cornelius suffered in July, and brother's eventual death on September 12, 1899.

1896. Registered the Vanderbilt colors, to initiate a long career of racing horses. Colors: Black cap, white jacket with a black hoop on sleeve. Had begun raising prize-winning cattle at Idlehour. Now began building the finest stable of racing horses in France, at Saint Louis de Poissy, which included a 2900 meter track.

1899. On April 11, shocked by news Idlehour burned to the ground, which included the loss of a rare-books library, antiques, family portraits, and international bric-a-brac. Commissioned R.M. Hunt's son Richard Howland Hunt to build on the site a 110-room English-Flemish brick mansion, to include a billiard room, indoor tennis courts, and a domed-glass Palm Garden; completed in 1901. (Now Dowling College.)

1902. Entered his horse Biltmore, having done so well in the finishes, in the Prix Bataille at St. Cloud. Won. Entered, on the same program, his horse Marigold in the Prix Soleil. Won.

1903. On April 25, married Anne Harriman Sands Rutherfurd, daughter of Oliver Harriman, at Saint Mark's Church, London. Became stepfather to her four children by previous marriages. Had no children by this marriage. Pleased that Anne supported his philanthropies and added those of her own.

1903. Permitted, voluntarily, the direction of N.Y.C.R. system, now comprising nearly 12,000 miles of track, to pass to a Rockefeller-Morgan-Pennsylvania combination. Continued to be dominant in ownership, a board member, and a material aid in increasing the Vanderbilt fortune.

1906. Entered his horse Maintenon in the Prix du Jockey Club, the French Derby, in Paris. Won.

1908–09. Again entered, in both years, horses from his stables in the Prix du Jockey Club. Won.

1909–15. Was generous in his charities: Gave $1,000,000, in 1909, to a housing development, between Avenues A and B in N.Y.C., for those who suffered from tuberculosis. Gave $113,750, in 1911, to enable Columbia Univ. to take the title to the north half of the block bounded by 118th St. Gave $100,000, in 1913, to the Y.M.C.A. Gave $500,000 toward the founding of the Vanderbilt Clinic by himself and other members of the family. Supported the charities of his wife Anne.

1914. Entered his horse Fortinbras in Prix Turenne at Chantilly. Won.

1916. Turned over, for the start and duration of WWI, over 800 acres of his estate Idlehour to the raising of potatoes for American troops.

1916 – 18. Funded the Lafayette Flying Corps. Integrated this Escadrille Lafayette into Amer. Army. Was elected honorary president of Escadrille.

1916 – 18. Gave $40,000 to American Hospital in Paris. Gave $200,000 to Italian Red Cross. Gave $40,000 to Neuilly Hospital where Anne worked.

1918 – 20. Was again generous in his charities: Gave $250,000 to Columbia Univ. Gave $50,000 to St. Mark's Church, Islip, L.I. Gave the Metropolitan Museum his lifetime collection of art, worth $1,005,000, which included: Rembrandt's "The Noble Slav" (also known by two other titles), painted in 1632; Jean Baptiste Greuze's "Broken Eggs," painted in 1756; and Francois Boucer's "Toilet of Venus," painted in 1751.

1919. Entered his horse McKinley in the Prix de Guiche. Won.

1919. Entered his horse Forearm in the Prix de la Grotte. Won.

1919. Entered his horse Tchad in the Prix du Jockey Club. Won, marking his fourth win of that prestigious race.

1920. Received the Cross of the French Legion of Honor for his aviation funding and achievements in air warfare in WWI.

1920. Was, previously and at this time, Director of the following railroad companies: Michigan Central, New Jersey Junction, New York and Harlem, New York Central, Pittsburgh and Lake Erie, St.

Lawrence and Adirondack, Shenango Valley, Wallkill Valley, West Shore, Western Transit; Pittsburgh, McKeesport & Yoghiogheny; Toledo, Canadian Southern and Detroit. And Director of: New York State Realty and Terminal Co.; and Niagara River Bridge Co.

1920. Was, previously and at this time, a Director of the following corporations: Canada Southern Bridge Co.; Canada Southern Railway Co.; Chicago & Northwestern Railway Co.; Chicago and State Line Railway Co.; Chicago, St. Paul, Minneapolis & Omaha Railway Co.; Cleveland, Cincinnati, Chicago and St. Louis Railway Co.; Detroit River Tunnel Co.; Detroit, Toledo & Milwaukee Railroad; Ft. Wayne, Cincinnati & Louisville Railroad; Indiana Harbor Belt Railroad Co.; Lake Erie & Western Railroad Co.; Coney Island Jockey Club; and Lake Island Motor Parkway, Inc.

1920. Was, previously, one of the organizers of the Metropolitan Club. Was a founder and President of the New Theatre. Was a former President of the Metropolitan Opera Co.

1920. Was, previously and at this time, a member of the following Clubs: Knickerbocker, Union, Racquet and Tennis, South Side Sportsmen's; New York Yacht, Aero Club of America, National Golf Links, Meadow Brook. Piping Rock, Turf and Field, St. Nicholas, and Cosmopolitan.

1920. On April 15, suffered a heart attack, while attending the races at Auteuil. Continued with the competition. Did not withdraw his entries until July 20.

1920. On July 22, at the age of 71, died of complications from the heart attack — with his wife, two sons, and daughter at his side. Received immediate tribute from the Duc de Gramont, stating, "I wish to express the grief of the French Jockey Club...It is fine and honorable sportsmen such as he, mindful of the best traditions of the turf, we delight in welcoming. His death will be a great loss to the French racing world." Was given a funeral, in France, at the American Church on Avenue d'Alina in Paris. After his body was returned to the U.S., was given a second funeral at his 660 Fifth Ave. chateau, in N.Y.C. — with family and friends present, during which time many more tributes were offered in his memory. Was laid to rest in the Vanderbilt mausoleum at New Dorp, Staten Island, N.Y.

1923. Was still astonishing the world when the appraisal of his estate was submitted in Suffolk County, N.Y., totaling $54,530,966.59. Included in his estate, he owned 289,375 shares in five railroad companies, plus 16,640 shares of Pullman. Had real estate holdings principally in: New York City; on Long Island; in Newport, R.I.; in Paris; Calvados, Normandy; Deauville; Poissy; and Seine et Oise. Having appointed his two sons as executors of his estate, gave them a free hand, allowing them almost unlimited power to sell or exchange the properties of the estate, to compromise claims, and not to be taxed for "errors of judgment or of fact" which might arise in their management of the estate. Generously remembered, in his will, his wife Anne and her children, his own three children, and his five grandchildren — either directly or indirectly. Paid, through his executors, an inheritance tax of $1,934,571.73, which was the highest yet exacted in Suffolk County, N.Y.

ALVA ERSKINE SMITH VANDERBILT BELMONT
1853-1933

Born January 17, 1853, Mobile, Alabama. Was second daughter and third of five surviving children of Phoebe Ann DeSha and Murray Forbes Smith.

Was a descendant, on her father's side, of two Edinburgh, Scotland families — the Stirlings and the Forbes. Was, on her mother's side, the granddaughter of Robert DeSha, Tennessee legislator, Congressman and militia general; and was niece of Joseph DeSha, Governor of Kentucky. Was an adventurous and determined child.

1861. Moved with her family to New York City, when the coming of the railroads greatly altered her father's export business in Mobile. Lived at 40 Fifth Ave.

1866. Moved, in the fall, to France, where her father still wished to reestablish himself in the export trade. Was educated in French schools, became fluent in French, was an unruly student, but made many friends and was known for her very long and beautiful auburn hair.

1870. Returned, with her family to N.Y.C.

1871. Was grieved by the death of her mother, always reliable in holding the family together. Became concerned over family finances and the continued inability of her father to adjust to the increased pace of doing business in N.Y.C.

1875. On April 20, married William Kissam Vanderbilt, son of the country's richest man, William H. Vanderbilt. Became a favorite of this new father-in-law, also of mother-in-law Maria.

1875. Was again grieved, this time by her father's death, only two weeks after her wedding.

1876. Began a concern that the whole Vanderbilt family was considered as new money and therefore not acceptable in Mrs. Caroline Astor's hierarchy of N.Y. society.

1877. On March 2, gave birth to her first child, daughter Consuelo.

1878. On October 26, gave birth to her first son, William Kissam, Jr.

1878. Approved husband's plans for Idlehour, a country home on their estate near Oakdale, L.I.; designed by architect Richard Morris Hunt in a Queen Anne style, completed by 1880.

1878. Assisted in drawing up plans, again using R.M. Hunt, to build a French chateau at 660 Fifth Ave., to assist Vanderbilt family in becoming recognized. Received approval of plans from father-in-law, who then agreed to fund the chateau. Saw it through, in every detail, to its completion in 1882 and the furnishing of chateau in 1882-83.

1879. Became annoyed at the difficulty of obtaining a box for the opera at Academy of Music at 14th St. and Irving Place. Began contacting all the Vanderbilts and other new-money families to collect funds to build a new opera house at 39th St. and Broadway.

1883. Required Mrs. Astor to leave her card, before she and her daughter Carrie would be welcome to attend the approaching costume ball and bring their rehearsed quadrille. Felt relieved, when card was delivered to her door, that Mrs. Astor was capitulating.

1883. On March 26, joined her husband in giving the costume ball of the century for 1200 guests, to assure the Vanderbilt position in N.Y. society and to introduce her guests to their new chateau. Was pleased that she and Mrs. Astor could now see eye to eye, since they were both the wives of second sons, and that she was assured all the Vanderbilts would henceforth receive Mrs. Astor's approval.

1884. On July 6, gave birth to a second son, Harold Stirling.

1886. On October 14, attended, with husband and family, the christening of their first yacht, *Alva*, named after her. Was responsible for designing its impressive interior and choosing its furnishings.

1887. Cruised with husband, children and guests to Cuba, Nassau, Port-au-Prince and to Georgia.

1887 – 88. Cruised with husband, children and guests to Europe, Turkey, Egypt and up the Nile; guests included Oliver Hazard Perry Belmont and Winfield Scott Hoyt. Realized, because of neglect, a rift was beginning between W.K. and herself.

1888 – 92. Saw plans underway, with R.M. Hunt, to design and build a summer home in Newport, RI. Assisted with interior and exterior. Hoped the project would hold marriage together; though W.K. paid the bills and presented house to her for her 39th birthday, he also unloaded responsibility of the house and further endangered the marriage.

1889. In February, took another cruise to Europe, with guests Belmont and Hoyt again included. Realized she and Belmont were attracted.

1890. From February to July, again cruised with husband and guests to Madeira and the Mediterranean.

1892. On August 19, formally opened, along with W.K., their Newport mansion, eventually called Marble House, to great approval.

1893. Entertained, though not always joined by husband, for the season at Marble House.

1893. On November 23, began cruise to India, with W.K., Consuelo, Harold, and guests which included Belmont and a N.Y. bachelor Winthrop Rutherfurd. Became opposed to growing attachment between W.R. and her daughter. Was left, by husband, in the company of Belmont.

1894. Left cruise, after an argument, in Calcutta. Went to Paris with W.K., Consuelo and Harold. Aware that differences over daughter and W.R. caused husband to leave for U.S.

1894 – 95. Conducted a search, for a year and a half, for a more desirable suitor for Consuelo. Carefully looked over eager possibilities and their financial and political status. Finally settled on, though Consuelo felt still attached to W.R., the Ninth Duke of Marlborough. Invited him to Marble House for an east coast tour.

1895. On March 5, divorced W.K. Vanderbilt on N.Y. State traditional grounds of adultery.

1895. On July 31, was saddened by the death of her beloved architectural mentor Richard Morris Hunt. Was asked by his wife Catherine to arrange the floral pieces at his funeral. Was impressed at the number of prominent architects, trained in Hunt's Studio Building atelier, who were present at the final rites.

1895. On November 6, was present with sons at the wedding of Consuelo and the Ninth Duke of Marlborough. Was relieved and grateful that her husband not only previously arranged the marriage settlement but that he also walked his daughter down the aisle. Still felt this European marriage would give her daughter more personal consideration and status than an American union. But also realized she was one of 500 parents now feeling the same thing, but were considered by the public as obtaining European titles in exchange for American money.

1896. On January 11, married O.H.P. Belmont. Arranged, because both were divorced, to have wedding at her house at 24 E. 72nd St., and to be married by William L. Strong, mayor of N.Y.C.

1896. Closed Marble House, which she had received in divorce settlement, and moved into her new husband's Belcourt, an interesting R.M. Hunt mansion at end of Bellevue Ave. in Newport. Began an active social life, which extended over the period of their marriage, entertaining celebrities and intellectuals. Began remodeling Belcourt.

1897. On September 18, welcomed birth of her grandson, the Marquis of Blandford and the Tenth Duke of Marlborough. Was present at his birth.

1898. On October 14, welcomed birth of her grandson Lord Ivor

Charles Spencer-Churchill.

1898 – 99. Supported the new political career of her husband, O.H.P., son of August Belmont, the American Rothschild, and chairman of the Democratic National Committee. Assisted in his publishing of newspaper *The Verdict*, beginning in 1899. Approved of his leadership of the William Jennings Bryan democrats.

1899. On September 7, joined her husband in holding the first electric car rally in Newport. Arranged the route, the decoration of the cars, the Belcourt pre-party, and the evening party at Gray Craig Park, Oliver's country home. Was gratified by praise from guests and the press.

1899. Supported her husband's continued interest in raising prize horses, also in racing horses at his family's Belmont Park on L.I., and acquiring one of New England's best collections of carriages.

1899. Joined her husband in beginning the plans for their chateau at 477 Madison Ave., N.Y.C., to house his additional art, book, antiques, and armor collection.

1900 Supported O.H.P. as delegate to the Democratic National Convention in Kansas City, Mo., which nominated William Jennings Bryan for President.

1900. Welcomed birth of Muriel, daughter of son William K., Jr. and his wife Virginia.

1901 – 03. Backed O.H.P. in his political career, representing the Hell's Kitchen 13th District in N.Y.C., in U.S. Congress, for two sessions within one term. When in Washington D.C., stayed at the Willard Hotel.

1903. Welcomed the birth of Consuelo, daughter of son William K., Jr. and his wife Virginia.

1904. Was deeply troubled by the failure of Consuelo's marriage, caused by the Duke's unreasonableness and infidelity. Visited her, along with O.H.P., at Blenheim Palace, ancestral home of the Duke, whenever possible. Joined O.H.P. in financing the maintenance of the Palace.

1904. Was proud of son W.K., Jr.'s attempt to begin the establishing of the American automobile through racing, on routes on L.I., calling it the Vanderbilt Cup Races. Was impressed by assistance of wife Virginia.

1904 – 08. Supported O.H.P.'s organizational activities at: Belcourt; chateau, 477 Madison; St. Regis Hotel; and home Brookholt, Hempstead, L.I.

1907. Welcomed birth of William Kissam III, son of W.K., Jr. and Virginia.

1908. On February 21, joined O.H.P. in grief over news of accidental death by asphyxiation of his daughter Natica; by former marriage to Sara Whiting.

1908. On June 10, was shocked by the sudden death of her husband, from complications after an appendectomy. Felt her life was over. Arranged for his burial at Woodlawn Cemetery in New York, instead of at Belmont family plot at Newport, R.I. Had sons of R.M. Hunt design and build a chapel at Woodlawn, to honor O.H.P. Belmont, and as a final resting place; eventually intended also for herself.

1909. Continued remodeling of Belcourt, with architect John Russell Pope, in order to put it up for sale. Also completed the chateau at 477 Madison Ave., which she and O.H.P. had begun.

1909. Resumed her interest in the American Woman's Suffrage Movement, being originally inspired by leader Anna Howard Shaw.

1909. On August 24, reopened Marble House and gave a public party to further the cause of suffrage. Gratified that 500 attended.

1909. Endorsed the Women's Trade Union League during the strike of the garment workers; repeated endorsement in 1913 strike.

1909. Wrote article, "Woman's Right to Govern Herself", published in November issue of *The North American Review.*

1909 – 10. Was founder and president of the Political Equality Association.

1910 – 14. Brought central office of National American Woman Suffrage Association from Warren, Ohio to N.Y.C. Rented and furnished office space, and founded their press bureau. Made speeches, walked picket lines, passed out leaflets, carried banners, organized soup kitchens, opened 11 suffragist settlement houses, and held public meetings and lectures at her Madison Ave. chateau.

1910. Wrote article, "How Can Women Get the Suffrage?", for *The Independent*, March 31.

1910. Wrote article, untitled, for *Harper's Bazaar*, March issue.

1910. Wrote article, "Woman Suffrage as It Looks To-Day", for *The Forum*, March issue.

1911. Wrote article, "Why I Am a Suffragist", for *The World To-day*, October issue.

1912. On May 4, led the shopgirl section of a suffrage parade, after working hours, up Fifth Ave., to Carnegie Hall for an evening rally.

1912. Financially rescued Max Eastman's socialist magazine *The Masses*.

1912 – 14. Commissioned Richard Howland Hunt and Joseph Howland Hunt, sons of R.M. Hunt, to design and build an elegant Chinese Teahouse, on the Cliff Walk edge of her Marble House property.

1913. Landscaped home Brookholt in Hempstead, L.I., but further used property for agricultural experiments begun by fellow suffragists in 1911.

1913. Offered her Paris house to Christabel Pankhurst and other British suffragettes who were fleeing the British police and their "cat and mouse game" of re-arresting suffragettes after their recovery from the adverse physical effects of forced feeding and incarceration.

1913. Wrote foreword to Christabel Pankhurst's "Story of the Woman's War" article in the November issue of *Good Housekeeping*.

1914. On February 12, became a member of the Congressional Union for Woman Suffrage, founded by Alice Paul and Lucy Burns.

1914. On July 8 and 9, held a suffragist event, The Conference of Great Women, at Marble House and its Teahouse; with daughter Consuelo as both guest of honor and one of the Conference's impressive speakers, regarding her extensive social work with both men and women in London.

1914. On July 24, formally opened the Chinese Teahouse with a lavish Chinese costume ball in the gold room of Marble House, preceded by colorful Chinese-theme dinners in the private homes of guests, given by the guests themselves.

1914. On August 30 and 31, held an executive meeting, at Marble House, to plan the strategy of boycotting political candidates who were not in favor of women's suffrage — a turning point in the Movement.

1914. Organized, assisted by her secretary, Doris Stevens, the U.S. lecture tour of Christabel Pankhurst, the English militant suffragette. (These women were called suffragettes in Great Britain as a nickname, but were called suffragists in the U.S.)

1914. In November, was approached by women from the Southern State Woman Suffrage Conference opposed to action on the federal level. Did not agree but gave them $10,000.00 to further suffrage activities in the South.

1915. Was an organizer of the Woman's Party Convention, held in San Francisco in September and in Washington, D.C. in December, composed of women delegates already given the vote in 12 states by 1915.

1915. Commissioned the sons of R.M. Hunt to design and build a castle at the ocean at Sands Point, L.I., on 18 acres of property and adjacent to the Sands Point Lighthouse (purchased later in 1924). Wished castle to combine several styles and periods and to rise five stories from the shore into the sky, with traditional battlements, balconies, turrets, towers and gables; and with its interior to be beautifully austere and to honor — with statues, murals and frescoes — Joan of Arc, a true figure-head of women's rights. Wanted castle to become a gathering place for members and leaders of the suffrage movement and to be an inspiration for them to continue their vigorous efforts until the vote was won.

1916. Sold Belcourt, for $100,000, to late husband's brother Perry Belmont, a lawyer, U.S. Representative in the 47-50th Congresses, and former U.S. Minister to Spain.

1916. Wrote and produced operetta "Melinda and Her Sisters", with music and lyrics by Elsa Maxwell; performed at the Waldorf Astoria with Marie Dressler, Marie Doro, Josephine Hull and Addison Mizener in the cast; attended by many N.Y. dignitaries, including Governor and Mrs. Charles W. Whitney; and considered a success, both as a fundraiser and as a theme-operetta on the suffragist cause.

1916 – 17. Worked toward a federal suffrage amendment, with Congressional Union for Woman Suffrage, serving on its executive board.

1917. Dictated her memoirs, in essay style, to co-suffrage-worker Sara Bard Field, using the convenience and privacy of her Chinese Teahouse.

1917. Served with the National Woman's Party, the new successor to the Congressional Union for Woman Suffrage.

1917 – 18. Felt her financial funds should be devoted to suffrage and not to the WWI effort, being assured many Vanderbilts were already serving in the various armed forces.

1919. Provided a house at Eze-sur-Mer on the French Riviera, where her daughter could come for medically recommended recuperation from exhaustion from her social work and from continued concern over the Duke's refusal to give her a divorce after 13 years of legal separation.

1919. Backed her fellow suffragists in the final push for a federal amendment: pleading with President Wilson; picketing the White House; and protesting being jailed and force-fed, attacked by the police, incarcerated in abandoned and unheated buildings, and jeered by the public.

1920. Financed, in late spring, the last push — the train trip of pro-suffrage lobbyists to Tennessee to convince their legislators that their crucial consensus would finally push the movement over the top.

1920. On July 22, was informed of the death of W.K. Vanderbilt, in France, from complications following an earlier heart attack. Knew, when his body was brought to the U.S., she would not be invited to his funeral to be held at the chateau at 660 Fifth Ave., but instead she paid her own private tribute to his memory —in respect for all his accomplishments, their shared years of marriage, and his being a good and caring father to their three children.

1920 – 22. Continued to use her Beacon Towers castle, during the season, as a recuperation refuge and a gathering place for fellow-suffragists, and made it the site of the 1920 N.W.P. Conference.

1920. On August 26, rejoiced with other leaders, over the certification, ratification, and declaration into law of the 19th Amendment. Simply toasted the victory at the National Woman's Party Headquarters in Washington, D.C., too exhausted to organize and hold a parade. But received word from N.Y.C. that a parade, though small, was being held, led by Carrie Chapman Catt down Seventh Ave.

1920. Button-holed Winston Churchill, asking him to convince his cousin the Duke that he must give Consuelo a divorce. In addition, berated Churchill for not politically defending the British suffragettes during their prolonged struggle.

1920. On May 14, felt relieved and rewarded that Consuelo was legally and finally granted a divorce.

1921. On July 4, rejoiced at marriage of Consuelo to Colonel Jacques Balsan, a French aviation pioneer, balloonist, and hero of WWI. But did not attend ceremony at Queen's Chapel in London. Was too aware the British newspapers blamed her for pressing for the divorce from the Duke, and did not wish news reporters to disturb the ceremony.

1921. Was elected president of the National Woman's Party. Was thereafter in Europe frequently, working for equality for women, including international citizenship for women who desired it.

1921. Contributed $146,000.00 for the purchase of a large house in Washington, D.C., as headquarters for the National Woman's Party. Attended 1922 opening. In 1927 sold house to U.S. Government for site of new Supreme Court Building. In 1928 purchased the Sewall mansion, at 144 Constitution Ave., Northeast. Was honored when, in 1931, it was named Alva E. Belmont House.

1922. Wrote article, "Women as Dictators", published in September issue of *Ladies Home Journal.*

1922. In November, wrote, with Alice Paul, a Declaration of Principles. Approved at N.W.P. headquarters, Washington, D.C.

1922. Wrote article, "What the Woman's Party Wants", published in December 23 issue of *Collier's.*

1923. Hired Clare Booth as her personal secretary when attended 75th Anniversary of Women's Rights, held at Seneca Falls, N.Y., in July. Saw Equal Rights Amendment (Lucretia Mott Amendment) approved and contributed to its writing.

1923. Decided to join the Balsans, now located on the French Riviera. Purchased villa at Eze-sur-Mer, naming it Villa Isoletta, and remodeling it. Joined the Balsans in entertaining international figures in politics and the arts.

1923. Sold her chateau at 477 Madison Ave. to U.S. journalist and publisher Arthur Brisbane; chateau was subsequently demolished.

1925. Was saddened that her former chateau at 660 Fifth Ave. was torn down. Was aware her late husband's wife sold the chateau and that her sons tried to save it. Also knew parts of it went to the Metropolitan Museum and to houses being constructed, but felt that N.Y.C. should revere and save its architectural treasures.

1926. Was surprised when Consuelo reported the Duke now wanted an annulment of their 1895 marriage. Was told this would allow the

Duke to become a full member of the Catholic church and to remarry Gladys Deacon in a Catholic ceremony. Realized an annulment would also allow Consuelo to be accepted by her husband's Catholic family, as no longer a divorced woman. So joined her daughter in applying for an annulment, from the Catholic Rota. Testified before an English tribunal of Catholic priests that she had forced Consuelo to marry the Duke, making her testimony as strong as possible to secure the annulment. Pleased when request was sent to Rota and granted and that it retained the titled validity of grandsons Blandford and Ivor; annulment granted on July 29.

1926. Was assured all procedures would be private. Was therefore shocked when the Duke later went to Rome to be received by the Pope as a no longer divorced man. So was not surprised that the *New York Times* discovered this and published the story. As always, took the ridicule she received, philosophically. Continued to live most of the year in France, but made annual visits to U.S. for N.W.P. events.

1926. Attended the convention of the International Woman Suffrage Alliance, in Paris.

1927. Sold Beacon Towers castle to Mr. and Mrs. William Randolph Hearst, to house their art and antiques collection.

1927. Purchased a chateau in France near Fontainebleau and near the chateau of Consuelo and Jacques purchased the year before, at Saint Georges-Motel. Restored and enhanced the interior. Improved the exterior, including paving its fore court with paving stones brought from Versailles, and doubling the width of its river. Again, with the Balsans, entertained a variety of international guests, including Alice Paul, who joined her in continuing the work of the International Council in Geneva.

1928 – 33. Furnished and maintained a recreation hostel for nurses from the American Hospital in Paris.

1928. Arranged for a statue of St. Joan of Arc to be placed in an old stone church in the village of Augerville-la-Riviere near her chateau. Asked, because she was an Episcopalian, her old friend Bessie Lehr, Mrs. Harry Lehr, a Catholic, to donate and present statue.

1929 – 30. Was able, through the National Woman's Party, to get President Hoover to change his mind on granting women equal citizenship.

1930. Urged, at the Hague Conference on the Codification of International Law, the removal of legal disabilities against women.

1930. Continued working toward the abolition of child labor. Continued contributing funds to the Episcopal Seaside Home for Children, even though earlier forced to resign from their board "because she was a divorced woman"; but retaliating in 1926, when asked to make a contribution to a St. John the Divine Cathedral, by refusing "as a divorced woman".

1930. Made a gift of $100,000.00 to the Nassau Hospital at Mineola, L.I.

1930. Was proud of son Harold Stirling Vanderbilt's America's Cup Victory, sailing his yacht *Enterprise*, over challenger Sir Thomas Lipton, sailing yacht *Shamrock V.*

1930. Took a 7-week tour of Egypt, up the Nile aboard houseboats, and touring the Valley of Kings with Howard Carter, man who discovered tomb of Tutankhamen. Accompanied by Consuelo, W.K. Vanderbilt, Jr. and friends.

1931. Was honored when son William K. Vanderbilt, Jr. named his new yacht *Alva*, and that it began a two-year cruise to circumnavigate the globe and bring back marine specimens for his Marine Museum at Eagle's Nest, his estate in Centerport, L.I.

1931. Wrote article, "Are Women Really Citizens?", published in September issue of *Good Housekeeping.*

1932. Reluctantly took back Belcourt from Perry Belmont and paid three year's of back taxes. Then willed Belcourt to nephew of O.H.P. Belmont, August Belmont IV.

1932. Suffered a stroke and became partially paralyzed, but still managed to be mobile by driving a pony cart each day around her garden. Was watched over solicitously by Consuelo and Jacques.

268

Felt so much sympathy for her nurses and employees that she installed a bowling alley on her property for their recreation.

1932. Was taken to her house in Paris for additional care.

1932. Sold Marble House to Mr. Frederick H. Prince of Boston and president of Armour & Co.

1933. On January 26, died of bronchial and heart complications as a result of her previous stroke. Was 80 years of age.

1933. On January 28, was given an Episcopal funeral, in Paris, at the American Cathedral Church of the Holy Trinity.

1933. On February 11-12, was given an Episcopal Funeral in the U.S. at St. Thomas Church in N.Y.C. Before her services, her funeral hearse was honored with a police escort up Fifth Ave. Was granted a two-day tribute by representatives of the National Woman's Party as honor guard, as her body lay in state for the public to pass by in homage. Was further honored by a "triumphantly symbolic" funeral service, "with suffrage societies flying their banners as they came up the aisle wave upon wave"; the official banner "Failure Is Impossible" was displayed; a poem "Weep, Ah Weep No More", which she had written, was sung as a hymn. Was paid great respect by those who attended, which included ambassadors, judges, supreme court justices, intellectuals of the time, and many persons involved in the arts.

1933. On February 12, was laid to rest, opposite her husband Oliver Hazard Perry Belmont, in the chapel she had built in Woodlawn Cemetery, N.Y.; a beautiful miniature copy of St. Hubert, the chapel at Chateau Amboise, in France, which was also the final resting place of Leonardo da Vinci. Was given the final honor that suffragist flags were placed beside her coffin by co-worker Alice Paul and secretary Doris Stevens. Was paid a last tribute by members of her family, which included: Harold Stirling Vanderbilt, William Kissam Vanderbilt, Jr., Col. and Mrs. Jacques Balsan, the Marquis and Marchioness of Blandford, Vanderbilt grandchildren, and representatives from the Belmont family.

1933. On July 8, was given a commemorative pageant at Sylvan

Theater in Washington, D.C.

1933 – on. Was memorialized in many personal, magazine, and newspaper acknowledgements for her lifetime of achievement. But for the past fifty years has not been memorialized in proportion to her achievements in the American Woman's Suffrage Movement.

1963. In December, was honored by the purchase of Marble House, with funds donated by her son Harold Stirling Vanderbilt, by the Preservation Society of Newport County from the Frederick H. Prince Trust. In additional tribute, received from the Prince Trust the return of most of the original furnishings, which had been placed in storage, of Marble House. Was paid great respect, along with Richard Morris Hunt, for the original design of the interior, by its subsequent restoration. And was granted additional honor by its being opened to the public for viewing, appreciation, and study.

1992. Honored by celebration of the 100th Anniversary of the Opening of Marble House, August 19, 1892. Commemoration arranged by Preservation Society of Newport County and held at Marble House in August, with exhibits and festivities open for members and the public to enjoy.

CONSUELO VANDERBILT BALSAN
(NINTH DUCHESS OF MARLBOROUGH)
1877-1964

Born March 2, 1877, New York City. First child and only daughter of William K. and Alva Vanderbilt.

Obtained education through tutors, instructors and a range of European governesses. Was early fluent in French. Was given lessons in dancing, voice, music, deportment, etiquette, grooming and dressing well. Was instructed by her mother, at their Long Island home Idlehour. Along with her two brothers, learned to sail a boat, ride a pony, drive a pony cart, and to also become proficient in the domestic arts.

In New York City, attended the opera, concerts, and St. Thomas Episcopal Church. Became a world traveler, accompanying her family on many world cruises. Began a lifelong habit of being an avid reader. Developed a charming and impish sense of humor.

1893. Fell in love, during a Mediterranean cruise, with guest passenger Winthrop Rutherfurd. Though her father approved, could not pursue romance because mother felt W.R. was too old, sophisticated, a playboy, and not serious about his law practice.

1894 – 95. Accompanied by her mother, conducted a search over Europe for a suitable husband — her mother being convinced a European wife received more consideration and status than an American. Was aware soaring taxation in Europe encouraged marriages with rich American girls, in fact 500 of them. Though still felt she was in love with W.R., finally settled on the Ninth Duke of Marlborough, who was invited to the Vanderbilt's mansion Marble House in Newport, R.I., in Aug. and Sept., 1895.

1895. On November 6, married the Ninth Duke of Marlborough in largest international wedding of its time, at St. Thomas Church,

Fifth Avenue. Was aware marriage contract, as arranged by her father, gave Duke appreciable railroad stock, 1.6 million in cash, and to each of them $100,000.00 annually.

1895 – 96. After a honeymoon at Idlehour, sailed to various Mediterranean cities. Returned to the Marlborough's ancestral home Blenheim Palace, at Woodstock, Oxford, England. Consuelo had always hoped to study foreign languages at Oxford Univ., but took up her duties as the Ninth Duchess of Marlborough. Became well liked though always treated as an American; an excellent horsewoman; and a great hostess — entertaining the Prince of Wales and his entourage among many other guests. Was presented at court to the Prince of Wales and Princess Alexandra and eventually to Queen Victoria.

1897. On September 18, gave birth to the Marquess of Blandford, the Tenth Duke of Marlborough, John Albert Edward William Spencer-Churchill.

1898. On October 14, gave birth to Lord Ivor Charles Spencer-Churchill.

1898. Received her news and gossip of the outside world regarding politics, the arts, and society from a new American friend of the Duke, Gladys Marie Deacon. Gladys gradually became a friend of the Duke, alone, leading to a future separation.

1899. Was opposed to the Boer War, though supported those who served in it, including the Duke and his cousin Winston Churchill.

1902. Was inspired by Churchill, during his Tory political campaigns, to deliver her first speech; to blind veterans and victims of industrial accidents, outlining ways in which they could be technically trained and find paying jobs.

1902. After the death of Queen Victoria, and with the approval of the new king, accompanied the Duke on a social visit to Russia. Amid the royal splendor, became very aware of the poverty of the people. Caught a severe cold, which though frequently treated, resulted in a hearing problem that troubled her for the rest of her life.

1902. On August 9, was one of four ladies in waiting to Princess Alexandra when she and Edward were crowned King and Queen.

1903. Accompanied the Duke to India, at the invitation of the new Viceroy Lord Curzon, for an Indian durbar to celebrate his coronation.

1903 – 04. As a gift from her father, received the newly built Sunderland House, a London residence for herself and the Duke. In the long gallery, placed a bas-relief of the original Duke of Marlborough and placed one of Commodore Vanderbilt opposite.

1904. With continuing estrangement from the Duke, began to build a new life for herself. Dealt less with royal and more with government circles which included Curzon, Asquith and Balfour. Plus ambassadors, admirals and generals. Gave a speech, at opening of East London flower show, on hard work and sound judgment of the working man as being more effective than the utopian talk of the time.

1905. Made a trip, accompanied by sons Blandford and Ivor, to Vienna for treatment of her hearing problems. At Imperial Palace, met Emperor Franz Josef. For six weeks, with her sons, enjoyed the sights of Vienna.

1906. Received Deed of Separation from the Duke, though not given a divorce by him until 1920. Had waited until their sons were in school — in preparation for entering Eton — before seeking Deed.

1906. Already having given over Sunderland House, her new residence, as a meeting place to discuss social causes, concentrated now on assisting released men and women prisoners. Fitted out two adjoining houses as a commercial laundry, sewing factory, and day-care center for the children. Interviewed ex-prisoners to help get them other jobs, as well.

1907. Purchased a small Tudor manor house, Crowhurst, in the North Wolds.

1908. Was inspired by Rev. Wilson Carlile and his Church Army to work in slums. Tried to set a minimum wage for women working at menial jobs in East London hovels. Had these women themselves, as a first, speak at Sunderland House for the Anti-Sweating League.

1909. Gave an international conference on eugenics, at S.H., with D.S. Jordan and Margaret Sanger present. Was appointed as only non-professional member of board of National Birthrate Commission. Encouraged birth control for wives and mothers, as set up by National Council on Public Morals. Began the establishment in London of a hospital entirely managed and directed by women doctors, surgeons and nurses.

1910. Was told by King George and Queen Mary she would be welcomed back into royal circles. Grateful, but still on the liberal left, she continued; S.H. could seat 300 and was used by the famous and unknown alike to further England's many causes. Believing the rich should take responsibility for their wealth, spent $2,000,000 of her own inheritance and devoted S.H. to fund raising. Was not a political radical. Gave frequent speeches saying everyone, rich or poor, should be compelled to work every day.

1910 – 14. Used S.H. as headquarters to curb traffic in women recruited as "white slaves" for overseas brothels. Supported the Y.W.C.A., Waifs and Strays Society, and Dr. Bernardo's Homes to clothe, house, educate and train these children in skills. Worked on Band of Hope, a temperance organization. Formed self-supporting hotels for single working women. Was given a home by Sir Edgar Vincent; made it into a vacation home for working women. Became a friend of the Fabian Society and such members as Sidney and Beatrice Webb and George Bernard Shaw. Helped unions found the British Labor Party; won seats in elections. Gave her famous Friday night dinners for a gathering of intellectuals, to gain what she wished in social rights, by confronting a powerful guest directly. Entertained at her country home Crowhurst; frequent guests were Prime Minister Asquith and wife Margot, David Lloyd George, and Lord Curzon.

1914. Invited by her mother to be guest of honor at the two-day Conference of Great Women at Marble House in Newport, R.I., July 8 and 9. Gave a speech about her work at S.H. Was well received and well covered by the press. Was pleased that the Conference was the turning point in the American Women's Suffrage Movement because those who attended voted the next month to boycott political candidates opposed to granting women the vote.

1914. Safely returned in August to England, having been warned of possible attack by submarines. Predicted WWI victory but felt it would be cruel and drawn out. Non-committal about U.S. neutrality.

1914 – 18. Grateful to Duke for giving over 1000 acres of Blenheim Park for raising vegetable crops and livestock, while Palace housed soldiers and medical units.

1914 – 18. Was first choice to chair the American Women's War Relief Fund. Opened a 400 bed London hospital. Advised English-women setting up Women's Emergency Corps and raised money for their mobile canteens. Enrolled to help the Red Cross. Opened basement of S.H. as a bomb shelter. Began to set up the very important permanent register of disciplined women volunteers, to continue their functions in peacetime. Organized employment service to search for jobs for 400,000 servants displaced by the wartime shutting down of mansions. Sought to raise the status of women in domestic service. Recruited women for the army of emancipation. Supported the 30,000 suffragette march, demanding the right to serve. Insisted on a girl driver to get her around London in her little French Renault. Had to give up S.H. because could no longer heat it; loaned it to the government; finally sold it. Moved into smaller quarters near Regent's Park, where son Ivor came to live with her.

1914 – 18. Was proud of the service of her two sons: Bertie left Eton, entered Sandhurst Military College; first served as an army officer, then as a subaltern in the First Life Guards. Though Ivor failed his medical exams to enter army, became a lieutenant in the Royal Army Service Corps. Was gratified that a new Deed of Separation was signed with the Duke, covering provision of allowances for their two sons.

1918 – 21. Witnessed British women's finally obtaining the vote, but only for 30-year-olds; the age later slowly going down to 21. Founded the Women's Municipal Party; became its president; introduced women candidates; threatened to vote with the opposition if wishes were not met. Won seat as councillor in her London area, without contest. Recognized as "the best-hearted of all the British duchesses."

1918. Transferred London apartment to Bertie. Saw Ivor continue his education at Oxford, training to be an art collector and critic.

1919. Went to her mother's newly purchased villa at Eze-sur-Mer for a prescribed rest.

1919. Sought divorce from Duke; obtained through her mother's convincing Winston Churchill to influence his cousin. Made required-by-law attempts at reconciliation, plus Duke's witness to unfaithfulness. Was granted by judge, costs and a decree nisi; divorce final May 14, 1920.

1920. Shocked by sudden illness of her father and went to France to be at his side. Attended Paris funeral of her father and also his services at 660 Fifth Ave., N.Y. Spent time with her mother at mother's Long Island Scottish Castle Beacon Towers at Sands Point.

1920. Attended wedding of her son Bertie and Mary Cadogan, daughter of Viscount Chelsea, at Church of Saint Margaret's, Westminster.

1920. Resigned her various posts in London. Bid a sad farewell to all her associates of 25 years. Was now 44 years old. Sold Crowhurst. Went to live in a small Paris house, a previous gift from her father. Was visited by her mother and her Aunt Jenny Tiffany.

1921. On July 4, married her longtime romantic attachment, French aviation pioneer and hero, Col. Jacques Balsan, war associate of her father in the Escadrille Lafayette. At Chapel Royal Savoy in London. (The Duke married Gladys Deacon in Paris on June 24, 1921.)

1921. Together with Jacques, furnished house in Paris which overlooked the Champs de Mars. Entertained French government and military dignitaries plus the Paris intellectuals of the time.

1922. Bought land and Romanesque convent of Le Thoronet, a

Cistercian abbey, on Rue du General Lambert, in Eze-sur-Mer near her mother, with a view of Cote d'Azur. Calling it Lou Sueil, The Hearth, again made home a center of entertaining, joined by her mother's own circle of friends and suffragists, now with international goals.

1926. Assisted French President Lebrun to raise funds for and build a 360 bed hospital at the fortress hill of Vincennes and dedicated to Marshal Foch. (After German occupation of it in WWII, Consuelo was named Honorary President at its 1950 rededication as Foundation Foch du Mont Valerian.)

1926. On April 13, welcomed birth of grandson George Vanderbilt Henry Spencer-Churchill; to be Eleventh Duke of Marlborough.

1926. Joined the Duke in seeking an annulment of their 1895 marriage; thus obtaining the opportunity to assuage the disapproving family of her husband Jacques by being remarried in a Catholic ceremony; and to give the Duke a long-awaited chance to become more than a divorced lay member of the Catholic Church. Received annulment from the Catholic Rota on July 29, 1926; also a declaration that sons Bertie and Ivor were legitimate offsprings.

1926. Sold Paris house. Purchased a chateau at Saint Georges-Motel, on the border of Normandy near the forest of Dreux; a tall, elegant house with towers, a moat, and an old mill; again ideal place for Bertie and Mary's sons George and Charles, and daughters Sarah, Caroline and Rosemary to visit. Conducted a summer play school for boys and girls. Built a children's hospital nearby, with playgrounds. (Chateau was occupied and used in WWII as headquarters for the German Luftwaffe.)

1931. Was given the Gold Cross as a member of the French Legion of Honor; pinned on by husband Jacques.

1931. Joined her mother, who had earlier obtained a chateau near Fontainebleau, in entertaining the dignitaries and celebrities of the world and also promoting an International Council to secure equal rights for women, co-directed by Alice Paul.

1933. Supervised her mother's last years after two strokes. Attended mother's funeral services in Paris. Accompanied her body to New York, attended two-day tribute and services at St. Thomas, and final interment at chapel mother build for herself and husband Oliver Hazard Perry Belmont at Woodlawn Cemetery.

1934. Founded a preventorium, a tuberculosis hospital for children, near her Saint Georges-Motel chateau, which later accommodated refugee children at beginning of WWII.

1936. Apprehensive of war, purchased an oceanfront villa near Palm Beach, calling it Casa Alva. Shipped their prized possessions there.

1939. Attended debutante ball of granddaughter Sarah in summer at Blenheim. Discussed approaching war with Winston Churchill. Became concerned over Nazi Soviet Pact of Aug. 23, 1939.

1940. Endured freezing winter at Saint Georges-Motel. Provided serums and certified milk for children of incoming refugees, with increase of refugees after invasion to Lowlands. Helped provide food and lodging. Bid farewell to Jacques who rejoined the French Army; and to Bertie who now served in Britain's Brigade of the Guards.

1940 – 45. Saw Blenheim Palace again be given over for war use, her son, the Tenth Duke, now being Military Liaison Officer to regular commander of Southern Region and Lt. Col. Liaison Officer, U.S. Forces. Proud also of son's wife Mary who became Chief Commandant in the Auxiliary Territorial Services, and later served in the British Red Cross.

1940. Informed by Red Cross she was marked on German list for capture and holding for ransom. Realized not protected by U.S. neutrality because now married to a French citizen.

1940. Pleased Winston Churchill was now prime minister. But knew Germans were advancing by tank and plane. Was very aware her region was now overwhelmed by refugees.

1940. Tried to move tuberculosis hospital to Pau, near Spanish border; later accomplished by artist Paul Maze, friend and tenant.

Heard Germans were occupying her chateau. Knew must flee. With Jacques protecting her, moved to Bordeaux. Told documents were inadequate and all money funds frozen. Went to Bayonne to obtain visa to cross Spain into Portugal. Finally got passports stamped. Hastened to Consulate of Spain. Were cleared to cross next day at San Sebastian. Sold car to get train fare to Lisbon. Grateful brothers Willie and Harold Vanderbilt had tickets waiting for them to cross Atlantic to U.S. on a clipper flying-boat to safety.

1940. Pleased about birth of Bertie and Mary's second son, Charles George William Colin Spencer-Churchill.

1941 – 45. Stayed in U.S. when Jacques returned to France to serve with Gen. Charles De Gaulle, organizing the Free French. Proud that son Ivor earned the French Legion of Honor for his work with the Free French. Saw her family fortune dwindle with failing railroad stocks and increasing taxation. Still continued to make contributions, for various causes.

1944. On January 8, shocked by death of her brother Willie, from a heart ailment. Impressed by the many tributes paid to him at time of his funeral and subsequently.

1946. Sold her Renoir painting, La Baigneuse, for $115,000 to buy food for French children. Sold Saint Georges-Motel chateau.

1946. Relieved Jacques returned from the war. Purchased a house with gardens at Oyster Bay on Long Island's north shore. Later rented an apartment in Sutton Place, N.Y.C.; purchased a house at Southampton, L.I. and one at Hypoluxo Island, Florida.

1946 – 56. Lived very happily in their various homes and entertained old friends. Tended Jacques faithfully when he became ill and finally bedridden at their home at Sutton Place. Wished also to be with Ivor, who had developed brain cancer. Knew he'd be cared for by wife Elizabeth Cunningham, also pleased at the birth of their son, Robert William Charles, in 1954, but distraught at the terminal condition of both men.

1956. On September 17, informed of death of Ivor. Arranged for him to be buried near Blenheim at Bladon Cemetery next to the chapel.

1956. On November 6, bid farewell to Jacques. Sadly accompanied his body back to France for burial in the Balsan family tomb. Then went to Bladon to lay flowers on grave of Ivor, to visit his family, and to visit Bertie and Mary and family at Blenheim.

1957. Was grateful and pleased that granddaughter Sarah came to U.S. to live with her. And loved Sarah's four daughters: Serena, Alexandra, Jacqueline and Consuelo. Was obliged to sell Casa Alva, also house at Oyster Bay, and many of her art treasures, in order to pay taxes.

1956 – 63. Continued to travel to France to Jacques' family, then to England to see Ivor's family and to see Bertie and his family at Blenheim.

1959. Was delighted by unexpected visit of Winston Churchill, after his being entertained at the White House by President Dwight Eisenhower and also by financier and statesman Bernard Baruch. Knew she, at age 82, and Winston, at age 84, had much "catching up" visiting to do, and was pleased it could all take place at her Southampton home.

1961. Was grieved by death of Bertie's wife Mary, the Tenth Duchess of Marlborough. Comforted the family. Chose, at their request, the music for Mary's funeral (which was duplicated for her own funeral at St. Thomas in 1964).

1964. On December 6, died at house at Southampton, after suffering a stroke. Planned own Dec. 9 funeral. Wished, according to Episcopal tradition, for no eulogy to be given. Having returned to the Episcopal faith, shortly after the 1926 annulment of her marriage to the Duke, granted by the Catholic Rota, she wished her funeral to be held at St. Thomas Episcopal Church; services were conducted by the Rev. Dr. Frederick M. Morris, of St. Thomas, and by the Rev. H.J. Gary, of Southampton. Selected the hymns to be sung: "Fight the Good Fight" and "Jesus Lives". Arranged for anthem "How Lovely Is Thy Dwelling Place" to be sung by a 60-voice choir. Requested a simple mahogany coffin, which was covered with a blanket of white roses, carnations, phlox, and Southern smilax.

Received a sheath of pink roses and carnations from her brother Harold Stirling Vanderbilt and his wife Gertrude, who could not attend. Also received a basket of pink and white gladiolas and carnations from one of her three surviving bridesmaids, Margaret (Daisy) Post. Was further honored by many floral pieces banking the chancel rail.

Would have been proud of others officiating: Head usher, Earl E.T. Smith, former Ambassador to China and former husband of her niece and namesake Consuelo, Mrs. N. Clarkson Earl. Other ushers and honorary pallbearers: Alfred Gwynne Vanderbilt II, William H. Vanderbilt III, Henry Francis du Pont, Hugh Chislom, Jr., Barclay Warburton, William L. Hutton, Joseph Meehan, Milton W. Holden, Winston Thomas, and Col. Serge Obolensky.

Would have been gratified at family and friends who attended: surviving son the Tenth Duke of Marlborough, the Marquis of Blandford; his brother Lord Spencer-Churchill; his sister the former Lady Sarah Spencer-Churchill, now Mrs. Edwin F. Russell; their four daughters Serena, Alexandra, Consuelo, and Jacqueline; Countess Lázló Széchényi, Countess Anthony Szapary; Mrs. Vanderbilt Adams; Mrs. William L. Hutton; Mrs. William A.M. Burden, daughter of Florence Vanderbilt Twombly; Mrs. Searle Whitney; Mrs. Harry Payne Bingham; Mrs. Lytle Hull, the former Mrs. Vincent Astor; Mrs. John T. Pratt, Jr.; Mrs. John J. Hammond; Mrs. Stanley Grafton Mortimer; Mr. and Mrs. William Jay Schiefflin; Mrs. Blake Lawrence; Mrs. John Henry Hammond; Mrs. George Henry Warren; Mrs. Winthrop Aldrich; and Mrs. McDonnell Ford, the former Mrs. Henry Ford the 2nd.

Wished her body to be taken to Kennedy International Airport and flown to England; accompanying the coffin on its flight, were the Tenth Duke of Marlborough, the Marquis of Blandford, Lord Charles, and Mrs. Edwin F. Russell.

1964. On December 11, following her wishes, her body was buried in an English country churchyard, in the Oxfordshire village of Bladon, near Blenheim Palace. Was paid a last tribute by her family and friends as they walked behind her coffin, covered with white chrysanthemums. Again according to her wishes, she was buried next to her son Lord Ivor Spencer-Churchill, her headstone reading

"In loving memory of Consuelo Vanderbilt Balsan—mother of the Tenth Duke of Marlborough — born 2nd March 1877 — died 6th December 1964." Would have been honored that her great friend Sir Winston Churchill chose the plot next to her in which to be buried, and chose plots adjacent to her grave and that of Ivor for Lady Churchill and his family's subsequent burial.

Would have been impressed by and grateful to her family and friends who braved the chill and fog of the morning to be present at her graveside services; among those being: her son, the Tenth Duke of Marlborough; her grandchildren, the Marquis of Blandford, Lord Charles, Mrs. Edwin F. Russell, Lady Caroline Waterhouse, and Lady Rosemary Muir; Lady Churchill, son Randolph, and daughters Sara and Mary (Sir Winston Churchill, at the age of 90, could not be present); two nephews of Col. Jacques Balsan, her late husband; the widow of her son Lord Ivor Spencer-Churchill, Lady Elizabeth Cunningham Spencer-Churchill; and the Marchioness of Blandford, the former Athina "Tina" Livanos, the former wife of Aristotle Onassis.

1965. Left a 17-page will, filed on December 11, in Suffolk County Surrogate's Court, Riverhead, L.I.; to be submitted for probate on January 25, 1966. Had realized only $2,000,000 remained from her share of the Vanderbilt fortune, but financially remembered her son, grandchildren, and other members of the family, her friends, and servants; with the bulk of the estate going to granddaughter Sarah; with substantial income from family trusts going to son Bertie; and with provision made for Ivor's widow, Elizabeth and son Robert William Charles. Was remembered by the people of Bladon for her former and long-standing kindnesses to them, both personal and financial, by their comment, "She's the best woman ever to be buried here."

WILLIAM KISSAM VANDERBILT, JR.
1878-1944

Born October 26, 1878, New York City. Second child and first son of William K. and Alva Vanderbilt. Nicknamed Willie.

1889. Showed early signs of being a daredevil. Rode, when only 11, a steam tricycle from the French Riviera's Beaulieu to Monte Carlo.

Attended St. Mark's School.

1894 - 96. Was already a veteran of many cruises on *Alva*, his parent's yacht. Began sailing, himself, by owning *Osprey*, a half-rater built at Herreshoff Mfg. Co. Chartered, at age 17, the sloop *Jessica* for the summer season. Observed his father's 1895 victory for the America's Cup.

1897. Entered Harvard Univ. Became associate business manager of "The Advocate."

1898. Captained *Carmita*, gift from parents, a sloop 70 feet over-all. Navigated, for two years, New England coast waters, managing to get along without a captain.

1899. Joined, when a sophomore, the Institute of 1770. Did not finish at Harvard. Purchased a Stanley Steamer automobile.

1899. On April 4, married Virginia Graham "Birdie" Fair, daughter of Senator James Graham Fair, who amassed $15,000,000 from the Nevada Comstock Lode; also sister of Teresa "Tessie" Oelrichs, subsequent owner of Rosecliff mansion, built in 1902, in Newport, Rhode Island.

1900. Welcomed birth of their daughter Muriel.

1900. Sold *Carmita*. Bought *Virginia*, a 70-foot sloop measuring 106 feet over-all, built to race off Newport. Observed the racing professionals and seemed amazed "I won a few cups during the season."

1901. Began racing automobiles, with "The Red Devil," a Mercedes imported from Germany. Raced against Foxhall Keene down Newport's Bellevue Avenue. Imported "The White Ghost," the first racing automobile in U.S.

1902. Competed in Europe. Raced in Madrid and Vienna. Drove from Monte Carlo to Paris in 17 hours. Resided at the Paris Ritz.

1902. Purchased *Tarantula I*, a 152-foot torpedo boat, built in England by Yarrow's, her Parsons turbines being first in Western Hemisphere.

1903. Began working for the New York Central Railroad.

1903. Welcomed birth of their second daughter Consuelo.

1904. On October 8, founded Vanderbilt Cup Races, to begin establishing the American auto through racing. Required, at first, that weight for racing cars range from 881 to 2,024 lbs. Included wife Virginia in assisting him and presenting trophies in early history of races. Had the handsome trophy cup (10 1/2 gallons) designed by Tiffany & Co. Continued races in various locations, after fighting Long Island route regulations.

1904. Won American Automobile Association Cup at Ormond Beach, Florida, setting a record by doing 1 mile in 39 seconds. Also did trick bicycle riding demonstrations outside Hotel Poinciana, astonishing spectators.

1906. Received gift of chateau from father, for himself and wife, designed and built by McKim, Mead and White, located at 666 Fifth Ave. and to blend with chateau of his father and step-mother at 660.

1907. Welcomed birth of their son William Kissam III.

1907 – 10. Joined wife Virginia in having a colonial mansion, Deepdale, designed and built by Carrere and Hastings, located along Lake Success, L.I., with a gatehouse designed by John Russell Pope.

1910. Was separated but not divorced (until 1927) from his wife Virginia.

1910. Lived, after leaving the 666 Fifth Ave. chateau, at 49 East Fifty-Second Street. Then at a maisonette in the apartment tower on the northeast corner of Park Ave. and Sixty-Seventh Street.

1912. Became vice-president of the New York Central Railroad.

1912. Began building Eagle's Nest, a 6-room Japanese style house, designed by Warren and Wetmore, located in Centerport, L.I. on Northport Harbor. Continued to alter and expand the house for the next 32 years.

1914 – 16. Took the Vanderbilt Automobile Cup Race west to California. Ran the ninth race in Santa Monica, Calif., the tenth race in San Francisco, and the eleventh and final race again in Santa Monica, fearing the accumulating interruption of racing by WWI.

1917 – 18. Did sea duty, serving from March 1917 to June 1918, on *Tarantula II*, purchased by him in 1913 and now renamed SP-124 and commanded by him. Purchased, after the war, the 148 feet over-all schooner *Genesee*. Then the steam yacht *Eagle*, of 362 gross tons.

1918. Wrote of his travels in his book *A Trip Through Italy, Sicily, Tunisia, Algeria and Southern France*, which was published privately.

1918. Became president of the N.Y.C.R., serving for A.H. Smith, on leave with the U.S. Gov't.

1918. Attended night classes at Merchant Marine School at the Seaman's Church Institute, N.Y.C. Studied under Robert Huntington. then held classes in his own N.Y. Central office, studying with Thomas Sheridan and M. Maurice Gaffet. Successfully obtained a Master's Certificate.

1920. On July 22 was at his father's side at time of his death. Resolved to carry on Vanderbilt tradition.

1920. Earned the rank of Lieutenant Commander in the U.S. Naval Reserve.

1922. Bought *Ara*, a 213-foot Diesel yacht, which had served in the French Navy as a sloop-of-war. Replaced its twin motors with 1,200-horsepower Diesels. Had crossed, by 1926, the Atlantic Ocean 5 times.

1926 – 27. Cruised to the Galapagos Islands, the haunt of friend William Beebe. Sailed as captain. Invited along expert fisherman and artist William E. Belanske, trained at the Amer. Museum of Natural History, to paint the unusual wild life of the Islands. Also invited friends, among them being Mr. and Mrs. Barclay H. Warburton, Jr. Kept a careful journal of this Galapagos excursion, listing: Galapagos herons, flightless cormorants, brown boobies, blackbellied mouth fish, paperheads, orange puffers, throat whiskers, sea devils, scarlet prawns, banded serranos, and the new species of band-tailed cat shark they discovered and named *Pristinius Arae Nichols*. When returned, established an on-going marine museum at his home Eagle's Nest.

1927. On June 2, was divorced from Virginia Fair Vanderbilt.

1927. On September 5, married Rosamond Lancaster Warburton, a guest on the Galapagos cruise, daughter of Mrs. John Lancaster and divorced in late 1926 from Barclay H. Warburton Jr., grandson of John Wanamaker. Was wed at the Mairie of the Sixteenth Arrondissement.

1927. Earned, from the U.S. Merchant Marine, a sailing certificate, endorsed for all oceans and for unlimited tonnage.

1928. Sailed, again as captain, yacht *Ara* around the world, capturing marine oddities. Was once more accompanied by Belanske, now curator of his marine museum at Eagle's Nest. Again kept a careful journal, listing specimens: Moorish idol, golden flutemouth, barked scale wrasse, calico razor wrasse, fringed pipefish, and bluelined butterfly fish. By now had traveled on the *Ara* a total of 135,991 miles.

1930. Ordered Cox and Stephens to draw up the plans for a new

286

ship, to be built by Krupp Germaniawerft, with two Diesel engines to insure a sustained sea speed of 17 knots.

1931. Christened this new 264-foot yacht *Alva,* named in honor of his mother. (Was the second *Alva;* the first, owned by his father, being sunk in summer of 1892 in collision during storm off coast of Martha's Vineyard.) Hired a required crew of 43. Now owned the world's most powerful yacht, built at a cost of $2,500,000 including decoration. Hired Mr. Benson C. Martin as chief engineer.

1931 – 32. Began a cruise, lasting from July 7, 1931 to March 4, 1932, to again collect rare specimens, with Belanske aboard. Wrote an invaluable log, published privately in 1933 by Edmund Garrett of New York, entitled *West Made East, With the Loss of a Day; A Chronicle of the First Circumnavigation of the Globe Under the United States Naval Reserve Yacht Pennant; An Account of Adventures in Navigation, Diversions, Picturesque Scenes, the Everyday Life of Remote Places, and the Taking of Specimens for The Vanderbilt Marine Museum.* Again included beautiful and accurate paintings of rare fish by Belanske; and new this time, excellent photographs by Alfred Gilks of Hollywood and his assistant Robert Bronner. Was joined on cruise by wife Rose, who did historical research on foreign places and typed up the daily notes. Invited guests, which included his daughter Consuelo and husband Earl Smith, Mr. and Mrs. Pierre C. Merillon, and (ship's physician) Capt. Harry Hamilton Lane. Hired a varied crew: American, English, German, Swedish and Dutch.

1932. Realized Vanderbilt family stock, which had soared to 256 1/2 in 1929, was soon to touch 8 3/4. Endured the 1931 Committee on Interstate and Foreign Commerce investigation, which finally recognized the Vanderbilts still held substantial investment in the railway carriers and still had strong voting power. Sustained his own following shares: 27,585 of N.Y. Central; 25,890 of Pittsburgh & Lake Erie; 45,400 of Lackawanna; and 4,250 of North Western preferred. Was also on board of directors of Western Union.

1933. Was stricken by the sudden news that his 26-year-old son, William Kissam Vanderbilt III, was killed in an automobile accident. Began plans for the building of a memorial to his son.

1934. Purchased a $57,000 seaplane, which he placed on the deck of yacht *Alva*. Had it flown by his personal pilot. Began writing accounts of his air flights.

1936. Had evolved his Eagle's Nest into a rambling 24-room Spanish Moorish-style mansion. Brought hand-wrought iron gates from Idlehour for his entrance driveway. Saved two iron eagles from old Grand Central Station and used them to guard his entrance drive. Used old bricks from newly paved N.Y.C. streets for his courtyard. Brought six Greek columns from Carthage for his harbor overlook. Installed marble lions from former home Deepdale for entrance to gardens. Saved statue of Richard Morris Hunt atop 660 Fifth Ave. from 1926 destruction of that chateau, locating statue near his bell tower and its 1715 cast iron bell. Furnished house with family treasures and portraits. Entertained, assisted by wife Rose, prominent guests such as Franklin D. Roosevelt, the Duke and Duchess of Windsor, William Randolph Hearst, Douglas Fairbanks, Sr., and Sonja Henie. Had entertainment include music from his Aeolian Duo-Art 1000-pipe organ installed in a special beautifully furnished room, where it could even play automatically.

1936. Added a Memorial Wing in memory of his son W.K.V. III. Had wing designed by Ronald H. Pearce, and let it become an extension of his marine museum, started in 1922, called Hall of Fishes. Displayed here more than 17,000 specimens of shells, marine animals, wildlife, artwork and photographs from his cruises; and called the new wing the Habitat. Prominently featured trophies and memorabilia of his son's wild game hunting expeditions, including his 1931 one in the Sudan memorialized in a mural. Continuing in true sporting style, had the roof of the building serve as the first tee of his 10-hole golf course. Provided, as his last addition, a library to contain and display the many logs and diaries of his sojourns and excursions around the world.

1936. On June 27, saw the revival of his Vanderbilt Automobile Cup Races, this time at the Roosevelt Raceway, using both American and foreign cars and drivers.

1936. Purchased a 9 3/4-ton Sikorsky S 43 amphibian airplane, which had two extra gasoline tanks and an improved instrument board. Had a private aircraft hangar built for it at Eagle's Nest.

1937. Circled South America in his Sikorsky, as flown by his pilot. Felt he was too old to receive a license, but flew the plane 104 hours of the flight time. Added to his airfleet a Fairchild Seaplane and a twin-engine Gruman Amphibian. Used the Sikorsky to fly back and forth to his private dock called Alva Base at Fisher Island, near Miami, Florida, where he moored his yacht *Alva*.

1937. Saw second year of revival of Vanderbilt Automobile Cup Races. Embarrassed that the German and Italian cars were so superior to those of the Americans. Again realized his Race was interrupted by an impending war, this time WWII.

1938. Realized market performance of railway stocks was dangerously down, in spite of multiple uses for Grand Central Station and creation of such new trains for the Vanderbilt roads as: the Southwestern Limited, the Knickerbocker, the Iroquois, the De Witt Clinton, the Fifth Avenue Special, the Commodore Vanderbilt, the Advance Commodore Vanderbilt, and the Empire State Express — all these added to the 50-year glory of the Twentieth Century Limited, which on January 7, 1929 operated eastbound in 7 sections carrying 822 pampered passengers. Saw the N.Y.C.R. suffer its greatest deficit at $20,145,357. Made the public statement, "In another ten years there won't be a single great fortune left in America. The country will come back — it always does, but *we* won't."

1938. On April 18, gave New York debut for his wife's daughter, Rosemary Warburton, at roof-garden suite of the Saint Regis; Rosemary's gown designed by Molyneaux; dance music by Emil Coleman's band; and flowers by conservatories of Constance Spry.

1938 – 44. Was generous with his charities. Gave $112,500 to Vanderbilt Univ. Presented the Long Island Motor Parkway to the people of New York.

1941. On November 4, donated his beloved yacht *Alva* to the U.S. Navy, as his personal contribution to the war effort. Transferred its personal furnishings to Eagle's Nest. Saw *Alva* renovated for active war use and placed in service flagged as the patrol gunboat U.S.S *Plymouth*.

1943. On August 5, felt a great loss when the patrol gunboat, U.S.S *Plymouth*, conducting convoy escort duties enroute to Key West, Florida, was torpedoed by a German U-boat 90 miles northeast of Cape Hatteras, North Carolina. Was proud, although *Plymouth* sank in two minutes, that Lt. Ormsby M. Mitchell, Jr., USNR, in command, was credited with rescue of 85 crew members and was awarded the Navy Cross; but went on feeling the loss of this beloved yacht. (Position of sinking provided courtesy of CDR Jeffrey J. Davidsson, USN, and John C. Reilly, director of the Naval History Center, Washington, DC.)

1944. On January 8, died of a heart ailment, at age of 64. Received many tributes from family friends, fellow yachtsmen, aviators, WWI Navy comrades, and recipients of his many generosities. Was considered to be the most prominent and active member of the Vanderbilt fourth generation. Joined the other members of the family when his body was interred in the Vanderbilt mausoleum in New Dorp, Staten Island, N.Y.

1944. Left a will which set up a trust fund of several million dollars to care for Eagle's Nest, and arranged for its presentation to the County of Suffolk, which maintains it today as the Vanderbilt Museum.

1944. Left an estate of $36,000,000, and, as predicted, $30,000,000 of the estate was paid in taxes. Provision was made for his wife Rose, daughters Muriel and Consuelo and their families, from the remainder.

HAROLD STIRLING VANDERBILT
1884-1970

Born July 6, 1884, Oakdale, Long Island. Third child and second son of William K. and Alva Vanderbilt. Nicknamed Mike.

Showed early talent for sailing, as encouraged by his mother and older brother W.K. Vanderbit, Jr. Accompanied his parents on many cruises of their yachts *Alva* and, later, *Valiant*.

1895. Skippered, at age of 12, his own 14-foot sloop.

1895. Observed his father's victory in defending the America's Cup with his yacht *Defender*, against British challenger the Earl of Dunraven with his yacht *Valkyrie III*.

Attended St. Mark's School. Awarded Founder's Medal for Scholarship.

1907. Graduated from Harvard, completing his undergraduate studies in three years; even while managing the football team.

1910. Received degree from Harvard Law School.

1910. Won his first schooner race to Bermuda.

1911. In January, became assistant to the general solicitor of the New York Central Railroad.

1911. Became member of the board of First National Bank of New York.

1913. Sailed from Portland, Maine to Lisbon, Portugal in 23 days.

1914. Was elected a director of the N.Y.C.R. Was a board member of Pittsburgh & Lake Erie, Chicago & North Western, and of the Pullman Co.

1917 – 18. Served in the U.S. Navy during WWI, with the rank of lieutenant, based at Queenstown, Ireland, on submarine chasing duty.

1920. On July 22, was at his father's side at time of his death. Resolved to carry on Vanderbilt tradition.

1920 – 22. Inherited Idlehour. Closed it. Had a Parke Bernet auction of its contents. Realized $132,962 from sale. In 1922 sold Idlehour to developers Edmund D. and Charles F. Burke.

1922. Became Commodore of N.Y. Yacht Club. Was saluted by the Forty-fourth Street Clubmen for his steel-hulled, 109-foot auxiliary schooner *Vagrant*, and for his methodical attitude toward yachting.

1922. Began winning the Astor Cup and the King's Cup, usually off Newport, Rhode Island. Won, from 1922-38, 5 Astor Cups and 6 King's Cups.

1922 – 25. Won races with *Prestige*, built as a modern class M sloop. Then he ordered built for cruising, *Vara*, a 150-foot-overall steel Diesel yacht.

1925. Could, when a child, harass his father at five-point euchre. Later played auction bridge. Discovered contract bridge on a 1925 cruise from Los Angeles to Havana, adopting a principle from the kindred French game of plafond, which permitted scoring only of tricks for which a player had bid or contracted. Named his new contract bridge Club Convention or Vanderbilt Club, prior to its being called simply Contract Bridge.

1926. Joined his brother W.K.V., Jr. in selling the traditional Vanderbilt box, inherited from their father after his death in 1920, at the Metropolitan Opera House, for $200,000.

1927. Made up a scoring table for the Whist Club of N.Y., after which they issued official rules.

1927. Ordered, after becoming interested in air yachts, the Atlantic Aircraft Corp. to build a Fokker Air Yacht; capable of cruising 90 miles per hour, with six passengers aboard; top speed, 115 mph.;

wing-span, 59 ft.; with remarkable 450-horsepower Napier engine; largest privately owned U.S. air yacht and third of his fleet.

1928. Donated silver cup for annual competition between contract bridge teams.

1929. Pleased by response to the publication of his book *Contract Bridge*.

1930. Again pleased by response to publication of his book *The New Contract Bridge* and that people around the world were using his new rules of the game.

1930. Won the America's Cup, in the summer sailing season at Newport, R.I., with his yacht *Enterprise*: Length Overall, 120 feet, 6 inches. Waterline length, 80 feet. Beam, 23 feet. Draft, 14 feet, 6 inches. Hull, bronze. Sail Area, 7,583 square feet. Owned by H.S. Vanderbilt and a New York Yacht Club Syndicate. Designer, W. Starling Burgess. Builder, Herreshoff Mfg. Co. Built in Bristol, R.I. Launched, April 1930. Challenger: Sir Thomas Lipton with his yacht *Shamrock V*. Realizing before the Race he was the smallest of 4 prospective defenders, H.S.V. devised a duralumin mast, plus a wide boom, with horizontal slides to obtain a better curve for the mainsail; mechanical devices to handle more of the running rigging below deck than ever before; and most of all, a crew of 25 trained to precision performance.

1931. Held following shares: 164,648 of N.Y. Central Railroad; 43,200 of Pittsburgh & Lake Erie; 46,000 of Delaware, Lackawanna & Western; 16,000 of North Western common; 8,250 of North Western preferred; and 10,000 of Union Pacific common. Began a process, over many years, of decreasing his holdings in the Vanderbilt family property, but remained the last Vanderbilt on the board of the N.Y. Central Railroad.

1931 – 32. Gave $50,000 for relief of unemployment. Gave $25,000 to the Republican Party.

1932. Had been working on, as a sailing innovator, the timed start, known subsequently as the Vanderbilt Start. Reduced Start to a mathematical formula, which could be modified for current, but resulted in "gutsy starts with full headway".

1932. Became, as a well-rounded sportsman, an excellent tennis player. Continued not only this sport but also golf throughout most of his life.

1932. Teamed up with, in his contract bridge tournament, Waldermar von Sedtwitz, P. Hal Sims, and Willard S. Karn, and won his own trophy. Was called by his mother "the professor", because of his strict adherence to his own rules.

1933. On August 19, at age of 49, married Gertrude Lewis Conaway, age 32, daughter of Mrs. W. Barklie Henry. Arranged honeymoon, crossing Atlantic aboard the *Rex* to Cannes, then chartering yacht *Argosy*.

1933. Resided, after returning to New York, in 17-room apartment of Hotel Barclay. Owned, during subsequent years, home "El Salano", a villa, created by Treanor and Fatio, in Manalapan, Palm Beach County, Florida; and a farm in Virginia.

1934. Won the America's Cup with his yacht *Rainbow*: Length Overall, 127 feet, 6 inches. Waterline length, 82 feet. Beam, 21 feet. Draft, 15 feet. Hull, steel topside, bronze underwater. Tonnage, 141 tons. Sail Area, 7,535 square feet. Owner, H.S. Vanderbilt and a New York Yacht Club Syndicate. Designer, W. Starling Burgess. Builder, Herreshoff Mfg. Co. Built, Bristol, R.I. Launched, 1934. Challenger: Sir Thomas Sopwith (British airplane designer), with his yacht *Endeavor*.

1934 – on. Was being recognized internationally as a formidable strategist and racing helmsman.

1936. Purchased a twin-engine, low-wing Lockheed Electra Monoplane: Designed by Cox and Stevens; its Wasp Junior motors had cruising speed of over 200 miles per hour; it carried 6 passengers and had a luxury club lounge which included a buffet and a card table.

1937. Won the America's Cup with his yacht *Ranger*: Length Overall, 135 feet. Waterline length, 87 feet. Beam, 21 feet. Draft, 15 feet. Hull, steel. Sail Area 7,546 square feet. Owner, Harold S. Vanderbilt. Designer, W. Starling Burgess, Sparkman & Stephens. Builder, Bath

Ironworks. Built, Bath, Maine. (Vanderbilt's wife, Gertrude, was a member of the crew.) Challenger: Sir Thomas Sopwith, again; with his yacht *Endeavor II*.

1937. Was proud that *Ranger* was the fastest large sloop to ever defend the America's Cup. Realized only one other skipper, Charles Barr — in 1899, 1901, and 1903 — had successfully defended the America's Cup three times. Had on his mantel in his library a tiny, silver America's Cup, a copy of the 27-inch high silver trophy, never presented to the winner to keep, but which had remained in American hands since 1851.

1939. In the racing season, defeated Sir Thomas Sopwith, once more; this time with his yacht *Vim*, designed by Sparkman and Stevens; crossing the Atlantic and racing in English waters and finishing first in 12 out of 17 events.

1939. Climaxed this racing season by winning the coveted International Challenge Cup.

1939. Wrote *On the Wind's Highway, Ranger, Rainbow and Racing*. Published by Charles Scribner's Sons, New York.

1940. Again won, in competition, his own Contract Bridge Trophy. Was impressed that his rules of the game were now being used and enjoyed internationally by 40 million people.

1940. Continued with his charities: Giving $700,000 to Harvard Univ. Giving $112,500 to Vanderbilt Univ. and serving as president of its Board of Trustees. And being one of the first donors to the planning and building of the Lincoln Center for the Performing Arts in N.Y.C.

1947. Developed, after WWII, new concepts of right-of-way rules because racing was turning to smaller sloops. Was pleased rules were adopted by the North American Yacht Racing Union.

1949. Again gratified his rules of right-of-way were adopted.

1954. Had continued, for four decades, as a director of the N.Y. Central Railroad, which had become part of the Penn Central

Transportation Co., as the financial power behind the Central network. Was very aware, beginning in 1947, that Robert R. Young, chairman of the Chesapeake & Ohio Railroad, was making a bid for a Central directorship but that Young was ruled out by the Interstate Commerce Commission. Was alert to Young's subsequent resignation, in January, and his announcement that he was the Central's largest stockholder and realized that Young demanded its chairmanship, but was refused by directors. Now knew he must fight with Young for proxies of the Central's shares, so both he and Young went to court. Lost the fight to solicit proxies for the management. Offered 20 million in vain for a key block of C. & O. shares. Was out-maneuvered by Young, who was supported by his Texas oilmen friends. Was present on May 26, when votes were cast at an annual meeting in Albany.

1954. On June 14, was defeated for the chairmanship of the Central. Even though was a director of 27 other railroad enterprises, plus a director of the First National Bank of N.Y., after June 14 there was, for the first time since the 1880's, no longer a Vanderbilt on the board of the Central.

1961. Purchased an estate in Newport, R.I. Called it Rockcliff. Placed, along with the assistance of his wife, throughout its interior, color prints of all the America's Cup defenders, also various King's Cups won by him on New York Yacht Club cruises, other Cups, and particularly "The Wheel" which was used by him on all of his yachts.

1963. Formulated a major revision of his right-of-way racing rules, not only again adopted by the North American Yacht Racing Union but also throughout the world.

1963. Gave the Preservation Society of Newport County money to purchase back his mother's Marble House in Newport, R.I., owned in the interim by Frederick H. Prince, president of Armour and Co. Arranged that the house be returned to its precondition, as far as possible, thanks to the generosity of the Prince Trust. Then arranged, through the Preservation Society that the house be made ready and opened to the public. Was greatly assisted in this project by his wife Gertrude.

1967. Continued his valued interest in the America's Cup, as a member of the syndicate which built the yacht *Intrepid* for the successful 1967 defense.

1969. In October, retired from the rules committee of the North American Yacht Union. Had been a member since it was formed in 1942.

1969. Was awarded the Nathaniel G. Herreshoff Trophy of the North American Yacht Racing Union, "in recognition of his contributions to yachting as a keen competitor and a superior helmsman in international competition and as the architect of a new and improved code of racing rules".

1970. Was a longtime member of the Following Clubs: New York Yacht, Knickerbocker, Racquet and Tennis, Sewanhaka Corinthian Yacht, Brook, National Golf Links, Creek, Meadow Brook, Whist, Garden City Golf, Piping Rock, and River.

1970. On July 4, died, after only recent years of declining health. Was just 2 days short of being 87 years old. Was buried in St. Mary's Episcopal Church Yard, Portsmouth, Rhode Island. Was survived by his wife Gertrude, no children resulting from the marriage.

1980. Was memorialized by the opening of the Harold Stirling Vanderbilt Room at Marble House, this room being arranged for by his widow Gertrude, previous to her death in 1978. Located in the enlarged former bedroom of William K. Vanderbilt, Jr., on the second floor, this display of tribute to H.S.V. includes trophies and yachting memorabilia of his distinguished career, as attractively shown by the Preservation Society of Newport County. The grand focal point of the room is a portrait, painted by Bouttet de Monvel, of Harold Stirling Vanderbilt at the traditional wheel of his yacht *Ranger*, winner of the 1937 America's Cup.

REFERRAL NOTES

1. Page 6. The others connected with New York opera would be the two women: Caroline Slidell Perry, Mrs. August Belmont, with the Academy; and Eleanor Robson, Mrs. August Belmont, Jr., with the Metropolitan Opera Guild.

2. Page 16. The Studio Building would be torn down in the mid-1950s. After Alva's death, of course — had she been alive, she perhaps could have saved it.

3. Page 33. Little did Alva realize her prediction. Richard Morris Hunt did the main building for the Chicago Exposition of 1893, a part of what was called the Great White City. It was to be a permanent "city" but unfortunately burned the next year.

4. Page 58. Considering her later involvement with the pulsating world of Women's Suffrage, Alva felt perhaps Caroline Schermerhorn Astor was her first true sight of female independence.

5. Page 60. Considering Alva's future career as "a friend of the worker", they might have been wise to do so. At least as a labor arbitrator.

6. Page 61. This was the sister of Alva, Mary Virginia, who later divorced Fernando Yznaga and married William Tiffany.

7. Page 68. How prophetic this Mrs. William B. Astor was. In fact, in Alva's lifetime, there would be *two* yachts named *Alva* — the second one belonging to her son, W. K. Vanderbilt, Jr.

8. Page 119. When Rockingham and Hurlingham, plus two other favorite horses, eventually died, O.H.P. Belmont had the bodies prepared and sent to France. There, a skilled taxidermist rekindled their likeness, returned them to Belcourt Castle, and they stood in the baronial hall, along with the collection of medieval armor.

9. Page 123. These two Vanderbilts each did exactly what they intended. George W. built the fabulous Biltmore mansion in Asheville, North Carolina, and scientifically supervised his 130,000 acres of forest land. He also became an expert at farming. Frederick, in turn, managed and invested so wisely that he ended up with more money than any of the Vanderbilts of his generation—$77,000,000.

10. Page 125. Alva had purchased the large and matching Savonnerie carpet for the room. But, over the years, the magnificent floors would be used for much dancing. Her carpet would end up in the New York Metropolitan Museum of Art!

11. Page 129. Their son, William K. Vanderbilt, Jr., would indeed, forty years later, christen his own yacht *Alva II*. And it would become a distinguished ocean-exploring vessel. Given to the U.S. Navy in World War II and newly flagged as *USS Plymouth*, it met its sad end when, as a part of a convoy, it was sunk by the Germans, August 5, 1943, ninety miles northeast of Cape Hatteras. (See Chronology for William Kissam Vanderbilt, Jr., page 283.)

12. Page 149. Years later, another Vanderbilt, Shirley C. Burden, would immortalize the chairs of the Tuileries in his charming photography-book-essay, *Chairs*.

13. Page 157. It was actually Alice and Cornelius Vanderbilt's second (living) daughter Gladys who married a title, Count László Széchényi. Gertrude married an American, Harry Payne Whitney.

14. Page 164. Since that night, Alva often wondered if Jacques Balsan had subsequently been brave enough to ask for Consuelo's hand in marriage, if she would have considered him. And if *she*, Alva herself, would have considered him. If so, Consuelo and Jacques would certainly not have had to wait twenty-seven years to finally marry.

15. Page 172. Years later as actual President of the French Republic, Deshanel paid an official visit to England. Consuelo was selected as his partner in the State Quadrille at the Court Ball at Buckingham Palace. Dancing opposite King George, the two recalled the days when he not only coveted but called her his "petit Philosophe rose."

Alva was blamed for the refusal, but she proved not so far wrong. After several undignified exhibitions of folly involving his government, he threw himself out of a railway train which was traveling through a tunnel. Soon afterward he died of his injuries.

16. Page 181. Years later, Consuelo told Alva it was a frequent question: "Where is the exact spot the Battle of Blenheim took place?" This victory over the French actually took place in South West Germany, on the Danube, in 1704.

17. Page 196. And other members of the R.M. Hunt family did. One by one. It was fourteen years before Catherine was laid to rest beside him, but not until she had begun a biography and finished scrapbooks of the life of her husband for all their children and grandchildren. An earlier illness had left Catherine with very little use of her right arm and hand. Her heart had also become weak, and she tired easily. So, collecting material for the biography and doing the scrapbooks was more than a labor of love. It was a physical triumph.

18. Page 212. Oliver Hazard Perry Belmont belonged to the following clubs: Brook, Raquet and Tennis, New York Athletic, Union, Knickerbocker, Manhattan, Lawyers', Meadow Brook, New York Yacht, Turf and Field, University, New York; Metropolitan Clubs of both N.Y. and Washington, D.C.; and served as Grand Master of the St. John's Lodge of Masons in Newport.

19. Page 220. Azar remained in the service of Alva, until the early Twenties, at which time he departed the U.S. to live in France.

20. Page 225. O.H.P. Belmont's butler at Belcourt Castle was Mr. Frederick Boucher. O.H.P. encouraged him to read every book in his art and antiques library, over the many years of Boucher's employment. Upon retirement, Boucher established a successful antiques gallery in New York City. After his death, his daughter continued with his work, as an authority in the art and antiques field.

21. Page 226. In 1956, Belcourt was purchased by the Tinney Family: Harold, his wife Ruth, son Donald, daughter-in-law Harle, and their Aunt Nellie Fuller. Furnishing Belcourt with their own

fine collection of impressive art treasures, the family began to manage and, to this year of 1992, still maintains this Castle for the enjoyment and pleasure of the public. A continuing and very devoted labor of love.

22. Page 233. In 1927, Alva sold Beacon Towers to Mr. and Mrs. William Randolph Hearst to house some of their art collection. Listed proudly as a Vanderbilt house, it, however, was torn down in 1945.

23. Page 238. Alva's bath-chair-donkey-cart was given by Col. and Mrs. Jacques Balsan to the museum of Compiegne, France, following Alva's death.

24. Page 241. Gertrude L. Conaway Vanderbilt is responsible for the excellent display in Marble House, to commemorate the career of her husband as one of America's finest yachtsmen.

25. Page 242. See section of separate Chronologies on each of the five members of the W. K. Vanderbilt family:
  William Kissam Vanderbilt
  Alva Erskine Smith Vanderbilt Belmont
  Consuelo Vanderbilt (Marlborough) Balsan
  William Kissam Vanderbilt, Jr.
  Harold Stirling Vanderbilt

Handwriting Analysis of Alva Vanderbilt Belmont

- Strong intellectual capacities
- Probably an excellent strategist in any undertaking
- Putting the achievement of goals first
- Pragmatist
- Genuinely liking people yet needing private time
- Strong sense of commitment
- Artistic inclinations
- Snappish on occasion
- Sense of family

Analysis by Ellen Bowers, Ed.D., President and Owner, GRAPHEX, (Scoring Graphological Psychograms), President, Council of Graphological Societies, P.O. Box 20175, Columbus, Ohio 43220

Letter above courtesy Special Collections, Western Manuscripts, Huntington Library, San Marino, California.

BIBLIOGRAPHY

MANUSCRIPT COLLECTIONS

The Huntington Library, San Marino, Calif. The Charles Erskine Scott Wood Collection: A first-draft, dictated autobiography of Alva Vanderbilt Belmont, received and prepared by Sara Bard Field, July and August, 1917. Dictated in essay form, with notes. At the Chinese Teahouse of Marble House, Bellevue Avenue, Newport, R.I.

The Newport Historical Society, Newport, R.I. Collection on The American Woman's Suffrage Movement rallies held by Alva Vanderbilt Belmont in Newport, R.I.

The William R. Perkins Library, Duke University, Durham, N.C. The Matilda Young Papers: The incomplete, typewritten manuscript memoirs of Alva Vanderbilt Belmont, plus correspondence, as prepared by Matilda Young, secretary to Mrs. Belmont.

The Preservation Society of Newport County. The personal scrapbook of Alva Vanderbilt Belmont, containing newspaper clippings covering the famed Masque Ball given by Mr. and Mrs. William Kissam Vanderbilt, March 26, 1883, at their new chateau, 660 Fifth Avenue, New York City. The original scrapbook was purchased at an auction by Mr. Benjamin Reed of The Historical Preservation Society, Newport, R.I., and then given to The Preservation Society of Newport County.

Mrs. Consuelo (Mimi) Russell, great-great-granddaughter of Alva Vanderbilt Belmont. A second personal scrapbook of Mrs. Belmomt, containing newspaper clippings covering the Conference of Great Women, which she held as a rally and benefit for The American Woman's Suffrage Movement, July 8–9, 1914, at her Marble House and its Chinese Teahouse, Newport, R.I.

The Sewall-Belmont House, 144 Constitution Avenue, N.E., Washington, D.C. Papers, information, and related photographs on the life and work of Alva Vanderbilt Belmont and The National Woman's Party.

The Arthur and Elizabeth Schlesinger Library on the History of Women in America, located at Radcliffe College, Cambridge, Mass. The Alice

Paul, Jane Norman Smith, and Doris Stevens Collections: Concerning The American Woman's Suffrage Movement papers of Alva Vanderbilt Belmont.

INTERVIEWS WITH:

Mr. Louis Auchincloss
Mrs. John Nicholas Brown
Mr. Shirley C. Burden
Mr. Allen Churchill
Mrs. Consuelo (Mimi) Russell
Countess Anthony Szapary
Mr. and Mrs. Donald Tinney
Mrs. Harold B. Tinney
Mr. J. Watson Webb, Jr.

BOOKLETS, BROCHURES, CALENDARS, EXHIBITIONS, GUIDE BOOKS, AND POSTERS

Cirker, Hayward. "Picture Postcards of Old New York." Mineola, N.Y.: Dover Publications, Inc., 1976, 1985.

Eastman, Max, editor. "Art for the Masses, 1911-1917." The Masses magazine sponsored program. Whitney Museum, N.Y., 1985. Exhibition organized by The Yale Univ. Art Gallery, 1985. shown at The Grunwald Center for the Graphic Arts, UCLA, and at The Boston Univ. Art Gallery.

Eisenberg, Bonnie. "Woman's Suffrage Movement, 1848-1920." Poster and display kit. National Women's History Project. P.O. Box 3716, Santa Rosa, CA 95402.

Ferguson, J. Walton. "Kingscote." "Rosecliff." Newport R. I.: The Preservation Society of Newport County, 1977.

Gavan, Terrence. "The Barons of Newport." A Guide to the Gilded Age. Newport, R.I.: Pineapple Publications, 1988.

Green, David. "Blenheim Palace." The Blenheim Estate Office. Oxfordshire, England: Alden Press, 1950, 1976, 1982, 1984.

———. "Blenheim Park and Gardens." The Blenheim Estate Office,

Woodstock. Oxfordshire, England: Alden Press, 1972, 1954.

Hopf, John T., text and photographs. "The Newport Mansions of the Preservation Society of Newport County." Newport, R.I.: Copyright by John T. Hopf, 1976, 1979-83.

Maconi, Carole J., in collaboration with the Tinney family. Photographs by Keith Maconi. "Belcourt Castle." Southborough, Mass.: Yankee Colour Corporation, 1978, 1983.

Memorabilia. "Vintage New York, 1987." Somerville, Mass.: Memorabilia Publishers, 1953, 1987.

The National Gallery of Art. Guide to the Exhibition, held Nov. 3, 1985 to March 16, 1986. "The Treasure Houses of Britain." Washington, D.C.: Published by The National Gallery of Art, 1985.

The National Women's History Project. Women's History Resources Service Catalogs. P.O. Box 3716, Santa Rosa, CA 95402.

The Newport Historical Society. "Newport History" Bulletins. Newport, R.I.: All issues for the past ten years with articles pertaining to the work and greater world of Alva Vanderbilt Belmont.

The Newport Restoration Foundation. "The Newport Restoration Foundation: Prescott Farm, Whitehorne House, and 57 Restored Houses in Newport, R.I." Southborough, Mass.: Yankee Colour Corporation, 1977.

Porter, Daniel R. Research by Jane McLeod Walsh. "The Hunter House, Mansion of Hospitality." Newport, R. I.: Published by The Preservation Society of Newport County, 1976.

The Preservation Society of Newport County. "The Breakers", "Chateau-sur-Mer", "The Chinese Teahouse", and "Marble House." Newport, R.I.: Published by The Preservation Society. Copyright for "The Breakers", 1952. Copyright for the remainder, 1971.

————. "A Guidebook to Newport Mansions." Newport, R. I.: Published by The Preservation Society in conjunction with the Fort Church Publishers, Inc., 1984.

Sharp, Lewis I., catalogue. David W. Kiehl, walking tours. "New York City Public Sculpture, by 19th Century American Artists." New York, N.Y.: Sponsored and published by The Metropolitan Museum of Art, 18 June 1974.

NEWSPAPERS

Brooklyn Eagle
New York Daily Tribune
New York Herald
New York Tribune
New York Journal
New York Mail
New York Sun
New York Times
New York World
Newport Daily News, R.I.

ARTICLES

Barkhorn, Jean Cook and Robin Whitney. "Summer in the Twenties "
  Town and Country, July 1991.

Barnett, Robert N. "Captains of Industry, Part XXIII: William Kissam
  Vanderbilt." *Cosmopolitan*, Vol. 36, No. 5, March 1904.

Belmont, Alva Vanderbilt. Articles arranged by the year published:

  "Woman' s Right to Govern Herself." *North American Review*, Vol. 190,
    No. 5, November 1909.

  (No title) *Harper's Bazaar*, March 1910.

  "Woman Suffrage as It Looks To-Day." *The Forum*, March 1910.

  "How Can Women Get the Suffrage?" *The Independent*, 31 March 1910.

  "Why I Am a Suffragist." *The World To-Day*, October 1911.

  Foreword to article by Christabel Pankhurst, "Story of the Woman' s
    War." *Good Housekeeping*, November 1913.

  "Women as Dictators." *Ladies' Home Journal*, September 1922.

  "What the Woman's Party Wants." *Collier's*, 23 December 1922.

  "Are Women Really Citizens?" *Good Housekeeping*, September 1931.

Multiple articles in national newspapers. National Woman' s Party Papers, 1913-1974. Available in the microfilm records of the National Woman' s Party, at Sewall-Belmont House (given by and named in honor of Mrs. Belmont), 144 Constitution Avenue, N.E., Washington, D.C. 20002.

Benway, Ann M. "The Chinese Teahouse on the Grounds of Marble House." Newport, R.I.: *The Preservation Society of Newport County*, 1982.

————. "A Guide to Newport Mansions." Newport, R.I.: *The Preservation Society of Newport County*, 1982.

Browne, T.C. "Rich Willie's Cup." *Automotive Yearbook of 1987*.

Buckley, Christopher. Photographs by Ira Block. "The Glitter and the Gold: Newport, Rhode Island." *National Geographic Traveler*, Spring 1987.

Burnham, Alan. "The New York Architecture of Richard Morris Hunt." *Journal of the Society of Architectural Historians*, Vol. XI, No. 2, May 1952.

Carlsen, Peter. "New York: Stanley Barrows, Recalling a Golden Era in Manhattan Design." *Architectural Digest*, November 1989.

Crowninshield, Frank. "The House of Vanderbilt." *Vogue*, 15 November 1941.

Evans, Meryle. "Newport, A Lively Landmark." *Cuisine*, September 1983.

Forbes Special Issue. The Eighth Annual Forbes 400. "The Richest People in America." *Forbes*, 23 October 1989.

Gray, Christopher. (Listed according to month and year.)
"Frozen in Time." *Avenue*, February 1987.
"Au Revoir to the French Style." *Avenue*, June-July-August 1987.
"Designs for Living." *Avenue*, November 1987.
"Presidents in Residence " *Avenue*, November 1988.
"Fashionable Facades." *Avenue*, December 1988.
"Growing Pains." *Avenue*, February 1989.
"Over My Dead Body." *Avenue*, May 1989.
"Show and Tell." *Avenue*, February 1990.
"The Plot Thickens." *Avenue*, June/July 1990.
"Architectural Cover-Ups." *Avenue*, August 1990.
"Mile of Style." *Avenue*, September 1990.
"Signs of the Time." *Avenue*, October 1990.

"New York Stories." *Avenue*, December 1990.
"Follies! " *Avenue*, February 1991.
"Watch on the Rhinelanders." *Avenue*, March 1991.
"Lofty Intentions." *Avenue*, April 1991.

Joyce, Henry. "The Marble House Project." *Newport Gazette*, The Preservation Society of Newport County. Winter 1991.

Kavaler, Lucy. "The Private World of High Society." *House and Garden*, September 1983.

Kisseloff, Jeff. "Opera Antics: Scene Stealers—a Century Ago " *Avenue*, October 1988.

Littlefield, Susan. Photograghs by Mick Hales. "Mrs. Belmont' s Chinese Fling." *House and Garden*, September 1983.

Lynes, Russell. "Chateau Builder to Fifth Avenue." *American Heritage*, Vol 6. No. 2, February 1955.

Maconi, Carole J. "Belcourt Castle." Southborough, Mass.: Yankee Colour Corporation, 1985.

McCarthy, Mary. "The Indomitable Miss Brayton." *House and Garden*, December 1983.

Merrick, Lenada Culver. "Magnificent Mansions at Christmas." *McCall's*, December 1988.

Patterson, Jerry E. "The Vanderbilt Heritage." *Town and Country*, December 1988.

The Preservation Society of Newport County. "Marble House: The William K. Vanderbilt Mansion." Newport, R. I.: *The Preservation Society of Newport County*, 1965.

Newport Gazette. Articles written and published by The Preservation Society of Newport County. All issues beginning with 1982.

Pryce-Jones, Alan. Photographs by Karen Radkai. "The Golden Age of Newport." *House and Garden*, June 1987.

Thomas, Lately. "Alva Smith Vanderbilt Belmont." *New York, N.Y.* book, as published by *American Heritage, The Magazine of History*, 1968.

Vanderbilt II, Arthur T. "Nous Nous Soutenons, Tales of Old New York." *Daily News Magazine*, New York, 14 January 1990.

Vogue special Issue. *"Vogue's* Eye View of 640 Fifth Avenue." *Vogue*, 15 November 1941.

Warburton, Eileen. "Secret Newport." *Connoisseur*, June 1990.

Weeks, Terry. Photography by Mathias Oppersdorff. "Newport." *Gourmet*, July 1990.

BOOKS

Algeo, Sara M. *The Story of a Sub-Pioneer*. Providence, R.I.: Snow and Farnham Co., 1907.

Amory, Cleveland. *The Last Resorts*. New York: Harper and Brothers, 1952.

———. *Who Killed Society?* New York: Harper and Brothers, 1960.

Andrews, Wayne. *Architecture in New York*. New York: Atheneum, 1969.

———. *The Vanderbilt Legend, The Story of the Vanderbilt Family, 1794-1940.*. New York: Harcourt, Brace and Co., 1941.

Auchincloss, Louis. *The Book Class*. Boston, Mass.: Houghton Mifflin Company, 1984.

———. *The Vanderbilt Era*. New York: Charles Scribner's Sons, 1989.

Baker, Paul R. *Richard Morris Hunt*. Cambridge, Mass.: MIT Press, 1980.

Balsan, Consuelo Vanderbilt (Ninth Duchess of Marlborough). *The Glitter and the Gold*. New York: Harper and Brothers, 1952.

Barlow, Elizabeth. *Frederick Law Olmsted's New York*. New York: Praeger Publishers, 1972.

Barrett, Richard. *Good Old Summer Days*. Boston, Mass.: Houghton Mifflin Company, 1952.

Bavier, Bob. *America's Cup Fever*. New York: Ziff-Davis Company, 1980.

Beebe, Lucius. *The Big Spenders*. Garden City, N.Y.: Doubleday and Company, 1966.

———. *Mansions on Rails*. Berkeley, Calif.: Howell-North, 1959.

Beken of Cowes. Introduction by Olin Stephens. *The America's Cup, 1851 to the Present*. New York: HarperCollins, 1990.

Belmont, Eleanor. *The Fabric of Memory*. New York: Farrar, Straus and Cudahy, 1957.

Bishop, George. *The Concise Dictionary of Motorsport*. New York: Mayflower Books, 1979.

Black, David. *The King of Fifth Avenue, The Fortunes of August Belmont*. New York: The Dial Press, 1981.

Bloom, Benjamin A. *Monograph of the Works of McKim, Mead & White: 1879-1915*. New York: Arno Press, 1977.

Birmingham, Stephen. *The Grand Dames*. New York: Simon and Schuster, 1982.

———. *Real Lace, America's Irish Rich*. New York: Harper and Row, 1973.

Brough, James. *Consuelo, Portrait of an American Heiress*. New York: Coward, McCann, and Geoghegan, Inc., 1979.

Burden, Shirley C. *Chairs*. New York. Aperture, 1985.

———. *The Vanderbilts in My Life*. New York: Ticknor and Fields, 1981.

Byron, Joseph. *Photographs of New York Interiors at the Turn of the Century*. New York: Dover Publications, Inc. 1976.

Cable, Mary. *Top Drawer: American High Society from the Gilded Age to the Roaring Twenties*. New York. Atheneum, 1984.

Cecil, William A.V. *Biltmore*. Asheville, N.C.: Biltmore Company, 1975.

Churchill, Allen. *The Improper Bohemians*. New York: E.P. Dutton and Company, 1959.

———. *The Splendor Seekers*. New York: Grosset and Dunlap, 1974.

————. *The Upper Crust: An Informal History of New York's Highest Society.* Englewood Cliffs, N.J.: Prentice-Hall, 1970.

Chyet, Stanley F. *Lopez of Newport.* Detroit, Mich.: Wayne State University Press, 1970.

Conrad III, Barnaby. *Absinthe, History in a Bottle.* San Francisco, Calif.: Chronicle Books, 1988.

Cowles, Virginia. *The Astors.* London. Weidenfeld and Nicolson, 1979.

Croffert, William A. *The Leisure Class in America.* New York. Arno Press, 1975.

Croffut, A. *The Vanderbilts and Their Fortune.* New York: Belford, Clarke and Company, 1886.

Crolius, Peter C., editor and publisher. *The Rhode Island Scene.* Wickford, R.I.: Dutch Island Press, 1986.

Crowninshield, Francis W. *Manners for the Metropolis.* New York: D. Appleton and Company, 1899.

Downing, Antoinette F. and Vincent J. Scully, Jr. *The Architectural Heritage of Newport, Rhode Island.* New York: American Legacy Press 1982.

Eliot, Elizabeth. *Heiresses and Coronets.* New York: McDowell, Obolensky, 1959.

Elliott, Maude Howe. *This Was My Newport.* Cambridge, Mass.: Mythology Company, 1944.

Flexner, Eleanor. *Century of Struggle: The Woman's Rights Movement in the United States.* New York: Atheneum, 1975.

Foreman, John, and Robbe Pierce Stimson. *The Vanderbilts and the Gilded Age, Architectural Aspirations, 1879–1901.* New York: St. Martin's Press, 1991.

Furnas, J.C. *The Americans: A Social History of the United States, 1587-1914.* New York: G.P. Putnam's Sons, 1969.

Gannon, Thomas. Photography by Richard Cheek. *Newport Mansions.* Little Compton, R.I.: Foremost Publishers, Inc., 1982.

313

Gates, John D. *The Astor Family*. New York: Doubleday, 1981.

Goldsmith, Barbara. *Little Gloria... Happy at Last*. New York: Alfred A. Knopf, 1980.

Hepburn, Andrew H. *Great Houses of American History*. New York: Bramhall House, 1972.

Hoogenboom, Art and Olive. *The Gilded Age*. Englewood Cliffs, N.J.: Prentice-Hall, 1967.

Howe, Julia Ward. *Reminiscences, 1819-1899*. Boston, Mass.: Houghton Mifflin Company, 1899.

Hoyt, Edwin P. *The Vanderbilts and Their Fortunes*. Garden City: N.Y.: Doubleday, 1962.

Jackson-Stops, Gervase, and James Pipkin. *The English Country House, A Grand Tour*. New York Graphic Society. National Gallery of Art, Washington, D.C., Boston, and Toronto: Little, Brown and Company, 1985.

Jackson-Stops, Gervase, editor. *The Treasure Houses of Britain, Five Hundred Years of Private Patronage and Art Collecting*. National Gallery of Art, Washington, D.C., New Haven, Conn., and London: Yale University Press, 1985.

Johnson, Harry, and Frederick S. Lightfoot. *Maritime New York, in Nineteenth-Century Photographs*. New York: Dover Publications, Inc., 1989.

Johnston, Johanna. *Frederick Law Olmsted: Partner With Nature*. New York: Dodd Mead and Company, 1975.

Kavaler, Lucy. *The Astors: A Family Chronicle of Pomp and Power*. New York: Dodd Mead and Company, 1966.

Kellner, George K., and Stanley Lemons. *Rhode Island, The Independent State*. Rhode Island Historical Society. Woodland Hills, Calif.: Windsor Publications, Inc., 1982.

King, Robert B. *The Vanderbilt Homes*. New York: Rizzoli International Publications, Inc., 1989.

Kirkland, Alexander. *Rector's Naughty '90s Cookbook*. George and Charles Rector. Garden City, N.Y.: Doubleday and Company, Inc., 1949.

314

Lane, Wheaton J. *Commodore Vanderbilt: An Epic of the Steam Age*. New York: Alfred A. Knopf, 1942.

Lehr, Elizabeth Drexel. *King Lehr and the Gilded Age*. London: J.P. Lippincott, 1935.

Lewis, Arnold, James Turner, and Steven McQuillin. *The Opulent Interiors of the Gilded Age*. New York: Dover Publications, 1987.

Lomask, Milton. *Seed Money, The Guggenheim Story*. New York: Farrar, Straus and Co., 1964.

Lynes, Russell. *The Tastemakers*. New York: Grosset and Dunlap, 1949.

Mayer, Grace M. Photography by Joseph Byron. *Once Upon a City, New York from 1890 to 1910*. New York: The Macmillan Co., 1958.

McAllister, Ward. *Society As I Have Found It*. New York. Cassell Publishing Company, 1890.

Menten, Theodore. *Victorian Fashion Paper Dolls from "Harper's Bazar"* (original spelling*), 1867-1898*. New York: Dover Publications, 1977.

Montgomery-Massingberd, Hugh. *Blenheim Revisited, The Spencer-Churchills and Their Palace*. London, Sydney, Toronto: The Bodley Head, 1985.

O'Connor, Richard. *The Golden Summers: An Antic History of Newport*. New York: G.P. Putnam's Sons, 1974.

Patterson, Jerry E. *The Vanderbilts*. New York: Harry N. Abrams, Inc., Publishers, 1989.

Randall, Monica. *The Mansions of Long Island's Gold Coast*. New York: Rizzoli International Publications, 1987.

Rogliatti, Gianni. *Great Collectors' Cars*. New York: Grosset and Dunlap Publishers, 1973.

Roper, Laura Wood. *FLO: The Biography of Frederick Law Olmsted*. Baltinore, Md.: Johns Hopkins University Press, 1973.

Seebohm, Caroline, and Christopher Simon Sykes. *English Country, Living in England's Private Houses*. New York. Clarkson N. Potter, Inc., Publishers, 1987.

315

Sherman, Joe. *The House at Shelburne Farms*. Middlebury, Vt. Ericksson, 1985.

Silver, Nathan. *Lost New York*. New York: American Legacy Press, 1967.

Sloane, Florence Adele. Commentary by Louis Auchincloss. *Maverick in Mauve: The Diary of a Romantic Age*. Garden City, N.Y.: Doubleday, 1983.

Stasz, Clarice. *The Vanderbilt Women, Dynasty of Wealth, Glamour and Tragedy*. New York: St. Martin's Press, 1991.

Stein, Susan R. *The Architecture of Richard Morris Hunt*. Chicago: University of Chicago Press, 1986.

Stephenson, June. *Women's Roots*. Napa, Calif.: Diemer, Smith Publishing Company, Inc., 1981.

Strange, Michael. *Who Tells Me True*. New York: Charles Scribner's Sons, 1940.

Tierney, Tom. *Great Fashion Designs of the Belle Epoque*. New York: Dover Publications, Inc., 1982.

Trahey, Jane. *Harper's Bazaar, 100 Years of the American Female*. New York: Random House, 1913.

Trecker, Janice Law. *Women on the Move, Struggles for Equal Rights in England*. New York: Macmillan, 1975.

Vanderbilt II, Arthur T. *Fortune's Children, The Fall of the House of Vanderbilt*. New York: William Morrow and Co., Inc., 1989.

Vanderbilt Jr., Cornelius. *Man of the World: My Life on Five Continents*. New York: Crown Publishers, 1959.

———. *Queen of the Golden Age. The Fabulous Story of Grace Wilson Vanderbilt*. New York: McGraw-Hill Book Company, 1956.

———. *Farewell to Fifth Avenue*. New York: Simon and Schuster, 1935.

Vanderbilt, Gloria. *Black Knight, White Knight*. New York: Alfred A. Knopf, 1987.

———. *Once Upon a Time*. New York: Alfred A. Knopf, 1985.

Vanderbilt, Jr., William Kissam. *West Made East With the Loss of a Day*, A Chronicle of Motor Ship *Alva* on The First Circumnavigation of the Globe Under the United States Naval Reserve Yacht Pennant. New York: privately printed, 1933.

Van Rensselaer, Mrs. John King. *The Social Ladder*. New York: Henry Holt and Company, 1924.

Vickers, Hugo. *Gladys, Duchess of Marlborough*. New York: Holt, Rinehart and Winston, 1979.

Vidal, Gore. *Empire*. New York: Random House, 1987.

Warbuton, Eileen. *In Living Memory, A Chronicle of Newport, Rhode Island, 1888–1988*. Newport, R.I.: published by Newport Savings and Loan Association/Island Trust Company, 1988.

Watson, Edward B. Contemporary Photographs by Edmund V. Gillon, Jr. *New York Then and Now*. New York: Dover Publication, Inc., 1981.

Wecter, Dixon. *The Saga of American Society: A Record of Social Aspiration, 1607-1937*. New York: Charles Scribner's Sons, 1937.

Weidman, Bette S., and Linda B. Martin. *Nassau County, Long Island, In Early Photographs, 1869-1940*. New York: Dover Publications, Inc., 1981.

Williams, Henry Lionel and Ottalie K. Williams. *A Treasury of Great American Houses*. New York: G.P. Putnam's Sons, 1970.

GENERAL REFERENCE BOOKS

Architectural League of New York and Catalogue of the Twenty-Seventh Annual Exhibition. New York: Galleries of the American Fine Arts Society, 215 West 57th Street, January 28 to February 17, Inclusive, 1912.

A Sense of History, The Best Writing From the Pages of American Heritage. New York: American Heritage Press, Inc., 1985. Boston, Mass.: distributed by Houghton Mifflin Company.

The Timetables of History, A Horizontal Linkage of People and Events. Bernard Grun, Editor. New York: Simon and Schuster, 1975, 1979. First Touchstone Edition, Simon and Schuster, 1982.

INDEX

Production Credits

Kristl Vision	Bailey's Mistake, Maine
Accu-Text	Hamilton, Rhode Island
Hog Alley Group	Calais, Maine
Debra Ames	Calais, Maine
Charles J. Cronin	Bangor, Maine
Beth Petrucci	Tucson, Arizona
Karen Wolfe	Columbia Falls, Maine
Barry Kaplan	Wickford, Rhode Island
Henry L.P. Beckwith	Wickford, Rhode Island
VIP	Machias, Maine
Graphic Color Service	Fairfield, Maine
Furbush-Roberts Co.	Bangor, Maine
BookCrafters, Inc.	Fredericksburg, Virginia